MW00851559

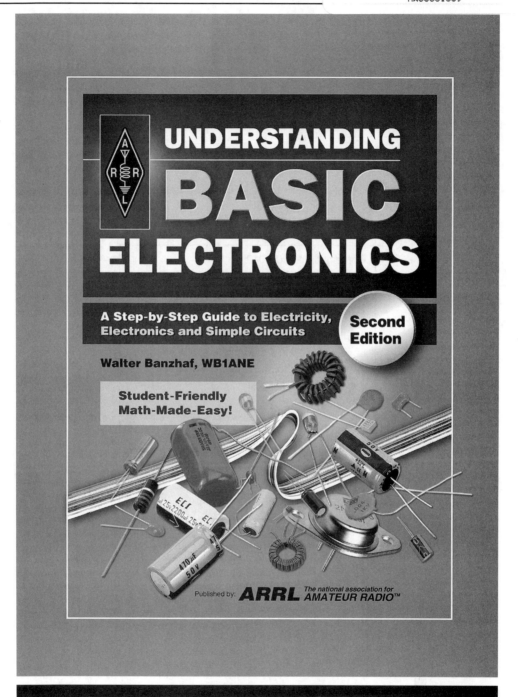

UNDERSTANDING BASIC ELECTRONICS

A Step-by-Step Guide to Electricity, Electronics and Simple Circuits

Second Edition

Walter Banzhaf, WB1ANE

Student-Friendly Math-Made-Easy!

Published by: **ARRL** *The national association for* AMATEUR RADIO™

Author
Walter Banzhaf, WB1ANE

Editorial Assistant
Maty Weinberg, KB1EIB

Production
Jodi Morin, KA1JPA
Shelly Bloom, WB1ENT
David F. Pingree, N1NAS
Carol Michaud, KB1QAW
Ed Vibert
Elaine Lengyl

Cover Design
Sue Fagan,
KB1OKW

Contents

Foreword

Electronics. The word conjures images of engineers and technicians huddled around their latest creation. Hot soldering irons and wire bits are scattered around. Cabinets full of resistors, transistors and other parts are nearby. Calculator in hand, an experimenter punches a few buttons and quickly selects a new component to try in the circuit.

But wait! You don't have to be an engineer or a math whiz to enjoy the thrill of experimenting with electronic circuits.

This book will teach you basic electronic principles. The only math skills you need are the ability to add, subtract, multiply and divide. Okay, to really understand *decibels*, knowing a bit about logarithms is desirable. This book will help you with all the math you need (including logarithms), and shows you how to use an inexpensive calculator to avoid tedious calculations. It is written in a light, easy-to-understand style that nontechnical readers will enjoy. Ample illustrations illustrate the electronics concepts to aid your understanding and help you to learn to use your calculator faster.

The text uses a modular approach to teaching. We normally present topics in two-page modules, and few modules are longer. This makes it convenient to study the book in small sections. It also makes it possible for you to skip modules that cover material with which you are already familiar, or modules that cover material you don't want to learn right now.

The ARRL's *Understanding Basic Electronics* is *not* a study guide for an Amateur Radio license exam. It is written in a friendly tone that makes it possible for any learner, young or old, to master the underlying principles of electronics.

Perhaps you have an Amateur Radio (ham radio) license, but want to gain a more complete understanding of basic electronics principles. Then this book is for you. Maybe you just want to learn about basic electronics without studying the FCC rules and other operating practices that ham radio operators need to know. This book is also for you.

The ARRL has an excellent series of study materials to help you earn an Amateur Radio license. Visit the ARRL Web site at **www.arrl.org** for information about the latest study materials, or write to New Ham Desk, ARRL, 225 Main Street, Newington, CT 06111-1494.

David Sumner, K1ZZ
Chief Executive Officer
Newington, CT
February 2010

Preface

The ARRL's classic book *Understanding Basic Electronics* has been used successfully by literally thousands of people like you over nearly a quarter of a century either to learn the fundamentals of electronics or to extend their knowledge of it. When I was approached by the ARRL to rewrite this fine classic and create this 2nd edition, little did I know how much work was involved, nor how excellent the 1st edition really is.

My admiration and appreciation for the many talents of Larry Wolfgang, WR1B, author of the 1st edition, is very high. Larry and those at the ARRL who helped him create the first edition did a superb job of making a very readable introductory book that works for a wide range of readers. But technology and teaching have of course advanced significantly since the 1st edition was written, and it was indeed time to create this 2nd edition.

A lot of the 1st edition lives on in this 2nd edition; the fundamentals of physics and electronics don't change. For example, a thousand years from now teachers still will put a sheet of paper over a magnet and sprinkle iron filings on the paper, thereby showing the invisible magnetic field lines that exist between the magnet's north and south poles, just as teachers do today. What has changed is how students learn, the availability of inexpensive calculators to do the tedious mathematics needed to understand electricity and electronics, and the development of new digital devices. This edition uses more effective ways of integrating math by presenting it "just in time" in the chapter where and when it is needed.

This 2nd edition of the ARRL's *Understanding Basic Electronics* is an introduction to the exciting world of electronics. Readers with little or no previous electronics knowledge will be able to understand and learn from the text. Radio amateurs who want to build on their foundation of electronics knowledge will find this book helpful.

I would like to express deep appreciation to Larry Wolfgang, WR1B (of course) and the many ARRL staff who created the 1st edition, my handling editor Mark Wilson, K1RO, and the talented production staff and graphic artists at ARRL Headquarters without whom this book couldn't have been printed. A special word of thanks to my wife, Mattie, whose eagle-eyed proofreading caught most of the goofs I made, and to Professor Saeid Moslehpour for scanning the entire 1st edition into electronic format for me to work with.

Finally, to all those who use this book, thank you. You are the real judges of whether the book meets its objectives. If it helps you learn some basic electronics, and leads you to further experimentation and/or enjoyment of ham radio, all the work has been worthwhile. Please share your suggestions and comments. There is a feedback form at the back of the book for this purpose, or send an e-mail to **pubsfdbk@arrl.org**.

Walter Banzhaf, P.E., WB1ANE
Professor of Electrical Engineering (Retired)

About Amateur Radio

There are many references to Amateur Radio throughout this book. We mentioned various types of Amateur Radio equipment in some of the examples and text discussions.

If you are a licensed Amateur Radio operator, you are familiar with the fun and excitement "hams" (as they are often called) enjoy every day! If not, you're probably wondering what this is all about.

Amateur Radio is about individuals communicating by means of radio signals through the air. It is about individual experimenters contributing to the advancement of the radio communications art. Amateur Radio is about the Federal Communications Commission providing a set of rules that encourage advancement of the communication and technical aspects of radio. Amateur Radio is about a national resource: a pool of trained radio operators, technicians and electronics experts ready to lend a hand during all types of emergencies. It is also about the international goodwill that develops when people communicate across national boundaries and around the world.

These five principles define the purpose of Amateur Radio. They also give you some hint of the wide variety of interests that Amateur Radio operators bring to their hobby (or avocation as it becomes for many).

What do Amateur Radio operators actually do? Most of all, they meet other people who like to communicate. They use many methods and a wide variety of radio frequency bands to carry out this communication. Small hand-held radios are popular for local communications. For longer distance communications, hams usually select the shortwave bands where they can reach just about any location on the globe. Many hams even send their signals "out of this world," communicating with astronauts in space, or using Amateur-built communications satellites or even the moon to relay their signals.

Amateur Radio communication takes many forms. Sure hams love to talk into a microphone. But they also thrill to the excitement of tapping out messages in Morse code, the oldest form of radio communication. Hams type messages and exchange data using digital communications — computers connected to radios. Amateur Radio operators even send and receive their own television pictures.

Amateur Radio operators enjoy building all kinds of electronics devices. They often build accessories to use with their stations. Many of them build complete radio transmitters and receivers. There is nothing quite like the thrill you get when you can proudly say of your equipment, "I built it myself!"

Anyone can become an Amateur Radio operator. There are no minimum (or maximum!) age requirements. Earning a license involves passing a simple written exam covering FCC Rules, elementary electronics principles and operating practices. You can begin with a Technician license; no Morse code is required.

For more information and answers to any questions you may have about Amateur Radio, contact:

ARRL — the National Association for Amateur Radio
225 Main Street
Newington CT 06111
1-800-326-3942 (toll free in the US)
e-mail **newham@arrl.org** or visit us on the Web at **www.arrl.org/hamradio**

About the ARRL

The seed for Amateur Radio was planted in the 1890s, when Guglielmo Marconi began his experiments in wireless telegraphy. Soon he was joined by dozens, then hundreds, of others who were enthusiastic about sending and receiving messages through the air—some with a commercial interest, but others solely out of a love for this new communications medium. The United States government began licensing Amateur Radio operators in 1912.

By 1914, there were thousands of Amateur Radio operators—hams—in the United States. Hiram Percy Maxim, a leading Hartford, Connecticut inventor and industrialist, saw the need for an organization to band together this fledgling group of radio experimenters. In May 1914 he founded the American Radio Relay League (ARRL) to meet that need.

Today ARRL, with approximately 155,000 members, is the largest organization of radio amateurs in the United States. The ARRL is a not-for-profit organization that:

♦ promotes interest in Amateur Radio communications and experimentation
♦ represents US radio amateurs in legislative matters, and
♦ maintains fraternalism and a high standard of conduct among Amateur Radio operators.

At ARRL headquarters in the Hartford suburb of Newington, the staff helps serve the needs of members. ARRL is also International Secretariat for the International Amateur Radio Union, which is made up of similar societies in 150 countries around the world.

ARRL publishes the monthly journal *QST*, as well as newsletters and many publications covering all aspects of Amateur Radio. Its headquarters station, W1AW, transmits bulletins of interest to radio amateurs and Morse code practice sessions. The ARRL also coordinates an extensive field organization, which includes volunteers who provide technical information and other support services for radio amateurs as well as communications for public-service activities. In addition, ARRL represents US amateurs with the Federal Communications Commission and other government agencies in the US and abroad.

Membership in ARRL means much more than receiving *QST* each month. In addition to the services already described, ARRL offers membership services on a personal level, such as the Technical Information Service—where members can get answers by phone, email or the ARRL website, to all their technical and operating questions.

Full ARRL membership (available only to licensed radio amateurs) gives you a voice in how the affairs of the organization are governed. ARRL policy is set by a Board of Directors (one from each of 15 Divisions). Each year, one-third of the ARRL Board of Directors stands for election by the full members they represent. The day-to-day operation of ARRL HQ is managed by an Executive Vice President and his staff.

No matter what aspect of Amateur Radio attracts you, ARRL membership is relevant and important. There would be no Amateur Radio as we know it today were it not for the ARRL. We would be happy to welcome you as a member! (An Amateur Radio license is not required for Associate Membership.) For more information about ARRL and answers to any questions you may have about Amateur Radio, write or call:

ARRL — the national association for Amateur Radio
225 Main Street
Newington CT 06111-1494
Voice: 860-594-0200
    Fax: 860-594-0259
    E-mail: **hq@arrl.org**
    Internet: **www.arrl.org/**

Prospective new amateurs call (toll-free):
800-32-NEW HAM (800-326-3942)
You can also contact us via e-mail at **newham@arrl.org**
or check out *ARRLWeb* at **www.arrl.org/**

Introduction

Modern technology touches every aspect of our lives. We must understand the basic concepts of technology to function effectively in our world. You explore new interests and learn about the world around you when you pursue a hobby, and using technology adds knowledge and great enjoyment too.

Electronics is a fascinating area of modern technology, and many have made it a life-long hobby. Wherever you look electronic devices, gadgets and gizmos are at work. From automobiles to US Postal Service ZIP code readers, nearly everywhere in our society there is some type of electronic circuitry present. Dogs can have ID microchips embedded in their bodies so they can be reunited with their owners if they become lost. Firefighters use thermal imaging cameras to locate victims in a burning house, or to look inside a wall to see if the fire has spread instead of tearing the wall open. Carbon monoxide detectors warn people if their heating system is leaking dangerous gas into their home. Air bag systems in cars detect a collision and inflate a fabric bag to protect occupants within a few thousandths of a second.

Of course you can use such devices even without knowing anything about electronics, but being familiar with some basic electronics principles will help you understand a lot more about the world around you.

There is no better way to learn how something works than to build it yourself. Many Amateur Radio operators enjoy building all kinds of electronics devices. From useful devices and gadgets for their radio stations to complete transmitters and receivers, many "hams" take great pleasure in saying "I built it myself." You, too, can use your electronics knowledge to build useful projects of all kinds.

This book's main purpose is to help you learn the important basic principles of electronics. You will become more confident of your ability to build projects and discover how they work. Many Amateur Radio examples throughout the text show you how to apply these principles. You will get experience with simple direct-current and alternating-current circuits, and you will gain knowledge of transistors and integrated circuits, which make modern electronics possible. Understanding these basic principles will help you to read and study more advanced texts, and you will become familiar with the technical terms and vocabulary of electronics and ham radio.

This book is made of chapters, and in each chapter there are *modules*. Modules separate each topic into bite-sized chunks to make it easier for you to digest them. These modules form the heart of the book.

Most modules cover two pages, although a few are a bit longer. Text explanations are in the simplest possible language. Important words and electronics terms are printed in *italic type* the first time they are used. Simple definitions appear with these important terms. Appendix F is a glossary of electronics and Amateur Radio terms. Refer to this glossary whenever you come across an unfamiliar term.

Good luck with your studies. We hope you enjoy learning about the fascinating field of electronics, and that this book makes it easy for you to do so.

UNIT 1

Introduction to Electronics

Electronics might be defined as the controlling of electrons (the outermost parts of all atoms) to perform jobs that are useful to humanity. Electronics makes possible a wide variety of the devices that we use and depend on so completely every day. Imagine not having an FM radio, cordless phone, cellular phone, computer, MP3 player, GPS navigation system, television, or — well, you get the point. We'd be a lot closer to living, by some measures, a rather primitive existence were it not for the electronic miracles that surround us.

It's important to make a distinction between *electrical* devices and *electronic* devices. An example of an electrical device is a wall switch, the kind that you use to turn lights in your home off and on. There's no subtlety about a wall switch. When it's up, electrons flow and the light is on, and when it's down, no electrons flow and the light is off.

Contrast a wall switch with a dimmer control. With a dimmer, the brightness of a lamp can be changed from completely off, to completely on, with a wide range of brightness levels in between. A dimmer is one simple example of an electronic device that uses *active devices* to control the flow of electrons.

Active devices include transistors and diodes, which are made today from specially manufactured "semiconductor" materials. Starting about 100 years ago, vacuum tubes were used as active devices, but they are seldom used today except in very specialized applications (such as high power transmitters for radio and TV stations). It's quite easy to make an active device control the flow of electrons, whether the flow is to a light bulb, or to headphones used for listening to music, or to a video display.

In this book you will learn about the exciting field of electronics and gain an appreciation for what you (yes, you) can do with it. It's a great hobby and can be a rewarding career. This book will help you to understand the fundamentals and underlying principles of electronics.

In This Unit You Will Learn
✓ some of the ways electronics plays important roles in daily life
✓ some basics of analog and digital electronic circuits, and how they differ
✓ about basic circuit building blocks

Electronics — What is it Good For? (Absolutely Everything)

Contents

Electronics in Our Daily Lives

This chapter lists a few of the many applications of electronics that we may take for granted, but which play important roles in modern life. As you read through them, think about the applications you are familiar with that are not listed, and even imagine those applications that will be developed during your lifetime.

Personal Computers

I'm writing this paragraph using my laptop computer, which has more ability to calculate, analyze and display information than all the computers, combined, on the planet earth only a few decades ago. A five-megabyte (5 MB) hard disk a few decades ago was the size of, and needed the electrical power of, several refrigerators, and had to be moved with a forklift. My four-gigabyte (4 GB) USB thumb drive is smaller than my pinky finger and uses less power than a small flashlight. Four GB is *4000* MB.

Cell Phones

Of course, the cell phone on my

Figure 1-1 — Thanks to continuous advances in electronics technology, mobile phones have gotten smaller and their features have multiplied.

belt is ready to connect me to anyone who may call me, from nearly any place in the world. The voice quality of a conversation on a cell phone or POTS (plain old telephone service) wired phone is now so good it's impossible to tell if the call is from the house next door, or from halfway across the world. In 2007, 26 years after the first cellular phone network was installed, there were about 3.3 billion mobile phone subscriptions worldwide. That represents one cellular phone for each of half the

people on earth.

To make a call, I could press the buttons on the numerical keypad, or I could just say "home" or "voice mail" or "George." Voice recognition technology based on digital signal processing was unavailable in any form a few decades ago. First available on a computer, voice recognition is now present in my little phone. Once trained to my voice, the phone dutifully calls the number associated with the word(s) I speak.

Toys

About three quarters of the toys demonstrated at the 2007 Toy Industry Association Toy Fair used microchips (tiny integrated circuits with stored programs) to make the toys speak, blink lights, respond to sounds, and so forth. Game systems like the *Wii* use microscopic integrated circuit accelerometers to sense the movement of the handheld controller, allowing the system to receive accurate data about how hard the virtual golf club hit the ball.

Electronics on the Go

Automobiles

While I'm driving my car, three computers are at work: one for the engine, one for the transmission, and the third for the car body. The engine computer makes the spark plugs fire at exactly the right time, whether it's a cold winter day or the hottest day of summer. It continuously monitors the exhaust gas, and adjusts the amount of fuel being injected into the cylinders.

The transmission computer shifts gears at just the right engine speed to give good gas mileage and performance. It even learns my style of driving after a few trips and shifts the gears accordingly.

The body computer locks the doors when the car reaches 15 miles per hour, turns off lights if I forget to do so after I park the car, beeps to warn me when I'm low on gas, and opens and closes doors without need to have a human touch the door handles. It also gives me a grace period of about 20 seconds, if I haven't put on my shoulder belt, before making loud and annoying sounds to induce me to buckle up.

Figure 1-2 — Modern cars often include an on-board computer that displays important information for the driver. This one shows outside temperature (80 degrees) and compass bearing (the car is driving SE, southeast).

Of course, my car's on-board trip computer tells me miles (or kilometers) traveled, instantaneous and average fuel consumption (in miles per gallon or liters per 100 kilometers), and the distance I can drive until the tank will be empty. That's another computer, but only a small one.

Electronics also helps make our cars safer. The airbag system (SRS,

Figure 1-3 — How did we ever find our way before GPS receivers? The Garmin Street Pilot 7200 is for automotive use, designed to display maps and driving directions and powered from the cigarette lighter jack. Battery powered, hand-held devices like the Magellan Triton are popular with hikers and other outdoor enthusiasts.

supplemental restraint system) in a car senses when the car has been in an accident and sends electrical current to an explosive device in the center of the steering wheel. Within a few thousandths of a second after the accident, the airbag is filled with gas and acts as a cushion to keep the driver's upper body from moving forward.

The ABS (anti-lock brake system) constantly monitors how fast each wheel is rotating. If a wheel is rotating slower than other wheels, it's skidding (perhaps because the road surface is slippery). The ABS pulses the brake fluid pressure to the skidding wheel, allowing it to grip the road, restoring control of the skidding car to the driver.

Some cars use the ABS system to let the driver know when a tire is low on air, since a low tire will be just a bit smaller than a properly inflated tire and will rotate just a bit faster. The ABS system can sense this slight difference in rotation speed, and it will tell the driver which tire is low on air.

GPS Navigation

I'm fortunate to have two global positioning system (GPS) receivers. One is hand-held, and I use it for hiking. The other is for my vehicle. Both can tell me (in different ways) my location anywhere on our planet Earth, with an accuracy of a few meters. All GPS receivers are totally dependent on a network of about 24 satellites orbiting a few thousand miles above Earth. Each satellite cost millions of dollars and contains atomic clocks that keep time accurate to a millionth of a second or so.

And yet the GPS receivers themselves cost somewhere around a couple of hundred dollars, are rugged and reliable, and are rather easy to use.

Making Life Safer

Smoke Detectors

For less than the cost of an inexpensive lunch you can buy a battery powered smoke detector that will sit on a wall in or near your bedroom, and for a year or so will detect the presence of smoke particles and sound a piercing alarm to awaken you while you sleep. Smoke detectors, CO (carbon monoxide) detectors, and flammable gas detectors (for propane and natural gas) provide us with reliable and effective early warning of a dangerous atmosphere in our homes.

Smoke detectors should be present in every home. If your home has any appliance that uses fuel of any kind (such as fuel oil, natural gas, propane or kerosene) for heating or cooking, you should also invest in a CO detector. If you use gas as a fuel, you should have a flammable gas detector as well. With modern electronics you can purchase all three kinds of detectors for about what it costs to eat dinner out once.

Medicine

Fifty years ago, for a patient with abdominal pain it was often necessary to perform exploratory surgery and cut that person open so the surgeon could explore and determine what was causing the pain. Today, with CAT (computer assisted tomography), MRI (magnetic

Figure 1-4 — Low cost, battery powered smoke detectors have saved thousands of lives. This one also includes a CO (carbon monoxide) detector. Modern technology allows smoke alarm batteries to last for many months or (with special batteries) many years.

resonance imaging), ultrasound and other noninvasive diagnostic tools it is possible to "see" electronically what is going on inside a body, without the need for surgery and its accompanying pain, expense, recovery time and risk of infection.

What's Next?

This chapter has presented a few of the ways in which electronics has improved and simplified our lives. Without electronic systems, we'd be living very primitive lives indeed. In the rest of Unit 1, we'll look at

Figure 1-5 — Magnetic resonance imaging (MRI) technology allows doctors to diagnose problems that may have required exploratory surgery in the not-too-distant past. Note the excellent detail in this image of the head and upper spine, including cervical and thoracic vertebras and the disks between them.

analog and digital electronic circuits and building blocks which are inside virtually every electronic product you can buy or use today.

Review Questions

1.1 The acronym "GPS" stands for:

a) Great Power Switch

b) Grey Poupon Sandwich

c) Global Positioning System

d) Gleeful People Singing

1.2 A home that uses fuel of any kind (fuel oil, natural gas, propane, kerosene, etc.) should have:

a) two cell phones

b) a carbon monoxide detector

c) an MRI machine

d) frozen pizza available

1.3 The acronym "SRS" stands for:

a) Serial Radiotelephone server

b) Semiconductor Recovery Service

c) Shortwave Radio Selector

d) Supplemental Restraint System

1.4 An example of an electronic device is:

a) a dimmer switch

b) a doorbell pushbutton switch

c) the on-off switch on a flashlight

d) a light switch on a wall

1.5 5 GB (gigabytes) equals:

a) 50 MB (megabytes)

b) 500 MB (megabytes)

c) 5000 MB (megabytes)

d) half a megabyte

1.6 A car's airbag system is set into action by:

a) sensing the force of the impact

b) weighing the driver

c) exploding the steering wheel

d) looking at oncoming traffic

1.7 A car's ABS (anti-lock brake system) can do all of these *except*:

a) sense which tire is low on air

b) determine how fast each tire is rotating

c) tell when a car is skidding

d) detect when the driver is using a cell-phone

Answers

1.1   c

1.2   b

1.3   d

1.4   a

1.5   c

1.6   a

1.7   d

Chapter 2

Analog Electronic Circuits

This table radio uses an analog circuit to tune in stations.

Contents

Analog Signals are Continuously Variable

We are all very familiar with devices that use analog or digital electronic circuits, even if we don't realize these circuits are present. Many modern devices use both. For example, a cellular phone (sometimes called a mobile phone) has analog and digital circuits. A computer has both. An older AM or FM radio that's tuned using a dial likely has no digital circuitry at all, while a radio with a digital display has both analog and digital circuitry.

So what's the difference between analog and digital? An analog signal is *continuously* variable, while a digital signal is broken into discrete

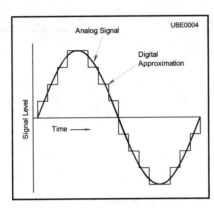

Figure 2-1 — An analog signal waveform has continuously varying signal levels, while the digital version of the same signal is approximated with discrete steps.

steps. For example, think of the face of a clock. With an analog clock, the second hand sweeps around in a smooth, continuous motion, showing the exact time at any instant. A digital clock display ticks off the time in one second steps, without showing the time in between.

Figure 2-1 shows an analog signal waveform with its continuously varying signal levels, and a digital signal that approximates the same waveform with discrete steps. Of course if the steps are small enough, a digital signal can very closely approximate its analog counterpart.

Linear Circuits

Analog circuits are sometimes called *linear* circuits, in which there generally is an input (such as the voice signal from the microphone in a public address system) and an output (a bigger, or amplified, version of the voice signal that comes out of the speaker). What makes such an amplifier *linear* is that if you increase the size (the fancy term for this is *amplitude*) of the input signal — perhaps by talking louder into the microphone — the output signal also gets bigger.

Figure 2-2A shows an amplifier with a small signal at its input, and a larger signal at its output. The output signal is three times the amplitude of the input signal; we can say the *gain* of this amplifier, in this example, is three.

In Figure 2-2B the input signal is larger, and the output signal is still three times as big as the input signal. No matter what the size of the input signal, the output will always be three times larger, until a point is reached

where the output signal can't get any bigger. You may have heard this occur when the volume on an inexpensive radio is turned up too high — it sounds distorted. At this point, the linear amplifier has reached the upper end of its linear range.

Analog circuits are found in virtually all devices. In a cell phone (**Figure 2-3**), there is an amplifier for the tiny voice signal coming from the microphone, which increases the voice signal to the right level for use in the outgoing transmitted signal. Another amplifier boosts the incoming voice signal (from the person on the other end of the cell phone conversation), making it big enough to drive the earpiece or the speaker of the cell phone.

Speaker/earphone

Figure 2-3 — A typical hand-held cell phone showing the microphone and speaker/earphone. (Photo courtesy Motorola, Inc.)

Microphone

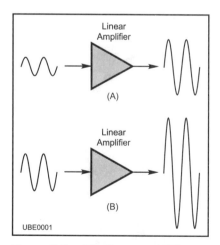

UBE0001

Figure 2-2 — The linear amplifier in part A increases the amplitude of the input signal by a factor of 3 (the gain = 3). In part B, the same amplifier has a larger input signal, which it amplifies by the same gain of 3. In both part A and part B, the output signal is three times bigger than the input signal.

Figure 2-4 — An analog guitar amplifier may have input jacks for signals from several instruments and microphones. Gain controls determine how much amplification is used (and how loud the amplified signals are). Other controls may affect the tone of the sound or add special effects. (Photo courtesy Roland Corp.)

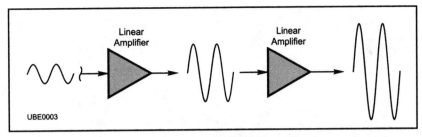

Figure 2-5 — Two linear amplifiers connected in cascade, with the output of one amplifier connected to the input of the next. Each amplifier, called a stage, boosts the amplitude of the signal at its input by a set amount. A guitar amplifier might have four or five stages between the microphone or guitar input and the speaker output.

So when you use your cell phone to order a pizza, the microphone amplifier makes the signal from your voice ("extra cheese please") bigger, and that goes into the cell phone's transmitter. The pizza chef receives your order, and asks "You want anchovies on that pizza?" That question is received on your cell phone, and is quite tiny indeed. The output amplifier in your cell phone helps to boost that weak signal so you can hear it clearly in your cell phone's earpiece (or speaker).

Another example of an analog circuit is a guitar amplifier, such as the one shown in **Figure 2-4**. When the guitar string vibrates, a "pickup" on the guitar turns these vibrations into tiny electrical signals. These signals are sent from the guitar to the amplifier through a cable. Inside the guitar amplifier are several different amplifiers that are connected so that output of one amplifier is connected to the input of the next amplifier, as shown in **Figure 2-5**. (The amplifiers are said to be connected in *cascade*.) Each amplifier boosts the amplitude of the signal in turn until it is big enough to make a large speaker fill a room with guitar sounds.

The world is inherently analog: sound levels, brightness of the sky, temperature and weight of your body, amount of water in a cup or a lake, speed of a car, altitude of an airplane, length of a blade of grass, to name a few. However, in order to measure, record and control analog parameters such as these, it's increasingly common for digital techniques to be used. Digital concepts and circuits are covered in the next chapter. Then, in Chapter 4, we'll return to the world of analog electronics by looking at some of the analog building blocks that are commonly used in a wide range of consumer electronics.

Review Questions

2.1 Analog circuits are:
a) present in only a few electronic devices
b) found only in battery-powered devices
c) the only circuits in cell phones
d) sometimes called *linear* circuits

2.2 An FM or AM radio that uses a dial for tuning likely has:
a) only digital circuits
b) only analog circuits
c) both analog and digital circuits
d) to be repaired at least once a week

2.3 In a cell phone the microphone you speak into is connected to:
a) the earphone
b) the antenna
c) the battery
d) an amplifier

Answers

2.1 d
2.2 b
2.3 d

Chapter 3

Digital Electronic Circuits

Modern Amateur Radio receivers use digital electronics to display the operating frequency.

Contents

Binary Numbers

As you know, there are a whole lot of electronic devices in the world today, and increasingly more and more of them involve digital circuits. First, let's try to understand what a digital circuit is.

Digital information is based on the *binary* system. Binary is a *base 2* system, using only the numbers 0 and 1. Humans are much more familiar with the decimal system, a *base 10* system with 10 symbols (0, 1, 2, 3, 4, 5, 6, 7, 8 and 9).

In digital electronics, a device can have only a finite number of states (as opposed to analog electronics where voltages or other quantities vary continuously). A good example of a binary device is a wall switch for a room light. The switch is either off (binary 0) or on (binary 1). That's it, 0 or 1, no other possibilities exist in the binary system. The binary digits 0 and 1 are called "bits" (*bit* is short for binary digit).

It's quite easy to make a digital electronic circuit using an active device like a transistor. The circuit can be either on or off, and it will work over a wide range of temperature and humidity, and with fresh batteries powering the circuit or nearly dead batteries. In practical circuits, voltage levels within a certain range may be used to represent binary 1 and 0 (**Figure 3-1**).

Conversely, it is quite difficult to make a circuit that can have a range of output voltages, representing a range of decimal numbers, that is stable with variations in temperature and supply voltage. That is why digital circuits, which are either on or off, use the binary system instead of the decimal system, and are used in so many applications.

More Bits, More Precision

Okay, now we realize there's a problem with the binary system if all we use is one bit. All we can express with one bit is *on* or *off*, yet so many things we care about (FM station frequency, body temperature, how much fuel is in a car's gas tank, price of a slice of pizza) require more numerical information than 1 or 0 (on or off). The solution is to use more bits, in fact as many bits as it takes to express numbers with the precision we need. For example, are we satisfied measuring our body temperature using a digital thermometer that can display 98 degrees Fahrenheit (°F), or 99°, or 100°, but not 98.62°? Probably we do want the extra precision of tenths of a degree (98.6° versus 98°). We can do that by using more bits to express the temperature in binary, then convert the binary information to decimal format.

Audio CDs use 16 or 18 bits to express a wide range of music amplitude levels. If 16 bits are used, there are 2^{16} or 65,536 voltage levels that can be used. If 18 bits are used, there are 2^{18} or 262,144 voltage levels that can be used. These very large numbers of voltage levels make it possible to accurately reproduce

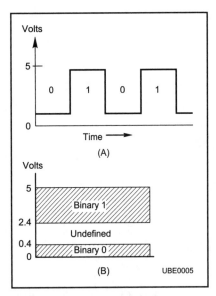

Figure 3-1 — Binary states 0 and 1 may be represented by two different voltage levels, for example 0 and 5 volts as shown at A. In practical circuits, 0 and 1 may be represented by a range of voltages as shown at B.

music that sounds just like the original analog sound before it was converted to digital form on a digital audio CD.

This technology gives very good audio reproduction of the original analog audio signal because it's possible to have very tiny differences of voltage (and the loudness of sound it represents) expressed with this many bits (high precision). Fortunately, using modern integrated circuit techniques, it's quite easy, and rather inexpensive, to add as many bits as is needed to a digital circuit.

In addition to audio, visual information is stored and transmitted in digital format as well (a DVD, for example). Many digital video files use 8 bits to express the brightness of each "pixel" (a tiny picture element, one of many on a display). Why only 8 bits for brightness, compared with 16 or 18 bits for loudness of a sound? Quite simply, 8 bits is enough for most human eyes. Eight bits allows 2^8 or 256 levels of brightness. Any more would be unnecessary, and the average person wouldn't be able to see any improvement in a picture in which more than 8 bits (256 levels) was used for brightness.

Similarly, if a thermometer display reported your body temperature as 98.6237° F, that is way too much precision to know if you have a fever. It would require far more bits than a display that showed 98.6° or 98.7°. This is less precision, but enough for the intended purpose.

Combining Digital and Analog Circuits

An AM or FM radio with a digital display of the frequency to which it's tuned has both analog and digital circuitry. The digital part does the tuning (setting of the radio station frequency to which the radio is tuned) and tells the user the tuned frequency. The rest of the circuitry in the radio is analog circuits. Here, too, the bits are limited to just what is needed. You tune your FM radio to 91.3 MHz, not 91.29735 MHz.

Most cell phones have a lot of digital circuitry, and a lesser amount of analog circuitry. The bottom line with a cell phone is that the input information is analog (the user's voice), and the output information is analog (the voice of the person you called). Frankly, it doesn't matter to the user how much of the cell phone is digital, as long as the pizza can get ordered, and it's very clear to the pizza restaurant if anchovies are requested, or not.

Storing Digital Information

Storing information is inexpensive, easy and reliable, if it's stored in digital format. A CD or DVD disk stores digital information in tiny spots (also known as *pits*; see **Figure 3-2**) burned by a powerful laser or molded into the plastic to store binary ones and zeroes in curved tracks on the disk. As shown in **Figure 3-3**, to read this digital information, a narrow beam of light from a less powerful laser is shined on a curved row of these tiny spots. Each spot either reflects the light back to a photodetector or scatters the light. As the disk rotates under the laser/photodetector, the electronic signal from the photodetector is a stream of ones and zeroes, representing letters and numbers (like Q, f, Z, 7, 4). When these letters or numbers are received and interpreted by other circuits, the result can be a document, a picture, or a song.

The pits are extremely small, with a width of 0.5 micrometer and a length of around 1.0 micrometer (micro means one millionth). To put that size in perspective, a typical mechanical pencil lead has a diameter of 500 micrometers. Because of the tiny size of the pits, a CD can hold around 650 million bytes, representing 5200 million bits.

It is important to understand the concept of a *byte*, which is the basic unit of many computer specifications. For example, a computer's memory might be 2 gigabytes (2 GB, meaning (two billion bytes), while the hard drive capacity is 100 GB.

So what's a byte? One byte is a sequence of 8 bits, and can be used to express symbols like letters, numbers and punctuation marks. The letter "A" expressed in ASCII (American Standard Code for Information Interchange) using 8 bits is 01000001. Some other 8-bit ASCII codes are: "DEL" (the "delete" symbol) is 01111111, "$" is 00100100, "a" is

Figure 3-2 — Pits on a CD, from a scanning electron microscope. The width of a pit is about 0.3 micron (0.3 µm). For comparison purposes, a human hair's diameter is about 75 µm. (Photo courtesy University of Rochester, Institute of Optics)

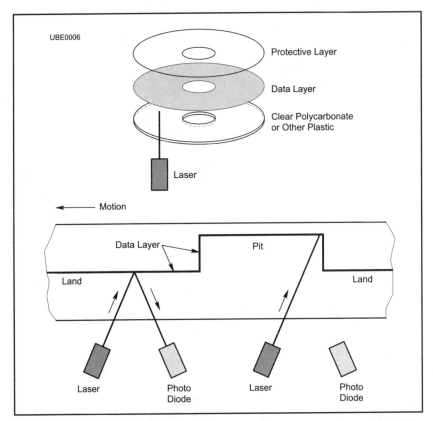

Figure 3-3 — A simplified diagram of how digital data is read from a CD. When the laser beam hits a *land*, the light is reflected into the photodiode; when the laser beam hits a pit, the light is scattered and doesn't reach the photodiode. The electrical signal coming out of the photodiode as the CD rotates is a stream of ones and zeroes, which is turned into *bytes* of information.

01100001, and "9" is 00111001. So on a CD, if your computer has stored the digit "9" using ASCII, there would be 8 spots (8 bits that make up 1 byte).

In Chapter 5, we'll look at some of the digital building blocks that manipulate bits and bytes, and are commonly used in cell phones and other consumer circuitry.

Review Questions

3.1 Digital circuits:
a) are found in only a few electronic devices
b) use many different voltage levels to represent numbers
c) are based on the binary number system
d) use fingers to express numbers

3.2 Audio CDs:
a) store music in analog form
b) use 16 or 18 b to store music amplitude levels
c) make really good coasters to put under glasses of iced tea
d) have millions of tiny lasers embedded within them

3.3 A *byte* is:
a) 8 bits
b) a between-meal snack
c) the unit of loudness of sound
d) equivalent to a pixel on a DVD

Answers

3.1 c
3.2 b
3.3 a

Chapter 4

Building Blocks of Analog Circuits

The oscillator circuit is an analog building block that generates a signal.

Contents

Amplifiers

Any piece of analog equipment, such as a radio or television, is made from a number of smaller circuits, or building blocks, that work together to make the final product. This chapter briefly discusses a few of the most important building blocks and what they do.

As discussed briefly in Chapter 2, an amplifier is a circuit that takes an input signal (such as a voice speaking into a microphone, or a radio signal picked up by an antenna) and makes the signal bigger (that is, it adds power). There's no such thing as free energy — the power that is added comes from a power supply, such as batteries or from the power company providing electricity to your home.

The output of the amplifier may go into a speaker or an antenna. Think of a hearing aid: A tiny signal from a microphone is amplified and the output goes into a tiny earpiece (a small speaker) in the ear canal of the wearer. This output power may be as small as a few thousandths of a watt. This is enough power to allow the person wearing the hearing aid to understand people speaking to him or her. And the tiny amount of output power means the battery will last a long time.

Figure 4-1 — Here's the inside of a ham radio amplifier that increases a 100 watt signal to 1000 watts. This unit uses a vacuum tube and draws power from the ac line.

On the other hand, a television station amplifier for the RF (radio frequency) signal carrying the video (the picture) information may have an output of 300,000 watts! This is enough power to supply the energy needs of about 300 homes, and this is the power needed to send the TV signal to millions of homes. The cost of the electrical energy for a commercial broadcast TV or radio transmitter is quite significant — thousands of dollars per day! **Figure 4-1** shows a more modest RF amplifier that might be found in a ham radio station.

As discussed in Chapter 2, it's common for two or more amplifiers to be connected together to raise the signal to the needed level in several steps. A very important concept is that *all* of this output power, be it thousandths of a watt or hundreds of thousands of watts, is supplied by an outside power supply.

Filters

A filter is used to select, or to reject, a range of frequencies. For example, the treble control on a stereo amplifier can either boost or cut the higher frequencies in an audio signal.

A *notch filter* might be used to remove noise or unwanted signals that interfere with the signal you want to hear. For example, a microphone at a rock concert may pick up noise at a frequency of 60 hertz (Hz) from the power lines (for the lighting) in the concert hall. A 60 Hz notch filter could be used to remove this interference from the microphone signal, while allowing frequencies above and below that 60 Hz notch to be sent on and amplified for the speakers in the concert hall.

A *band-pass filter* can be used to allow a

range of frequencies to pass through while rejecting frequencies below and above that range. For example, the frequencies important in a human voice for understanding speech range from about 300 Hz to 4000 Hz. A band-pass filter for that frequency range would be important in a hearing aid, to eliminate low frequencies (like the many rumbling sounds in a car as it drives down the road) and high frequencies (like wind noise in a car). If those sounds are prevented from reaching the ear of the person wearing the hearing aid, speech is easier to understand.

Band-pass filters are also used in radio and TV receivers, to select the

one station you want to listen to (or watch) and to reject all others. Think of the FM broadcast band, ranging from 88 MHz to 108 MHz. Your favorite FM station is assigned one frequency in that band; mine is 91.3 MHz (the University of Hartford nonprofit radio station). Your FM receiver's task is to receive all the stations' signals from 88 to 108 MHz, use a band-pass filter to separate the one you want from the many, and to send the signal to one or more amplifiers so you can hear it. It does this job with a band-pass filter, rejecting all stations except 91.3 MHz.

Filters are often used when signals from electronic devices interfere with the operation of other electronic devices. The filter shown in **Figure 4-2** is designed to block radio signals that might be picked up through the ac power cord.

Figure 4-2 — An ac line filter is designed to block interference to electronic devices that occurs when radio signals are picked up by the power line.

Mixers

Let's be really clear about mixers. In the world of audio, a "mixer" is a box that takes several audio inputs (microphones and/or instrument pickups) and produces an output signal by adding some of each input. The person operating the mixer board can select how much, if any, of each audio input is sent to the output.

In the world of analog electronics, a *mixer* is a very different circuit building block. Here, a mixer will take two different inputs, and will create an output that contains *sum* and *difference* frequencies. For example,

RF Input
91.3 MHz

Mixer

Output
102 – 91.3 = 10.7 MHz
102 + 91.3 = 193.3 MHz

102 MHz

Local Oscillator
(LO)

UBE0007

Figure 4-3 — A mixer takes two different input signals and creates an output that contains signals at the sum and difference of the input frequencies.

if one input is an FM radio signal at 91.3 MHz, and the other signal is a pure sine wave at 102.0 MHz, then the two output signals from the mixer will be 10.7 MHz (102.0 – 91.3) and 193.3 MHz (102.0 + 91.3). See **Figure 4-3**.

It turns out that nearly every FM receiver amplifies the radio signal to which it is tuned by first converting the received frequency (91.3 MHz in the example above) to 10.7 MHz, and then feeding that new frequency into several amplifier stages tuned to 10.7 MHz. So no matter to what frequency the FM radio is tuned, the *IF* (*intermediate frequency*) amplifier in the receiver provides the amplification to increase the signal's amplitude. By the way, the IF amplifier includes a band-pass filter.

Oscillators

The function of an oscillator is to produce a pure signal with no noise or distortion at a single frequency. All that's needed is an amplifier, and a filter, and some "feedback." The amplifier increases signal amplitude (*gain*) with a *feedback* circuit to route some of the amplifier's output signal back to its input as shown in **Figure 4-4**.

When the amplifier's gain and the amount of feedback are properly adjusted, the oscillator circuit's output will be self-sustaining. This is called *oscillation*. To make an oscillator produce an output at the desired frequency, the feedback circuit must include a filter so that feedback is present at only the intended frequency.

A common example of oscillation is a PA (public address) system in an auditorium, when the volume control of the amplifier (the gain) is

Figure 4-4 — A block diagram of an electronic oscillator. While many amplifiers have an input signal (perhaps from a microphone or antenna), and the output signal is fed to another device (like a speaker), the oscillator creates its own signal. The frequency at which it oscillates is determined by the filter and the feedback path.

turned up just a bit too high. Nearly everyone has heard, and grimaced at, the loud shrieking sound that results until someone either re-aims the microphone or turns down the volume. The filter in this electro-acoustic oscillator is actually an acoustic filter, a combination of the microphone, the speaker and the acoustic properties of the room, and how they respond to different frequencies. In this kind of system, oscillation is highly undesirable.

But for many purposes in electronic circuits, oscillators and the sinusoidal output waveforms they produce are highly desirable and useful. Variable frequency electronic oscillators are used to tune radios and TVs. They are also used to test amplifiers, speakers, and even human hearing.

Power Supplies

A power supply is a circuit that provides the electrical energy that allows other electronic circuits to work. A simple example of a power supply is in a flashlight. The two D cells provide the energy to light the bulb and are its power supply. A cell phone has a battery, and the power supply circuitry in the phone provides several different voltages needed by the analog and digital circuits in the cell phone.

Some power supplies operate from the ac power line and convert that 120 volt ac (V ac) line voltage to provide one or more dc voltages to other electronic circuits. A television, for example, may require four or five different voltages for

Figure 4-5 — A "wall wart" power supply. It plugs into the ac *mains* (120 V ac) and delivers a dc voltage to the device it powers. There are literally hundreds of configurations of wall warts — different voltages, different maximum current capabilities, and even different polarities (+ on center pin or – on center pin).

its circuits, all from one power supply.

A power supply may be as tiny as one integrated circuit, the size of your thumbnail, in your cell phone. It might be a power cube (sometimes called a "wall wart" — **Figure 4-5**) used to provide power to, or to charge, many electronic devices (PDA, MP3 player, answering machine, cell phone). For a large RF transmitter (radio or TV station), the power supply might be as big as a car. Whatever its size, the power supply's job is the same: to provide the energy required by the electronic circuit, or system, to which it is connected.

Review Questions

4.1 All *amplifiers*:
a) have high-power output signals
b) require external power input from power supply
c) must have more than one input
d) can be used for audio signals

4.2 A *filter*:
a) must be used when making coffee
b) amplifies very small signals
c) passes, or rejects, a range of frequencies
d) makes your drinking water taste better

4.3 In the world of analog electronics, a *mixer*:
a) is used when more than one microphone is connected to a guitar amplifier
b) makes better brownies than stirring with a spoon
c) adds or subtracts binary numbers
d) creates sum and difference frequencies

4.4 A *wall wart*:
a) is a power supply that plugs into an electrical outlet
b) can be avoided by washing a wall twice per day
c) oscillates to tune a radio
d) converts radio signals to audio signals

Answers

4.1 b
4.2 c
4.3 d
4.4 a

Chapter 5

Building Blocks of Digital Circuits

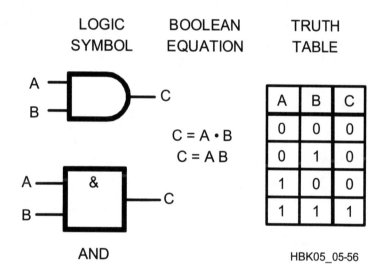

Digital logic gates are one of several building blocks described in this chapter.

Contents

Handling Bits

This is a brief introduction to the kinds of functional blocks that are used in digital circuits and systems. Recall that digital circuits, at their basic level, need to handle and sometimes store *bits* that represent 1 or 0 (on and off). Once a basic circuit that handles one bit is designed, it's very easy to replicate that basic circuit and make larger circuits that handle huge numbers of bits.

For example, as I'm writing this paragraph, every few minutes I tell my computer to save the document. It saves the document to a 4-gigabyte (GB) memory stick (thumb drive) on the USB port of my PC. That memory stick is less than half full, and stores nearly everything I've written and done (except for photos) in the last two years.

This tiny 4 gigabyte thumb drive holds as much information as 833,333 sheets of paper.

To show the incredible storage capacity of a 4 gigabyte (4 GB, or 4,000,000,000 bytes) thumb drive, if one page of a document has 60 lines, and 80 characters per line, storing that page would require about 60×80 = 4800 bytes of memory. To see how many pages the thumb drive can hold, if we divide 4,000,000,000 bytes by 4800 bytes per page, we get 833,333 pages.

A ream of paper is about 2.5 inches thick and holds 500 sheets of paper. So 833,333 pages divided by 500 pages per ream gives us 1667 reams of paper. That's a lot of paper indeed! Multiply 1667 reams by 2.5 inches per ream and that's a stack of reams of paper 4167 inches (347 feet) high. All that text information could be stored on one tiny thumb drive.

Digital Devices

The simplest digital devices are switches and relays. Electronic digital systems, however, are created using *digital ICs* — integrated circuits that generate, detect or in some way process digital signals. Whether switches or microprocessors, though, all digital systems use common mathematical principles known as *logic*.

In binary digital logic circuits, each combination of inputs results in a specific output or combination of outputs. Digital circuits add, subtract, multiply and divide, but normally do it using the binary number system (base 2) using two states represented by the numerals 0 and 1.

Logic Gates

A *logic gate* is a single digital

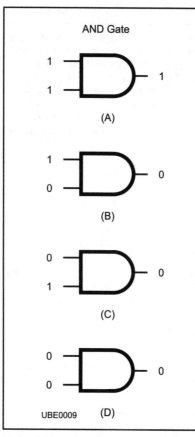

Figure 5-2 — The AND gate is shown above with all possible input combinations. Note that only when all inputs are 1 is the output 1 (part A). If any input is 0, or both inputs are 0, then the output is 0.

block with one or more inputs and generally one output. The simplest logic gate is the *inverter*, which has one input. As shown in **Figure 5-1**, if the input is 1, the output is 0. And if the input is 0, the output is 1.

A common logic gate is the *AND gate*, which has two or more inputs and one output. Only if all inputs are 1 is the output 1; all other input possibilities make the output be 0 (**Figure 5-2**). One example of an AND situation is when you want to turn on a car radio. The key must be in the ignition switch turned to the "on" position, AND the radio switch must be on.

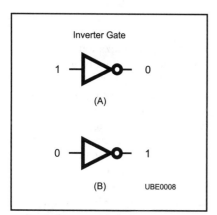

Figure 5-1 — The inverter in part A has a "high" logic level = 1 at the input, and a "low" logic level = 0 at the output. In part B, the 0 on the input produces a 1 on the output.

Figure 5-3 — A NAND gate is made by adding an inverter to the output of an AND gate. Logic designers have found that complex designs (for example, a digital watch or the logic part of a cell phone) can be made more simply using NAND gates.

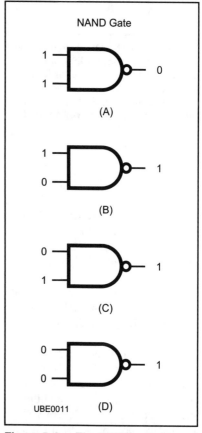

Figure 5-4 — The NAND gate is shown above with all possible input combinations. Note that only when all inputs are 1 is the output 0 (part A). If any input is 0, or both inputs are 0, then the output is 1.

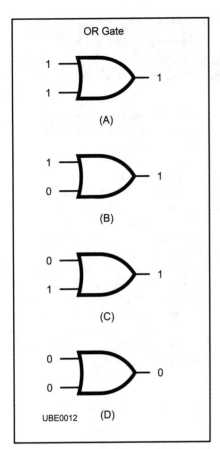

OR Gate

1
1 ⟩— 1

(A)

1
0 ⟩— 1

(B)

0
1 ⟩— 1

(C)

0
0 ⟩— 0

UBE0012   (D)

Figure 5-5 — The OR gate is shown above with all possible input combinations. Note that only when all inputs are 0 is the output 0 (part D). If any input is 1, or both inputs are 1, then the output is 1.

NOR Gate

UBE0013

Figure 5-6 — This NOR gate is made by putting an inverter at the output of an OR gate. Only if both inputs are 0 is the output 1; if one, or both, inputs are 1, the output is 0. Logic designers have found that, like the NAND gate, complex designs can be made more simply using NOR gates.

Digital Oscillator (Clock)   UBE0014

Figure 5-7 — A digital oscillator, or clock, is the metronome for a digital system. Clocks are found in watches, cell phones, computers, DVD players, and in fact in all digital devices. The output is a square wave, with a fixed, and very stable, frequency.

Sometimes an inverter is connected to the output of the AND gate, which creates a *NAND gate* (**Figure 5-3**). Only if all inputs are 1 is the output 0; all other input possibilities make the output be 1, as shown in **Figure 5-4**. NAND gates offer more design flexibility than AND gates.

An *OR gate*, like the AND gate, has two or more inputs and one output. Only if all inputs are 0 is the output 0; all other input possibilities make the output be 1 (**Figure 5-5**). A good example of an OR situation is the dome light in a car. If any door is open, or if more than one door is open, then the dome light is on. Another way to say this is the dome light is off only if all doors are closed.

If an inverter is tied to the output of an OR gate, then a *NOR gate* is the result (**Figure 5-6**). NOR gates allow more design flexibility than OR gates. The output of a NOR gate is the opposite of an OR gate's output.

Timing

A *clock* in a digital system is an oscillator that is made with logic gates and puts out a steady stream of precisely spaced pulses (see **Figure 5-7**). Like the conductor in an orchestra, a clock determines when all the other digital circuits will have their outputs change.

Often this clock is precisely controlled in frequency by a crystal. Your digital watch has such a clock, controlled by a crystal which vibrates at 32,768 hertz (cycles per second). A chain of digital circuits (called flip-flops) connected to this clock divide the 32,768 hertz frequency by 2, first to 16,384 hertz, then to 8192 hertz, 4096 hertz, 2048 hertz, and so on until 1 hertz is reached. This 1 hertz signal allows your digital clock to keep track of time in very accurate 1-second increments.

Memory Devices

A *latch* is a memory device that can be made using logic gates. It will "remember" (by storing as a voltage level) a binary value (0 or 1) that was put in briefly. An elevator button is a good example of a latch. If you want to go up in an elevator, you briefly press the up button, and a latch circuit remembers your request and lights up the up arrow. You don't have to hold the up button, or press it repeatedly (although many of us do this).

A *flip-flop*, also known as a *bistable multivibrator*, stores one bit of information. It is like a latch, but differs in that it has a "clock" input. Changes at the output of the flip-flop occur in synchronization with the digital pulses coming from the clock. While a flip-flop can store only one bit, combinations of flip-flops can be used to make counters and registers. The clock input is important, making sure all the digital circuits perform their tasks at the same time.

A *register* is a collection of flip-flops that is used to store multiple bits (often 8 bits, or one byte). So when you press a number on a calculator, a register in the calculator remembers that number, which will be used subsequently in a calculation.

Counters are a collection of flip-flops that are used for several purposes. One is to count up or count down. A watch and a stopwatch are examples of counters that count up. A counter that counts down is the timer in a microwave oven. You set it for 30 seconds, and it counts down from 30 to 0, warming up your cold leftover pizza.

Converters

Analog-to-digital (A-to-D) converters take electrical signals

Figure 5-8 — At the top of the display are two oscilloscope traces of a pure sine wave, which is the analog input signal to an 8-bit analog-to-digital (A/D) converter. The bottom eight traces are the digital levels (0 or 1) of the A/D converter output. D0 is the *least significant bit*, while D7 is the *most significant bit*. As the analog signal varies in amplitude, the 8-bit digital word (a byte) varies from 00000000 (when the sine wave is at its minimum) to 11111111 (when the sine wave is at its maximum).

(voltages) from microphones, video cameras, electronic thermometers, pressure sensors or photocells and convert the voltages to digital information. The number of bits on the output depends on how the information will be used. Quality audio may require 16 or 18 bits, while the audio in your telephone answering machine may have 8 bits. Because fewer bits are used, answering machine messages don't have the sound quality of a CD player, but they generally give adequate sound reproduction for voices. **Figure 5-8** shows an analog sine wave signal at the input of an A-to-D converter, and the equivalent digital waveforms at the output.

Digital-to-analog (D-to-A) converters take digital inputs and produce analog voltages at the output. A CD player uses a D-to-A converter to take the digital signal's 1s and 0s

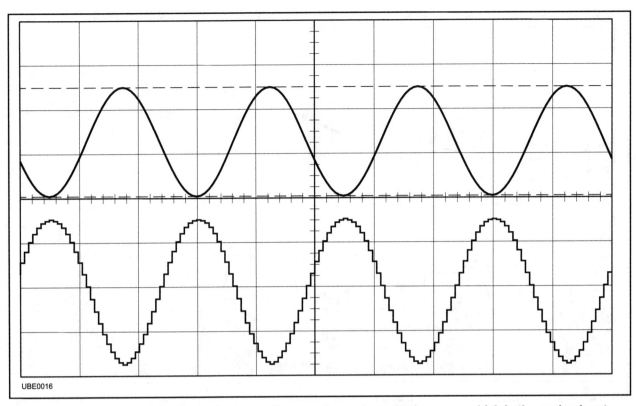

Figure 5-9 — At the top of the display is the oscilloscope trace of a pure sine wave, which is the analog input signal to an 8-bit analog-to-digital (A/D) converter. The bottom trace shows the (inverted) analog output from a digital-to-analog (D/A) converter whose input is the 8-bit digital signal from Figure 5-8. Notice that the analog output signal is an inverted and distorted approximation of the input signal. We can see that it jumps from level to level, instead of varying smoothly, because the input analog signal is changing faster than the A/D converter can handle. Any time that an analog signal is converted to digital format, some distortion will occur. Having a fast A/D converter, and having a lot of bits (for example, using 16 bits instead of 8 bits), will make the distortion negligible.

that come off the CD and recreate an analog signal that is the music stored in digital format on the CD. As with A-to-D converters, the number of bits is an important D-to-A specification. **Figure 5-9** shows the result of a slow D-to-A converter having its 8-bit digital output converted to a distorted analog signal.

There are other digital building blocks (including multiplexers, demultiplexers, buffers, decoders, arithmetic logic units and shift registers) that are beyond the scope of this introductory chapter. What has been presented gives the reader an introduction to the basic circuits that are found in digital systems.

Review Questions

5.1   An *AND logic gate*:
a)   has one input and one output
b)   should be closed so the cows don't escape
c)   has a "high" output only when all its inputs are "high"
d)   has one input and two outputs

5.2   A *clock* in a digital system:
a)   creates a stream of precisely spaced pulses
b)   should be set to *daylight savings time* in April each year
c)   tells the user the date and time
d)   uses AAA batteries

5.3   A *latch*:
a)   keeps the pasture gate closed, so only the farmer can get it
b)   has three output states: high, low or maybe
c)   has a clock input
d)   is a digital memory device which remembers a "1" or a "0"

5.4   In a digital circuit, a *counter*:
a)   is another name for a clock
b)   is a collection of flip-flops, used to count up or count down
c)   is the place where you sit when you're at a diner having lunch
d)   converts time information into binary format

5.5   A *digital-to-analog* converter can be used to:
a)   convert analog information into digital format
b)   convert digital information into analog format
c)   provide more complete combustion of a car's exhaust gases
d)   change Euros into rupees

Answers

5.1 c
5.2 a
5.3 d
5.4 b
5.5 b

UNIT 2

DC Electrical Circuit Concepts

Now that we've seen in Unit 1 some of the neat and useful jobs that electronic circuits can perform and the building blocks that are used to make electronic systems, we should now become familiar with some of the language and concepts of electricity and electronics.

Most electronic circuits process a signal in some way. A signal can be as simple as the electrical pulse created by closing the contacts of a switch. Most signals are more complex, however. A radio receiver takes signals it picks up from an antenna and turns them into sound. A television takes signals it picks up and forms pictures on the screen. Radio and TV signals change constantly. The radio or TV receiver makes more changes to the signal as it converts it to sound or a picture. There are many electronic parts in

The chapters in Unit 2 describe many of the components and concepts used to make electronic circuits.

such a circuit. When you look inside a radio you might think it would be impossible for you to understand how such a circuit works.

Each part has a specific job in the whole circuit. Each part behaves in a certain way when those signals come along. We analyze circuits by looking at each part's task. Then we study the effects it will have on the signal coming into it. In this way, we can understand even the most complicated circuits.

We won't begin our study of electronics by looking at how circuits affect changing signals. Just keeping track of what the signal is doing can be tricky. We'll begin by looking at what happens to a constant, unchanging signal. That way you can concentrate on learning the basic principles without trying to keep track of what the signal is doing.

Your first task, then, is to study the effects of steady, unchanging signals in an electronic circuit. Such signals tell us much about how electronic circuits operate. Once you know how to analyze a circuit with steady signals, it will be much easier to understand the effects of changing signals.

For an unchanging signal, the electricity flows only in one direction. Electricity that flows only in one direction is a *direct current* signal. Electricity that changes direction, flowing first in one direction and then in the other, is an *alternating current* signal. We often use the abbreviations *dc* and *ac* when we describe these two types of electricity. Sometimes the amount of electricity in a dc signal changes, but it still flows only in one direction. In this unit we will concentrate on dc signals that do not vary.

Unit 2, Chapters 6 through 13, will give you the background to understand why:

- lights in a house may dim when the refrigerator starts
- car jumper cables are so thick and heavy
- circuit breakers trip (or fuses blow) when too many things are plugged into an outlet
- your electric bill can be way more than you would expect
- trees may explode when hit by lightning
- powering something with batteries is much more expensive than plugging it in
- a TV or computer monitor can give a nasty shock days after it has been unplugged
- the power company runs very high voltage (around 13,000 volts) quite near your house

But some of what we will be studying requires not only a new vocabulary (volts, amps, ohms, joules, watts) but also some mathematics (don't worry, we'll be using a calculator to make things easier) and a clever way of expressing numbers that are quite small, and others that are quite large, using *scientific notation* and *engineering notation* to make things easier.

In This Unit You Will Learn

✓ about voltage, the pressure that makes electricity move through a circuit

✓ about current, a measure of the amount of electricity in a circuit

✓ what an electric field is by comparing it with magnetism and by observing some effects of electric force acting through space

✓ that we can control how easy it is for electricity to flow through a circuit by selecting conductors, insulators or resistors to make up the circuit

✓ there are two basic kinds of electrical circuits: series circuits and parallel circuits

✓ that a series/parallel circuit is easily understood as a combination of series, and parallel, circuits

✓ how to use Ohm's Law, an important electronics principle, to calculate circuit conditions

✓ about two other important electronics principles, Kirchhoff's Laws

✓ what electrical energy is

✓ how to calculate power, the rate of using that energy

Chapter 6

Electrical Terms: Voltage and Current

You probably know that a wall outlet supplies 120 volts ac for your home, but what does that mean?

Contents

Voltage — The Pressure of Electricity

Most everyone has heard the term *voltage*. A car battery is rated at 12 *volts*, while a toaster or TV is plugged into a wall socket that provides 120 *volts* to make it work. Sometimes we see a "Danger, High Voltage" sign where there are power lines and electrical power company *substations* near buildings. I guess we'd better explore some of the significance to the word *voltage*.

It is dark outside, so you pick up a flashlight before stepping out the door. When you turn on the switch, a bright beam of light shines ahead of you. Have you ever stopped to think about the magic that goes on inside that flashlight? What happens during that moment when you push the switch? The battery inside the flashlight stores electricity. When you close the switch, you complete a path for that electricity to travel to the bulb, and it lights.

The battery stores energy in the chemicals inside it, and when needed the chemical energy is converted to electricity. (You can learn more about how batteries work later.)

A battery pushes electricity through the bulb. Something about the battery pushes the electricity, forcing it to light the flashlight. You also may have noticed that different kinds of flashlights produce different amounts of light.

A small light that uses a single AA-cell battery makes a pretty small beam. A flashlight that uses four or more D-cell batteries usually produces a much larger, brighter light beam. Eventually the batteries begin to die, however, and the light beam becomes smaller and weaker. Batteries such as AA, AAA, C and D cells have a rating of 1.5 volts. Other batteries have different voltage ratings. For example, small "transistor batteries" have a 9-volt rating. Lantern batteries (the kind with coiled springs on top) have a 6-volt rating. Car batteries have a 12-volt rating. Still others, like small watch batteries, have various voltage ratings. **Figure 6-1** shows several battery types.

These voltage ratings tell us something about how much pressure

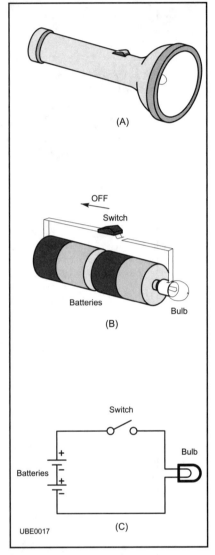

Figure 6-2 — A flashlight is a good example of a simple electronic circuit. There are three main ingredients to any electronic circuit. You must have a voltage source, which in this case is the flashlight battery. You must also have some wires or other conductors to carry the electricity. Finally, there must be a load, or something for the electricity to do. In this example, the flashlight bulb serves as the load. Part A shows a flashlight and B shows a view of the components of the circuit inside the flashlight. Part C is a schematic diagram of the circuit. Schematic diagrams use special symbols to represent circuit components.

Figure 6-1 — Common batteries come in all shapes and sizes. You must select the proper battery voltage for each application. Otherwise you risk destroying part of the circuit, or at least not having the circuit work properly.

will be pushing the electricity that battery will send through a circuit. You must select the proper battery for a particular job, or the circuit won't receive the proper amount of electricity. If you tried to connect a 12-volt car battery to your AA-cell flashlight, the bulb would burn out very quickly (from too much voltage). A single 1.5-volt AA cell wouldn't do much good trying to light your car's headlights, either, since they are designed to glow properly with 12 volts applied to them.

Find a couple of batteries and take a close look at them now. All batteries have two *terminals*, or places to connect wires. One terminal has a + (plus) and the other a – (minus) symbol.

Some electrical devices (a flashlight bulb is one example) can be connected without worrying about which side of the bulb is connected to the plus terminal of the battery. Other circuits (almost any electronic device — a calculator, watch or radio) will work only if they are connected with the proper *polarity*, meaning the plus input of the circuit must go to the plus terminal of the battery.

Figure 6-2 shows the electrical circuit of a flashlight. An electrical circuit forms a complete path (a loop) for the electricity to flow through. The electricity starts flowing from one end of the battery, flows through the wires connecting the battery to the *load* of this circuit (think of the flashlight bulb as the *load,* the part

of the circuit to which energy is delivered in this simple example). Then the electricity returns to the other end of the battery. If the circuit is not complete, the electricity will not flow through it. This is why the switch on your flashlight turns the light off. It opens, or breaks, the circuit, and if there isn't a complete path for the electricity to flow through, no electricity at all will flow.

The unit called the *volt* (often abbreviated V) measures the amount of pressure, or push, in an electric circuit. This push is the force that moves electricity, so we sometimes refer to a voltage as an *electromotive force*, abbreviated *EMF*. Another name we often use for voltage is *electrical potential*, or just *potential*.

Water Pressure Analogy for Voltage

A good way to think of voltage is to relate it to something you are already familiar with: water pressure. Many of us have used a garden hose, to water plants, or to wash a car, or to squirt a friend on a warm summer day. The higher the water pressure, the more water will flow out the end of the hose.

Figure 6-3 shows a container nearly full of water in part A. Some of the water is pouring out through a hole near the bottom of the container. What is forcing the water out of the container? The pressure of the water in the container is exerting a force to push some water through the hole. When the container is full, as shown in part A, the pressure is highest. The water will shoot out farthest from the bottom when the container is full.

When the container is nearly empty, as shown in part B, the pressure is much lower. Now the water doesn't shoot out as far. The amount of water pressure depends on how high the water is above the hole in the container. The more water in the container, the greater the pressure

pushing water out a hole in the bottom.

This example can help you better understand electrical pressure because it is similar to water pressure. The amount of EMF, or voltage, indicates how much electricity that voltage source can move in a circuit. An EMF of 100 volt is much stronger than one of 10 V. A higher voltage can move more electricity than a lower one.

So how can we change the potential, electromotive force, or voltage we apply to an electrical circuit? One way is to use more cells or batteries. A single AA cell produces a voltage of about 1.5 volt between its terminals. If we take two AA cells, and put one atop the other, we have created a battery with 1.5 + 1.5 = 3.0 V. A car battery uses 6 cells, each producing about 2 volt (the chemistry of a cell in a car battery — lead and sulfuric acid — is different from the chemistry of an AA cell).

In **Figure 6-4** we can see that one cell produces 1.5 V, and two cells can

be connected two different ways: in *parallel*, or in *series*. Most flashlights that use more than one cell put the cells in series to increase the voltage.

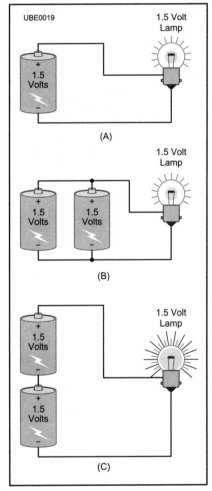

Figure 6-4 — In part A, the 1.5-V lamp glows normally with 1.5 V applied to it. In part B, the two 1.5-V cells are in *parallel*, the voltage across the lamp is still 1.5 volts so it glows normally, and the two cells will last twice as long as the one cell in part A. In part C, the two cells are in *series*, so the voltage across the lamp is now 3.0 V, and the lamp, designed to operate on 1.5 V, will be extremely bright and will burn out quickly.

Figure 6-3 — The height of water in a container determines how much pressure the water exerts on the container bottom. In Part A, the container is full, so there is a lot of pressure. The water shoots far out of the hole in the container. In Part B, the container is nearly empty, so there is only a little pressure. The water does not shoot out as far.

Current — The Flow of Electricity

When you switch on an electronic circuit, something happens. A flashlight shines your way in the dark, a radio begins to play, a cell phone beeps or a computer comes to life. A voltage source (like a battery, or the electric power company) supplies the force, or pressure, to move electricity through a circuit. As we just saw, we measure this force in *volts*. A higher voltage pushes more electricity through the circuit. How do we measure the *amount* of electricity, though?

A unit called the *ampere* describes the amount of electricity flowing in a circuit. We often abbreviate ampere as amp, or simply A. The amount of electricity flowing in a circuit is called the circuit current. Besides requiring a specific voltage, electronic circuits also require a certain current to operate properly. For example, an Amateur Radio transceiver may require a circuit that supplies a current of 20 amperes (A) at 12 volts (V) of electrical pressure. A 60-watt (W) household light bulb requires 0.5 A with 120 V applied to it. Small portable radios often use 9-V transistor batteries. Such a radio may only require a few thousandths of an ampere (known as *milliamperes*) to operate. Other circuits may use only a few millionths of an ampere (known as *microamperes*) to operate; a digital wrist watch is an example of a circuit that uses such a tiny current.

Metric Prefixes

This is a good time to introduce "metric" prefixes. We have heard of millimeters (1 millimeter is one-thousandth of a meter) and kilograms (one kilogram is one thousand grams). Metric prefixes are often used for many of the units in electricity in electronics. **Table 6-1** shows the most commonly used ones.

The third column shows the value of the metric prefix in *engineering notation*. See Appendix A to learn

more about *scientific notation* and *engineering notation*. There are lots of examples and practice questions to help you get familiar with these time-saving notations.

Note that the metric prefixes for big numbers (G, M, k) are upper-case letters, except for kilo (k). The reason for this is that upper-case K is used for temperature expressed in Kelvins, used for science and engineering work. So the prefix kilo, which logically would have used upper-case K, instead uses lower-case k.

Figure 6-5 is a *schematic diagram* of a simple electronic circuit (a flashlight). A schematic diagram uses special symbols to represent the parts of a circuit. The diagram shows how those parts are connected to form a circuit. Do you remember that a voltage source always has two connections? One might wonder "which way does electricity flow out

of the battery"? That is an important question because the answer determines which direction the current flows. Unfortunately, there are two answers to the question.

Benjamin Franklin conducted some experiments with electricity hundreds of years ago, long before scientists knew as much about electricity as is understood today. Franklin decided that the electricity came out of the positive terminal of the battery, went through a circuit, and came back into the negative terminal. **Figure 6-6** shows the current going from the positive battery connection, around the circuit (causing a light-emitting diode to glow) and back to the negative terminal. Engineers refer to this as *conventional current*.

Because a huge amount of experimentation and discovery about electricity and electronics

Figure 6-5 — This drawing is a *schematic diagram* of a simple electronic circuit. This circuit represents a flashlight. We labeled each symbol on the diagram to help you identify the circuit parts.

UBE0020

Table 6-1

Metric Prefixes Common in Electronic Circuits

Prefix	Symbol	Value	Value
Giga	G	10^9	1,000,000,000
Mega	M	10^6	1,000,000
Kilo	k	10^3	1,000
milli	m	10^{-3}	1/1,000
micro	μ	10^{-6}	1/1,000,000
nano	n	10^{-9}	1/1,000,000,000
pico	p	10^{-12}	1/1,000,000,000,000

Figure 6-6 — This drawing shows a circuit with the conventional current direction added. Conventional current moves from the positive battery terminal, through the circuit and back to the negative terminal.

Figure 6-7 — This diagram shows the direction of electron flow through the circuit of Figure 6-6.

happened in the 19th century based on Franklin's assumption, the mathematics of modern electronics follows this convention: current flows from positive to negative.

Many years after Franklin's experiments, scientists learned that negatively charged particles called *electrons* actually make up the electrical current. (You'll learn more about the important role of these electrons in the next few chapters.) Today, we know that electrons actually flow from the negative terminal, through the circuit, and back to the battery. **Figure 6-7** shows the direction of this *electron flow* through our circuit.

Can't we just ignore the old *conventional current*? Well, often

Figure 6-8 — This drawing shows the schematic diagram symbol for a diode. The symbol's arrow shows the conventional current direction through the diode.

we can. But it's important for us to be aware of conventional current since it's used by engineers for many calculations. We continue to use it because it provides a convenient mathematical solution to many problems. Often a schematic diagram will include some type of arrow, and

these arrows point the direction of conventional current through that part. For example, **Figure 6-8** shows the schematic diagram symbol for a *diode*, and the arrow points in the direction of conventional current through the diode.

In this book, we have been very careful to distinguish between conventional current and electron flow. Most references in *The ARRL Handbook* and other ARRL publications also carefully make this distinction. Not all publications are as careful, however, so as you read other books to learn more about electronics, be sure you understand whether the book means electron flow or conventional current when it refers to current.

Review Questions

6.1 DC is an electrical term that refers to:
a) the nation's capital, where the president's house is
b) electrical current that flows in only one direction
c) electrical current that changes direction
d) dielectric constant

6.2 EMF is an electrical term that means the same as:
a) current
b) power
c) energy
d) voltage

6.3 When a battery is connected to something that uses electrical energy, that something is called a:
a) wire
b) ammeter
c) load
d) duck

6.4 An *electronic* (or *electrical*) *circuit* is:
a) a complete path through which current can flow
b) found only when batteries are used
c) where the energy source is located
d) going to make lots of sparks – run for your life!

6.5 In most flashlights, two or more batteries:
a) make a complete path through which current can flow
b) are used to keep the cost to a minimum
c) are put in parallel to increase the charge
d) are put in series to increase the voltage

6.6 Imagine that you are asked to explain to a 3rd grade student the difference between *voltage* and *current*. Consider using the *water* analogy to do this. What would you say?

6.7 We know that electrical current is really the flow of electrons from the negative terminal of a battery to the positive terminal through a *load* (perhaps a flashlight bulb). Yet many books on electronics show the current flow as going from the positive terminal of a battery to the negative terminal. Why is this done?

Answers

6.1 b
6.2 d
6.3 c
6.4 a
6.5 d
6.6 *Voltage* is the electrical pressure which pushes current through a circuit, similar to the water pressure in a hose. *Current* is the amount of electrical charge that flows through a circuit each second, similar to the amount of water flowing in a hose.
6.7 *Conventional current* is considered to flow from a battery's positive terminal to its negative terminal, through a circuit. It was an incorrect decision made by Benjamin Franklin long before electrons were known to be the actual carriers of electrical current. Since the science of electricity and magnetism that was developed in the 1800s was based on this incorrect decision, conventional current is still used today. We all know electron current is what's really happening, but the mathematics and equations still used today use conventional current.

Chapter 7

Conductors, Insulators and Resistors

Resistors come in all shapes and sizes.

Contents

Conductors

There are some materials that allow their electrons to move from one atom to another rather easily; these are called *conductors*. Other materials hold tightly to their electrons, and are not so willing to let go; such materials are called *insulators*. The amount of electrical pressure, or voltage, it takes to move electrons through a material depends on how free its electrons are. If lots of electrons flow through a material with only a small voltage applied, we call that material a conductor. The main reason for using conductors in an electronic circuit is to provide a path for electrons to follow.

Most metals are good conductors. Copper is probably the most common conductor. Silver is one of the best conductors available, although it is expensive. Gold is also a good conductor, but not as good as copper. The main advantage of using gold is that it won't corrode like copper will. A light coating of silver or gold on switch contacts or connector surfaces will help maintain good contact. Aluminum is not as good a conductor as copper, but it is less expensive and lighter.

Iron conducts electricity, but it is not a very good conductor. (It takes only a small voltage to produce a certain current through a copper wire. It takes quite a bit more voltage to produce the same current in an iron wire.) Mercury, a metal that is a liquid at normal temperatures, will conduct electricity. While it is not one of the best conductors, mercury has some interesting uses because it is a liquid.

The *conductivity* of a material tells us how good a conductor

that material is. We won't go into the details of how to measure conductivity here. Just remember that a material with a large conductivity is a better conductor than one with a small conductivity. In fact, we seldom use the actual conductivity of a material in electronics calculations. It's common practice to use a number that compares the conductivity of one material with the conductivity of copper. Any material with a relative conductivity greater than 1 is a better conductor than copper. Materials with a relative conductivity of less than 1 are not as good as copper. **Table 7-1** lists many of the metals commonly used as electric conductors. This table also shows the relative conductivities of the metals listed. The best conductors appear at the top of the list, with the poorer ones shown last.

Figure 7-1 shows a section of copper wire. To help you better understand how electrons move in a conductor, this drawing shows a simplified picture of the copper atoms. It only shows one electron with each atom. That one electron is free to move from atom to atom. Suppose the electron from atom

---

Table 7-1
Some Common Conductors of Electricity

Relative Conductivity (compared to copper)

Silver	1.064
Copper	1.000
Gold	0.707
Aluminum	0.659
Zinc	0.288
Brass	0.243
Iron	0.178
Tin	0.151
Mercury	0.018

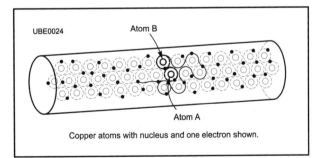

Copper atoms with nucleus and one electron shown.

Figure 7-1 — This drawing shows a simplified model of the atoms in a copper wire. It shows the nucleus of some atoms, along with one electron from each atom's electron cloud. The electrons shown can move from atom to atom with little difficulty. The solid line represents the path followed by one electron as it moves around.

Copper atoms with nucleus and one electron shown.

Figure 7-2 — If we connect a piece of copper wire to a voltage source (like a battery) the electrons drift toward the positive terminal. Individual electrons may only move a few inches each second. Electrons are constantly moving from the negative side of the voltage source onto the wire. Other electrons are constantly moving from the wire to the positive voltage source.

A moves over to atom B. Atom A immediately attracts an electron from another atom to fill the space left by the moving electron. Electrons normally wander randomly from atom to atom, but don't move away from the general area of the atom with which they started.

Now let's apply a voltage to the wire. The positive side of the voltage immediately attracts electrons. As the electrons move from atom to atom, they drift toward the positive end of the wire. **Figure 7-2** shows this electric current in a wire. We use the word drift when describing the movement of individual electrons because each electron moves rather slowly through the wire. If you could watch an electron move through a wire, you'd find that the electron only moves a few inches every second.

This sounds like a pretty slow speed for electrons to move through the wire. How can an electric light come on so fast when you turn the switch, if the electrons move so slowly? What you have to remember is that when you turn the switch, electrons are already in the wire at the light bulb. They are just waiting for the voltage to push them through the bulb. So as soon as we apply a

voltage to the wire, electrons begin to move. Electrons in the center of the wire begin moving toward the positive end. Electrons at the negative end move farther into the wire and electrons from the negative voltage source move onto the wire. At the positive end of the wire, electrons immediately begin to move off the wire and into the positive voltage source. We don't measure an electric current by how *fast* individual electrons move through a wire. We measure current by how *many* electrons are moving.

Figure 7-3 shows a thin slice taken out of a copper wire that is conducting an electric current. By counting the number of electrons that move through this slice each second, we can measure the current. There is 1 ampere of current for every 6.24×10^{18} electrons moving through this slice in one second! 6.24×10^{18} could be written as 624×10^{16} or 6,240,000,000,000,000,000 electrons. (Yes that sure is a lot of electrons! Atoms are very small, though. There are many times that number of electrons in a thin slice of even a small wire.) To light a 100 watt light bulb requires a current of almost 1 ampere, if the applied

voltage is 120 volts.

Of course we don't actually have to count electrons to measure the current in a wire. We'll discuss more of the details about measuring current in a later section. You might also realize there are many more atoms in a slice from a thicker wire than from a thinner one. Larger currents can flow through the thicker wire more easily (with less resistance) because there are more electrons available to move.

It's interesting to note that the electrons don't follow a straight path through the wire. Instead, they move from atom to atom, possibly even moving back toward the negative side of the voltage sometimes. As we increase the voltage applied to the wire, however, the electrons move more directly toward the positive end.

We can compare the movement of electrons through a wire with water flowing through a pipe. If there is more pressure pushing the water, more will flow. A higher voltage pushes more electrons through a wire. If we use a larger diameter pipe, it is easier to force more water through the pipe, as shown in **Figure 7-4**. This is similar to using a thicker wire to carry more current.

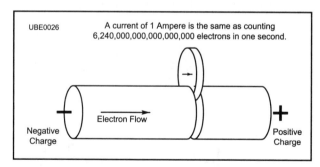

Figure 7-3 — We've taken a thin slice out of a copper wire so we can watch the electrons more easily. Imagine being able to count the electrons as they moved through this section. If you could do that, it would give us a measure of the current in the wire. There is 1 ampere of current for every 6.24×10^{18} electrons that move through this section each second.

Figure 7-4 — We can compare electric current flowing through a wire with the example of water flowing through a pipe. More water flows if there is more pressure, or if we use a larger diameter pipe.

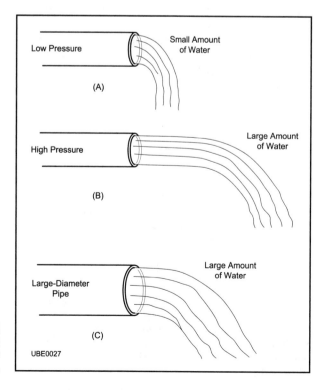

Insulators

Some materials hold tightly to their electrons. These materials don't allow their electrons to move when there is a small voltage across them. Anything that doesn't conduct electricity easily is an *insulator*. You should know, however, that it is possible to make an electric current flow through every material. If the voltage is large enough, even the best insulators will break down and allow their electrons to move. Insulators are important in electronics because they help to keep the voltages and currents where you want them in the circuit. Insulators also help to protect us from the dangerous voltages.

Figure 7-5 shows a spark jumping through an insulator. Once the voltage causes a spark to jump, a current will often continue to flow even at much lower voltages. The spark actually punches a hole in the insulator.

Just as not all conductors are as good as others, all insulators aren't equally as good either. Some will break down and conduct at lower voltages than others. Any insulator will hold up against a higher voltage if we use thicker material, however.

Let's discuss a couple of examples of insulation breakdown that you're probably already familiar with. Nearly everyone has had the experience of walking across a carpeted floor and receiving a shock while reaching for a metal doorknob. You'll notice that you don't receive the shock while you are halfway across the room. You do receive it just before you actually touch the doorknob, though. In this example, your body builds up an electric charge as you walk across the carpet. The air between your finger and the doorknob serves to insulate that charge from the metal conductor. As you move closer to the doorknob, you reduce the thickness of air insulating you from it. At some point the voltage is large enough to cause a spark to jump through that insulator.

You could conduct a small experiment by first shuffling your feet across a room with a thick pile carpet. Carefully approach a metal surface and point your finger as you reach toward the metal. Move gradually closer, until a spark jumps between your finger and the metal, giving you a small shock (**Figure 7-6**). How close did your finger get before the spark jumped? Try walking around the room to build up a bigger electric charge on your body. If the charge is larger, what do you know about the voltage between the metal doorknob and your body? Is the spark likely to jump a bigger or smaller distance?

Lightning gives us another example of an insulator breaking down when there is a large voltage across it. Lightning is an electric spark that jumps between clouds or from a cloud to earth (**Figure 7-7**). How does the voltage that produces lightning compare with the voltage that gives you a shock after walking across the carpet? Of course the voltage that produces lightning is *much* larger, because it moves electrons through a much thicker layer of air, often thousands of feet!

The example of water pressure in a pipe may help you understand insulator breakdown. The hollow opening in the pipe is like a conductor and the pipe itself is like the insulation on a wire. If we block one end of the pipe and increase the water pressure, eventually the pipe will burst. Water will shoot out through the break, instead of remaining inside the pipe. No matter how strong the pipe is, if the pressure is large enough, the pipe will burst.

Table 7-2 lists some materials that we often use as insulators in electronic and electrical circuits. The list is in decreasing order of ability to withstand high voltages without conducting. Rubber is one of the best

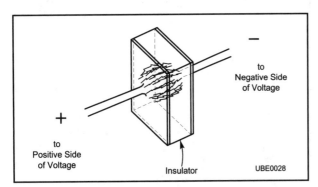

Figure 7-5 — You can make a spark jump through any insulator by applying a large enough voltage. Such a spark will punch a hole in the material, often destroying the insulator.

Figure 7-6 — Have you ever received a shock from touching a doorknob?

Figure 7-7 — Lightning is a natural source of electricity. A layer of air makes an insulator between clouds or between a cloud and the earth. An electric charge builds up on the clouds and the earth, producing a voltage between them. When the voltage is large enough, a spark jumps through the layer of air separating them. *(Photo courtesy C. Clark, NOAA photo library)*

Figure 7-8 — Sometimes the dirt and moisture on an insulator will conduct an electric spark, allowing the spark to jump around the insulator. *(Photo courtesy of Lapp Insulator Company, Le Roy, NY)*

Table 7-2

Common Insulators

Mica	Plastics
Rubber	Glass
Wax	Fiberglass
Porcelain	Dry wood
Bakelite	Air

Table 7-3

Voltage Needed to Puncture

Insulator (1 cm thick)

Mica	500,000 V
Oiled paper	400,000 V
Paraffin	350,000 V
Glass	250,000 V
Air	30,000 V

insulating materials known. Mica is another excellent insulator. (Mica is a mineral that easily separates into thin layers and is almost clear, with slight color variations.) Paper can be a good insulator, especially if it is first soaked in some types of oil or wax. Porcelain and most ceramic materials are very good insulators. Bakelite is

a brittle plastic material often used as an insulator in older electronic equipment. Glass and fiberglass are also common insulators. Air can serve as an insulator, although its voltage breakdown characteristics vary quite a bit depending on temperature and humidity. You can use wood as an insulator as long as it is dry. Modern electronic circuits also make use of various types of plastics as insulators.

Remember that each material has a limitation on how high a voltage you can safely apply to it. **Table 7-3** lists the approximate voltages that will cause a spark to jump through some of the common insulators. These numbers aren't exact, but they will give you some idea of how much voltage the insulators can withstand.

There is another item that you should consider about insulators. Dirt and moisture may serve to conduct electricity around an insulator. Notice that this is not a case of the insulator itself breaking down from the applied voltage. The insulator could probably withstand a much higher voltage, but the dirt provides a path for the electrons to flow around it. See

Figure 7-8. Sometimes accumulated dirt can lead to problems with electronic circuits. It's important to keep things clean so the insulators can do their job.

In Florida, near the Atlantic coast where onshore winds carry tiny drops of sea water with salt, insulators on high-voltage power lines can be coated with a layer of sea salt. In humid conditions (very frequent in Florida) this could cause dangerous arcing, where the high voltage causes large currents to flow across the surface of the insulator. To prevent this arcing, special trucks spray a fine mist of distilled water (water from which dissolved salts have been removed) on the insulators without turning off the electricity! As long as the water used is free of contaminants, the water spray removes the salt deposits from the insulators and improves the reliability of the electric power transmission lines.

Resistors

"Some materials allow a controlled opposition to electron flow."

All materials present some opposition to the flow of electrons. If that opposition is relatively small, the material is a conductor. Insulators are materials that have a large opposition to electron flow. This can be very handy, for example when we plug in a toaster or a lamp. The blades on the plug are metal (a good conductor like brass), while the body of the plug is a good insulator (a plastic that keeps us from having electricity flow through our fingers).

Some materials have too much opposition to be good conductors, yet they allow too much current to be insulators. Such materials are useful in electronic circuits because of their opposition to electron flow. This kind of material is used to make *resistors*. Resistors oppose the flow of electrons through them.

Examples of resistors in non-electronic circuits are a toaster, electric oven, hair dryer, or space heater. See **Figure 7-9**. In all these devices, a metal with far more resistance than copper (a good conductor) provides so much opposition to the flow of current that a lot of voltage is required to force the current through. Together, current and voltage produce electrical power, and in this case the electrical power is converted to heat. This is a good result, for these devices are designed to produce heat. These devices often use *nichrome* (an alloy of nickel, chromium and iron) wire, which has much lower conductivity, and much higher resistance, than copper.

Other examples of not-so-good conductors performing a useful function are fuses and incandescent light bulbs. Fuses such as those shown in **Figure 7-10** are used to protect circuits (and houses) from too

much current flowing. Many fuses have a small piece of high resistance wire or flat ribbon made of a metal or alloy inside a plastic or glass housing. If the current exceeds the current rating of the fuse, the wire or ribbon gets hot and melts (yup — the metal turns to a liquid). This opens the circuit, stopping the flow of current completely.

A light bulb's job is to have the metal (tungsten) inside a glass shell get so hot that it glows white and gives off light. Tungsten has a higher resistance than copper, and also has

a melting point much higher than other metals, so it can glow white hot without melting. So tungsten is a wonderful material for a light bulb, but would make a terrible fuse since it wouldn't melt and open the circuit when it got hot because of excessive current flow.

We've just spoken about electric circuits (toasters, hair dryers, irons, electric ovens) in which the resistor is chosen specifically to generate heat. However, in most electronic circuits, resistors are used to control things (sound level coming out of

UBE0030

Figure 7-9 — All electronic circuits produce some heat. Most of the time we don't want this heat, but sometimes producing heat is the main purpose of a circuit.

Figure 7-10 — Fuses come in a wide variety of sizes, shapes, housings and current ratings. These fuse types are commonly found in electronic circuits. The housings are made of glass, plastic and ceramic (all are insulators), with two metal contacts for each fuse.

an amplifier, brightness of a display, station to which a radio is tuned). Unlike hair dryers and toasters, in most electronic circuits heat is an undesirable result of having a resistor in the circuit. Safely removing that heat from the circuit is an important part of designing electronic circuits.

When we describe electronic circuits, it is helpful to make drawings of the various parts and their connections. We call drawings like this *schematic diagrams*. Special schematic symbols represent each part in a circuit. **Figure 7-11** shows the schematic symbol for a resistor. The zig-zag line appears to create a traffic jam for electrons. It's as though the electrons must slow down to wind their way through the resistor.

You can control the amount of current in an electronic circuit by carefully selecting the amount of resistance in that circuit. So one important reason to use a resistor in a circuit is to limit the current in some part of the circuit. For example, a resistor can make an LED (light-emitting diode) glow with the desired brightness; an adjustable resistor would allow you to make the LED give off more or less light. Carefully selected and properly placed, resistors will guide exactly the right amount of current to each part of the circuit. See **Figure 7-12**.

Current flowing through any resistance will produce heat. There will be more heat when there is a larger current. Most of the time in electronic circuits, this heat is a waste product that we must remove from

Figure 7-11 — This symbol represents a resistor on schematic diagrams of electronic circuits.

Figure 7-12 — Resistors give us a way to control the amount of current going to different parts of an electronic circuit.

the circuit. Occasionally, however, we will *want* to produce some heat with a circuit.

Some metals have a resistance that is quite a bit greater than the resistance of copper, which is the most common conductor. By selecting a type of wire with higher resistance (like nichrome) you can control the amount of current in a circuit. There will be much less current through a nichrome wire than there would be through a copper wire of the same thickness.

Another way to control the amount of current in a circuit is to select the proper diameter wire. It is much harder for electrons to flow through a thin wire than through a thick one.

So by carefully selecting the diameter of wire used in a circuit you can allow just the right amount of current. Remember though, if it's harder for the electrons to flow through the thinner wire, then the current will produce more heat. If there is too much heat the wire may start a fire, or it may melt and break. It's important to be sure that any resistor can get rid of the heat it produces without damaging itself, or anything nearby. See **Figure 7-13**.

Automotive "jumper" cables are used when a car has a weak or dead battery, and the car won't start. The jumper cables connect a healthy battery from another car to the weak battery, and the energy from the

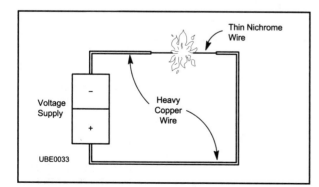

Figure 7-13 — If the current through a resistor produces too much heat, the resistor may melt, or even start a fire.

Figure 7-14 — This cutaway view shows typical construction of wire-wound resistors.

healthy battery starts the car with the weak battery. These cables have large diameter wires, to minimize the resistance (and the heat, and the drop in voltage) that smaller wires would have.

The length of wire that the electrons must flow through helps determine the amount of resistance for a particular piece of wire. You can wind a length of thin wire around a piece of wooden dowel or other form to make a resistor. The exact amount of resistance depends on the type of wire and on its length and diameter. Can you guess why we call resistors like this *wire-wound resistors*? **Figure 7-14** shows how a wire-wound resistor is made.

Carbon, a black, powdery substance, has a resistance that is quite a bit greater than copper. In fact, carbon is called a *semiconductor* for that reason. Manufacturers mix carbon with clay and form it into thin cylinders, or pellets. Then they attach wire leads to the ends, forming resistors that we can conveniently connect into an electronic circuit. The clay serves to hold the powdery carbon together. By changing the amount of clay in the mixture, manufacturers can also control the resistance. As you might have guessed, we call resistors made in this way *carbon-composition resistors*, and for many years they were very common in electronic circuits. **Figure 7-15** is a cutaway view of a carbon-composition resistor.

Modern resistors are usually made another way. The manufacturer starts with a cylinder of ceramic material, which is an insulator. Next, a thin film of carbon is placed over the ceramic. Then leads are attached and the resistor is coated with a layer of epoxy sealer to insulate and protect it. Resistors like this are *carbon-film resistors*. A similar construction method uses a thin film of metal on the ceramic base. Resistors made in this way are *metal-film* types. **Figure 7-16** shows a cutaway view of film-resistor construction.

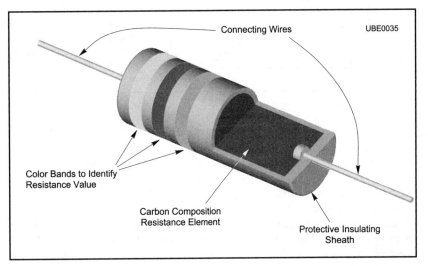

Figure 7-15 — This cutaway view of a carbon-composition resistor shows how this type of resistor is made. The resistance material is a mixture of powdered carbon and clay.

Figure 7-16 — This is a cutaway view of a film resistor. Both metal-film and carbon-film resistors use the same basic construction techniques. The metal or carbon film is trimmed away in a spiral to control the resistance. Part B shows a resistor trimmed with a lathe. The resistor at Part C was trimmed with a laser.

Review Questions ———————————————————

7.1 **Can you name five common conductors?**

7.2 **What determines if a material (an element) is a good conductor?**

7.3 **About how many electrons moving in one second represents a current of one amp?**
a)   7
b)   about a million (10^6)
c)   about a billion (10^9)
d)   about a billion billion (10^{18})

7.4 **If a material requires a very large amount of voltage to make electrons move through it, that material is called:**
a)   uncooperative
b)   an insulator
c)   a semiconductor
d)   a conductor

7.5 **Can you name five common insulators?**

7.6 **What are two common metals that are not good conductors, but are very useful and are found in nearly everyone's house?**

7.7 **Another very useful application of a metal that is not a good conductor is:**
a)   speaker wires
b)   extension cords
c)   fuses
d)   headphone cords for listening to music

Answers ————————————————————————

7.1 Silver, copper, gold, aluminum, mercury, iron, tin, lead; in general, metals.

7.2 The number of electrons in the outermost electron shell of an element's atom determines how good a conductor that element is. Silver and copper have one "free" electron in the outmost shell, and they are the two best conductors of electricity.

7.3 d. One ampere of current is when 6.24×10^{18} electrons flow each second! One billion is 10^9; 10^{18} a billion billion.

7.4 b. Insulators protect us from dangerous voltages. The plastic around the copper conductors on an extension cord is but one example of how insulation does this.

7.5 Rubber, mica, paper, oil, porcelain, most ceramics, glass, air, and many plastics are good insulators.

7.6 Nichrome (an alloy of two metals — nickel and chromium) is used for heating elements in toasters, hair dryers, space heaters, electric ranges and ovens. Tungsten is used as the filament in incandescent light bulbs.

7.7 c

Chapter 8

Electricity and Magnetism

PIECE OF PAPER
ON TOP OF MAGNETS

N   S

IRON FILINGS SPRINKLED ON TOP OF PAPER

**Two magnets and some iron filings allow you to
visualize the lines of force in a magnetic field.**

Contents

Electric Charge

We usually think of electricity as a modern development. It wasn't until the late 1800s that people began to use electricity for the benefit of society. Actually, the discovery of electricity took place more than 2000 years ago! Ancient Greece is known for the philosophers, mathematicians and scientists who lived there. They wanted to discover more about the world around them. They found a kind of rock that seemed to have magical properties when they rubbed it with a piece of fur or cloth. This rock, which they called *elektron*, would attract small bits of dried leaves, wood shavings, straw and other materials. (Today we call this rock *amber*.) Our word *electricity* comes from the Greek name for this rock.

It wasn't until 1733 that anyone realized there might be two kinds of electric charge, or force. Charles DuFay noticed that a charged piece of glass attracted some electrically charged objects but repelled others. He concluded there are two types of electricity. Then in the mid 1700s, Benjamin Franklin conducted some further experiments with electricity. It was Franklin who gave the names *positive* and *negative* to the two kinds of electric charge.

In Ben Franklin's time, scientists thought that electricity was a kind of fluid found in all objects. If there were more of one type of fluid, the object would have the charge of that type, either positive or negative.

Today's scientists have identified very tiny particles that carry the electric charges. *Protons* carry the positive charges and *electrons* carry the negative charges. These particles are much too small for you to see with your eye. In fact they are even too small to see with a powerful microscope. Scientists have found ways to detect these particles by the effects they produce. Protons and electrons are present in every material

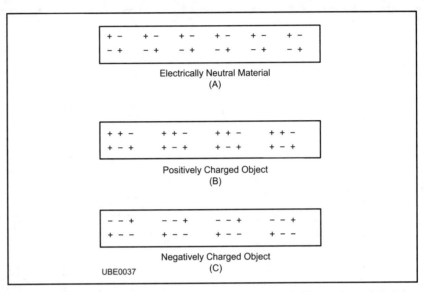

Figure 8-1 — The normal condition for an object, like the metal bar shown, is to have the same number of positive and negative charges. The bar shown in part A is electrically neutral. If an object has more positively charged particles than negative ones, the object has a positive charge (Part B). If an object has more negatively charged particles than positive ones, the object has a negative charge (Part C).

known. In fact, they are some of the basic building blocks of all matter.

The amount of negative electric charge on an electron is the same as the amount of positive electric charge on a proton. So the relative numbers of electrons and protons in an object determine what kind of electric charge that object has. If it has more electrons, it has a negative charge; if it has more protons, it has a positive charge. The normal condition is to be electrically neutral, or to have the same numbers of electrons and protons. See **Figure 8-1**. A charged object will exert a force on other objects. The objects do not have to be in direct contact for this force to be exerted, since the force acts through space.

By now you are probably wondering how an object can become electrically charged, if its normal condition is to be neutral. Let's consider a couple of examples. The

ancient Greeks discovered that they could charge a piece of amber, or *elektron* as they called it, by rubbing it with a piece of animal fur. The friction between the fur and the rock causes the rock to pull some extra electrons away from the fur. Thus, the rock becomes negatively charged. (Actually, it is the heat produced by the friction of rubbing the fur that frees some electrons from the fur.)

You're probably familiar with what happens when you shuffle your feet across a carpet and then touch something metal, like a doorknob! You also can conduct a simple experiment based on this principle, as shown in **Figure 8-2**. First, tear up a few small pieces of paper and place them on a table. Next, take a comb made from hard rubber or nylon, and run it quickly through your hair a few times. The friction that this rubbing produces will pull electrons away from your hair and onto the comb.

Figure 8-2 — A negatively charged object will attract small bits of paper or other lightweight objects.

UBE0038

UBE0039

Figure 8-3 — You can give a positive electric charge to a glass rod by rubbing it with a piece of silk cloth.

In this way, the comb gets a negative charge. Now bring the comb close to the bits of paper. Notice how the paper jumps onto the comb? The electric charge on the comb exerts a force on the paper, attracting it to the comb.

Would you like to try another example? Blow up a balloon and rub that against your hair. Then carefully stick the balloon to a wall or ceiling. Again, the friction of rubbing the balloon through your hair has given the balloon a negative electric charge.

That charge exerts an electric force to attract the balloon to the wall.

All materials don't become negatively charged when you rub them. Rub a piece of glass, like a glass rod, with a piece of silk cloth (**Figure 8-3**). The heat produced by this friction will free some electrons in the glass. That will leave the glass with a positive electric charge. The glass rod will still attract small bits of paper and other lightweight items, however. An object with a positive charge exerts an electric force, just as a negatively charged object does.

It would be helpful to have a number that we could associate with the amount of electric charge on an object. A simple measurement would allow us to compare one charged object with another. In electronics we use the *coulomb* to measure electric charge. A charge of 1 *coulomb* is approximately equal to 6.24×10^{18} (that's 6,240,000,000,000,000,000) electrons. (Recall that 6.24×10^{18} electrons flowing per second is a current of 1 amp.) Of course it's impossible to count the number of extra electrons on a charged object. That's not how we measure a coulomb. Instead, we measure the effects of the charge. The effects are greater for an object with more charge.

Rules of Attraction and Repulsion

In the last section you learned there are two types of electric charge, *positive* and *negative*. If an object has more of either type of charge than the other, it will exert an electric force on nearby objects. In this section you will learn how to determine whether an object has a positive or a negative electric charge. You also will learn some rules about the electric forces exerted by such charged objects.

Figure 8-4 shows an electroscope.

This is a simple device that illustrates the effects of electric charge on an object. The metal rod and gold leaves are inside a glass jar, mainly to protect the delicate gold foil. When the two leaves of gold foil are electrically neutral, they hang straight down, as shown.

Now let's bring a negatively charged object close to the metal ball on top of the jar. (This might be a hard-rubber rod that we rubbed with fur.) Some electrons move away from the ball and onto the gold foil. When the two gold leaves have extra electrons, they push away from each other. This force causes the leaves to stand out to the side, as shown in **Figure 8-5A**.

Remove the hard-rubber rod without touching the electroscope. The electrons will return to their normal positions and the gold-foil leaves will go together. Figure 8-5B shows the electroscope in an uncharged, or neutral, position.

Figure 8-4 — An electroscope illustrates the effects that electrically charged objects cause. The main purpose of the glass jar is to protect the delicate gold-foil leaves.

Figure 8-5 — When we bring a negatively charged object near the top of the electroscope, electrons from the metal ball move onto the foil. With extra electrons on them, the gold leaves push away from each other. The leaves stand out to the sides, as shown in part A. When we take the negatively charged object away, the electrons move back to the top of the electroscope. Then the gold foil is neutral again and the leaves hang straight down, as shown in part B.

Figure 8-6 — Touch the negatively charged rod to the ball on top of the electroscope. Some of the excess electrons will move onto the gold foil, as shown in part A. Then, when we remove the rod, the charge will remain on the electroscope. The gold leaves will stay apart, as shown in part B.

Figure 8-7 — When we bring a positively charged glass rod close to the negatively charged electroscope, the gold leaves will go down. This is because the positively charged glass rod pulls electrons to the top of the electroscope, leaving the foil leaves neutral again.

If we touch the rod to the top of the electroscope, some electrons will flow from the rod onto the metal ball. Now take the negative rod away from the electroscope. The extra electrons keep the gold-foil leaves negatively charged. The leaves remain apart until they become electrically neutral again. See **Figure 8-6**.

These examples illustrate an important rule for electric charges: electrically charged objects that are charged alike (with the same charge — positive and positive or negative and negative) will repel each other. We say: *Like charged objects repel*. If

the objects have only a small amount of charge, there will be a small force trying to push them apart. If the objects have a large electric charge, though, there will be a bigger force trying to push them apart. With an electroscope, you also can observe how the strength of the force varies. As you bring the charged rubber rod close to the electroscope, the gold-foil leaves begin to move apart. As you bring the rod closer to the electroscope, they move farther apart. If the rod has quite a large amount of charge, you can make the gold leaves stand almost straight out.

Let's go back to the negatively charged electroscope, as shown in Figure 8-6. Now suppose we take a glass rod and rub it with a piece of silk cloth. The silk cloth pulls electrons away from the glass, leaving it with a positive charge. When we bring the charged glass rod close to the electroscope, the leaves go down, as shown in **Figure 8-7**. Why is this? The positively charged glass rod attracts electrons from the gold leaves to the top of the electroscope. That removes the negative charge from the gold foil, allowing the leaves to hang straight down again.

Now we'll touch the ball on top of the electroscope with the positively

Positively Charged
Glass Rod

Electrons jump onto glass rod
to neutralize the positive
charges on it. The electroscope
is left with a positive charge.

UBE0044

Figure 8-8 — The positively charged glass rod can recharge the negative electroscope when it touches the ball on top. The gold leaves of the now positively charged electroscope again repel each other, and stand out to the side.

charged glass rod. **Figure 8-8** shows how the gold leaves will spring out to the side again. Some electrons jumped from the electroscope to the glass rod, replacing a few of those pulled off by the silk cloth. The glass rod has less positive charge now than before we touched it to the electroscope. The gold foil has a positive charge, though, because it gave up some of its electrons.

From this discussion you should realize there is a force of attraction between positive and negative electric charges. This brings us to the second important rule for electric charges and the forces they exert: *Oppositely charged objects attract.*

It is very important that you understand and remember these two rules of electric forces. They will help you understand many important principles of electronics. Remember: *likes repel, opposites attract.*

The Structure of Matter

We have been studying electric charges and electrically charged objects. You know there are two kinds of electric charge, and that electrons and protons are small particles that carry these charges. You are probably wondering how these electric charges move around on an object and how they move from one object to another. To understand the movement of these charges better, we'll have to look at the makeup of all matter.

Matter is a scientific term describing every kind of material. Matter can be a solid, a liquid or a gas. Let's begin our brief study by looking at a cup of water. Normally, we think of water as a liquid. Keep in mind, though, that we can turn water into a solid by freezing it. We also can turn water into a gas by boiling it. After any of these changes, the material is still water. (When we boil the water, it turns to steam and the steam leaves the cup, but it is still water.) See **Figure 8-9**.

Imagine taking smaller and smaller amounts of water, until eventually we have a single molecule of water. A *molecule* is the smallest particle of any material that will still have the properties of that material.

We can't make a water molecule any smaller. We could split the molecule, however, and end up with an atom of oxygen and two atoms of hydrogen. **Figure 8-10** illustrates a water molecule splitting into hydrogen and oxygen atoms. *Atoms* are the smallest particles of elements, which combine to form molecules of other materials. An *element* is the simplest form of matter. Scientists have found more than a hundred different elements. Each element has certain characteristics to help identify it. Copper, gold, nitrogen, silicon and uranium are all elements.

Scientists who study matter look for ways to break particles into smaller and smaller pieces. From our discussion so far, you can see they have been quite successful in finding smaller particles that make up everyday materials.

As you might imagine, scientists weren't content to stop when they found atoms. They wanted to know what atoms were made from, too. Individual atoms are so small they are impossible to see, even with a very powerful microscope. Through some

UBE0046

Oxygen

Water Molecule

Hydrogen

Hydrogen

Oxygen

Hydrogen

Hydrogen

Oxygen and Hydrogen Atoms

Figure 8-10 — One oxygen atom and two hydrogen atoms make up each water molecule. We can divide water molecules into these individual atoms, but the resulting material will be oxygen and hydrogen rather than water.

Figure 8-9 — A cup of water shows the three states of matter. At room temperature, water will be in its liquid form. If the temperature is low enough, the water will turn to its solid form, ice. If we heat the water on a stove it will boil and turn into a gas, steam.

UBE0045

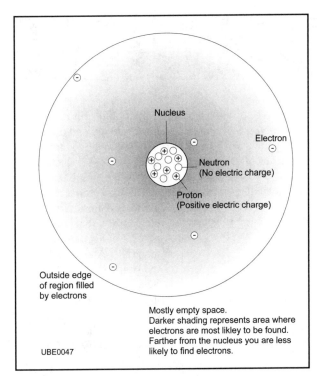

Figure 8-11 — This drawing shows a simplified model of an atom. There is a small central core, called the nucleus. The nucleus contains positively charged protons and electrically neutral neutrons. Surrounding the nucleus is a larger region of (mostly) empty space. Negatively charged electrons occupy this space. The number of electrons surrounding the nucleus is the same as the number of protons in the nucleus. Atoms are electrically neutral.

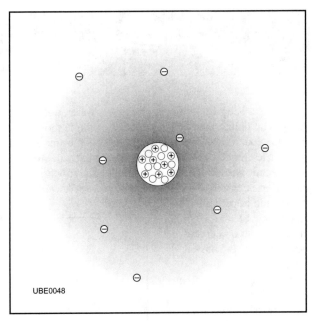

Figure 8-12 — This drawing is a simplified sketch of an oxygen atom. There are eight protons in the nucleus and eight electrons in the electron cloud surrounding it. There are also eight neutrons in this particular oxygen atom. There could be anywhere from five to twelve neutrons in an oxygen atom!

experiments, however, scientists learned a lot about how atoms are put together.

Atoms are mostly empty space. There is a small solid center in an atom, and that center, or *nucleus* has a positive charge. Surrounding the nucleus is a rather large, (nearly) empty space that has a negative charge. See **Figure 8-11**. There are the same number of positively charged particles in the nucleus as there are negatively charged particles around it. The overall effect is that atoms are electrically neutral.

The negatively charged particles surrounding the nucleus are *electrons*. These electrons move very fast. Scientists found two kinds of particles inside the nucleus. The positively charged particles in the nucleus are *protons*. You also might find *neutrons*, which are electrically neutral, in the nucleus. The protons and neutrons are almost 1840 times heavier than the electrons. That helps explain why the electrons can move so much more easily than protons or neutrons.

The number of protons is the same as the number of electrons in any atom. The number of neutrons varies. It is the number of protons (or electrons) that determines what element a certain atom is. For example, a hydrogen atom has one electron and one proton. A helium atom has two electrons and two protons while a carbon atom has six of each. Oxygen has eight protons in its nucleus and gold has 79.

Figure 8-12 shows a drawing of a simple model of an oxygen atom. The nucleus contains eight protons and eight neutrons. There are eight electrons flying around in the space surrounding the nucleus. Although most of the space around the nucleus is empty, the electrons effectively fill the space because of their motion. It might help to think of the space occupied by the electrons as a cloud surrounding the nucleus. There isn't a definite edge, or boundary, to the cloud. Sometimes an electron might fly out a bit farther from the nucleus and at other times it might be in much closer.

Maybe you could use some help understanding the relative size of an atom and its nucleus. Imagine a tiny grain of sand in the middle of a football field. Now let the grain of sand represent the nucleus of an atom. Then the electrons will fill a space the size of the football field, in all directions. The model of an atom developed by scientists includes a definite, detailed electron structure. You don't need to know about those details right now, however. Just remember that some elements have electron structures that are more stable than others. With some elements it is not very difficult for an electron to leave one atom and move on to another one. The atoms of some elements will gladly accept an extra electron or two. There are other elements, however, that simply won't allow any more in their electron clouds.

If an atom loses an electron, then it has one more positive charge than negative charges. When we rub a glass rod with a silk cloth, we pull electrons away from some of the atoms. These atoms now have a positive charge, and so the glass rod itself has a positive charge. Similarly, if an atom gains an electron it has one more negative charge than positive charges. Some of the atoms in a hard rubber rod each pick up an extra electron when you rub the rod with fur. The atoms in the rod have a negative charge, and so the rubber rod itself also has a negative charge.

It is important to remember that electrons move from one atom to another. Normally, atoms have as many electrons as protons, so they are electrically neutral. Electrons give atoms a negative charge if there are too many of them. They also give atoms a positive charge if there aren't enough of them. The atoms of some elements, like copper, gold and silver allow their electrons to move from one atom to another rather easily. The atoms of some other materials hold on to their electrons very tightly. This prevents electrons from moving from atom to atom.

Magnets and Magnetic Fields

Most readers are familiar with some of the basic properties of magnets. As shown in **Figure 8-13**, there are two ends to any magnet, and these ends represent "opposite" kinds of magnetism. These opposite kinds of magnetism are the north-seeking pole and the south-seeking pole of the magnet. The north-seeking pole of a magnet will turn to point toward the Earth's north pole, if it is free to move. This is why we call that pole the north pole of the magnet (**Figure 8-14**).

Either end of a magnet will attract a piece of iron that is not magnetized. Some metals besides iron can be magnetized or attracted by a magnet. Many metals are nonmagnetic.

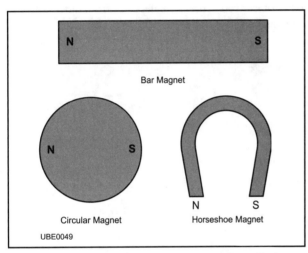

Figure 8-13 — Every magnet has two ends, called *poles.* These poles represent "opposite" kinds of magnetism.

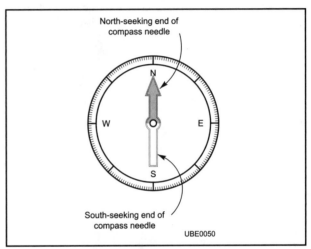

Figure 8-14 — The poles of a magnet are *north-seeking* and *south-seeking* depending on which of the Earth's magnetic poles they point toward.

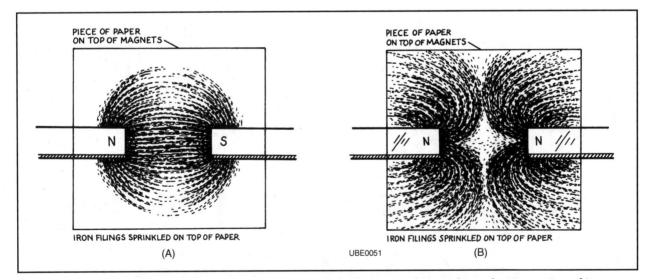

Figure 8-15 — To illustrate the lines of force in a magnetic field, we can place a piece of paper on top of two magnets. Then if we sprinkle some iron filings on the paper, they will line up with the lines of force. If there are many lines between the two magnets, the magnetic field is strong. If there are only a few lines, the field is not as strong. The number of lines represents how strong the force of attraction or repulsion will be. If the lines extend from one magnet to the other, as at A, the magnets attract each other. If the lines leaving one magnet return to the same magnet, as at B, the magnets repel each other.

UBE0052

PUSH ON CHAIR

CHAIR PUSHING BACK

FLOOR PUSHING BACK   FEET PUSHING ON FLOOR   CHAIR PUSHING ON FLOOR
FLOOR PUSHING BACK

Figure 8-16 — There are many examples of forces that require contact between the objects exerting the forces.

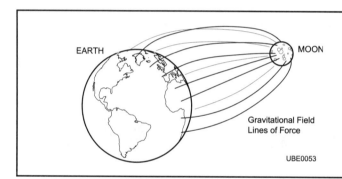

EARTH   MOON

Gravitational Field
Lines of Force

UBE0053

Figure 8-17 — There is a gravitational field between the Earth and the moon that holds the moon in orbit around the Earth. The lines represent the lines of force for this gravitational field.

(Cobalt and nickel are slightly magnetic. Aluminum and copper are examples of metals that are not magnetic.)

There is one other important property of magnets that we should think about here. The forces of attraction and repulsion that magnets exert on each other and on other materials act through space. The objects do not have to be in contact for magnetic forces to act. Lines of magnetic force are illustrated in **Figure 8-15**. This is different from many other natural forces with which you are probably familiar.

For example, consider what happens when you push or pull on a chair to slide it across the floor (**Figure 8-16**). There are several

forces acting because of the objects in contact with each other. You must be touching the chair to move it. You can't look at the chair from across the room and make it move! There is also a friction force that tries to keep the chair from moving. It acts because the chair legs are in contact with the floor.

There are many other examples of forces that act only when objects are in physical contact. The force of exploding gasoline vapor pushing down on the piston in a car engine is one. The difference in air pressure that results in the "lift" that makes an airplane fly is another.

Gravity is a natural force that acts without contact. Pick up a small stone and hold it in the air. Can you feel the

Earth trying to pull the stone back to the ground? If you let go, the stone will fall. Gravity forces also can act over very large distances. The pull of gravity between the Earth and the sun keeps the Earth in orbit around the sun. Similarly, a gravitational field holds the moon in orbit around the Earth (**Figure 8-17**).

You might call the forces that act through space *invisible forces*. Scientists have a special name for these *invisible forces*. They call them *fields*. A field also refers to the region of space through which the force acts. When scientists describe a force of gravity, they call it a *gravitational field*. Likewise, they describe a magnetic force as a *magnetic field*.

Electric Fields are Similar to Magnetic Fields

The two ends of any magnet represent "opposite" kinds of magnetism. The force that these magnetic poles exert on each other produces a *magnetic field*, as shown in **Figure 8-18**. The two kinds of electric charge, *positive* and *negative*, are similar to the two magnetic poles. A positive electric charge attracts a negative electric charge in much the same way that a magnetic north pole attracts a magnetic south pole. Two electric charges of the same kind push each other apart in much the same way as two like magnetic poles would. The electric charges do not have to be in contact with each other to produce these forces. The electric force acts through the space between the charges. As you probably guessed, we call this electric force an *electric field*.

Let's consider some of the properties of an electric field. Like the magnetic field, the electric field is invisible. Try the experiment shown in **Figure 8-19**. Tear a few small bits of paper and place them on your desk or table. Then run a plastic comb quickly through your hair four or five times. Now bring the comb slowly toward the paper bits. What happens? Does the paper jump one or two centimeters off the table to meet the comb? Can you see anything reaching out from the comb to pick up the paper?

When the comb runs through your hair, friction pulls electrons off your hair and onto the comb. In this way the comb becomes negatively charged. You can collect more electrons on the comb by running it through your hair 15 or 20 times instead of five times. (There is a limit to how much negative charge you can collect on the comb, however. You probably won't collect a bigger charge by running the comb through your hair 50 or 100 times rather

Figure 8-18 — **A magnetic field represents the invisible force between two magnets. When two opposite magnetic poles face each other, there is an attraction force between the magnets. If like poles face each other the force would try to push the magnets apart, or repel each other.**

Figure 8-19 — **Try this simple experiment. Tear a few small bits of paper and put them on a table. Then run a comb through your hair a few times. Slowly bring the comb toward the paper bits and watch what happens.**

than 20 times!) Does the paper jump farther off the table when you approach it with the comb now? It should. When the comb has a larger negative charge, it exerts a larger force on the paper bits. The electric field between the comb and paper must be stronger when there are more electrons.

We can conduct the same experiment with a positively charged object. Rub a glass rod with a silk cloth. The silk pulls electrons off the glass in much the same way the comb pulls electrons off your hair. The glass rod will have a positive charge after you rub it.

We represent the electric field between charged objects by drawing a series of lines. This is similar to the way we draw a magnetic field. **Figure 8-20** shows the electric field between a positively charged ball and a negatively charged ball. Notice that

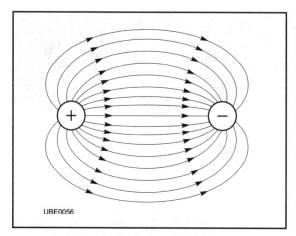

Figure 8-20 — An electric field represents the invisible force between two electrically charged objects. This diagram shows the electric field between a positively charged ball and a negatively charged one. Notice that the electric-field lines go from the positive charge to the negative charge.

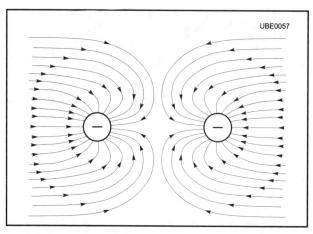

Figure 8-21 — This drawing shows the electric field between two negatively charged balls. Notice that the electric-field lines point toward the negatively charged balls. The electric field between two positively charged balls looks similar, but the lines point away from the charged objects.

the arrows on the lines point from the positive charge to the negative charge. These arrows represent the direction of the electric field.

Figure 8-21 shows the electric field between two negatively charged balls. A similar picture would represent the electric field between two positively charged balls.

The number of lines indicates the strength of the electric field. A stronger field has more lines than does a weaker one. An electric field represents the strength of the force between the charged objects.

The force of an electric field can move electrical charges. The paper bits in our comb-and-paper experiment jumped up to the comb. The comb pushed electrons away and attracted the positive charges. We refer to this ability to move electric charges as an *electrical potential*. (The field has the *potential* — or possibility — of moving charges.) Voltage is another name for electric potential. Voltage is like a pressure that moves electrons through a wire.

Is an electric field the same as a voltage? No. They are related, but they are not the same. You don't have to know the exact details to understand basic electronics, so we'll stay away from the more difficult mathematics in this book. Just remember this important idea: Any time there is a voltage or potential difference between two charged objects, there is also an electric field.

Electric Fields — An Experiment for You to Do

In the earlier sections of this chapter you learned about electric charges and electric fields. You can't see an electric charge, nor can you see an electric field. Yet both are real. You can observe some effects of charges and fields, however. It can be difficult to understand something you can't see. Hands-on observations of their effects may help you gain some insight into these concepts.

This experiment will take about 5 minutes to set up. Don't be surprised if you spend much more than that observing the results, however. The results are fascinating!

Begin with a strip of aluminum foil about 1 to 1.5 inches wide. A standard roll of foil is 12 inches wide. Tear your foil strip into two 6-inch lengths. Roll these pieces into two small foil balls. Next, you'll need two

pieces of sewing thread. You don't need an exact length; 10 to 20 inches each should be plenty. You'll also need a sewing needle, a pencil and a nylon or hard-rubber comb. **Figure 8-22** shows all the pieces ready for assembly.

Figure 8-23 — Attach one piece of thread to each aluminum-foil ball. Use a sewing needle to pass the thread through the foil. Then secure the thread by going around the ball and tying a knot.

Now for the hard part. Use a needle to pull the thread through each one of the foil balls. Pull the end through, and leave a few inches to work with. Take the short end around the ball and tie it to the longer piece using a small knot. Tie the strings to a pencil or a small piece of wooden dowel. **Figure 8-23** shows the detail of the string tied to one foil ball. Now tie the free string ends to the pencil, so both balls hang to the same level.

Finally, find some way to hang your experiment so the foil balls can swing freely. The balls should hang about ½ inch apart. **Figure 8-24** shows one way, using a ruler under some books on a shelf. In this example, the pencil balances on the ruler. You may

Figure 8-22 — Here is the equipment you will need for a simple electric fields experiment. Make the aluminum-foil balls by tearing two pieces of foil, about 1 to 1.5 inches wide and 6 inches long. The thread length doesn't have to be exact; two pieces 10 to 20 inches long will serve. You will attach the balls to the string and suspend them from the pencil. A pen or piece of wooden dowel also will work.

Figure 8-24 — Tie the strings to the pencil so the aluminum-foil balls hang at the same height. Suspend the pencil so the foil balls are away from any objects that might interfere with their movement. Here, some books hold a ruler, and the pencil balances on the ruler. Keep the strings toward one end so both strings are on the same side of the ruler. The foil balls should be about ½ inch apart.

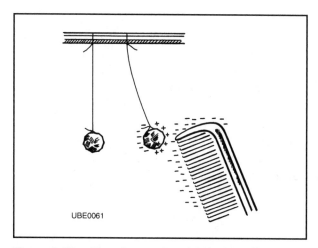

Figure 8-25 — Run the comb quickly through your hair to give it a negative charge. Now bring the comb close to the foil balls. Notice how the comb attracts the balls? What happens if you run the comb through your hair longer or faster? Try running the comb through other family members' hair. You also can experiment with your dog's or cat's fur.

Figure 8-26 — After you experiment with the comb attracting the foil balls, allow the balls to touch the comb. Notice how they immediately swing away from the comb? Experiment with pushing the foil balls around with the comb. Swing the balls out to the side and make them touch the comb again. Do the balls become more negatively charged? How can you tell? Repeat the process a few times to see how much stronger you can make the force between the foil balls and comb.

think of better ways to suspend the experiment.

Now you are ready to conduct your experiment. Run the comb through your hair a few times. This puts a negative electric charge on the comb. Bring the comb close to the foil balls and watch what happens.

At first, the balls swing toward the comb, because the negative charge attracts them. You can pull the balls around without touching them because of the effects of the electric field surrounding the comb. **Figure 8-25** shows that the negative charge on the comb pushes electrons away from the side of the ball it approaches. This leaves that side of the ball positively charged. That is why the comb attracts the ball.

Allow one ball to touch the comb. Notice how the ball jumps away immediately after touching the comb? When the ball touches the comb, it takes some electrons from the comb. Then the foil ball becomes negatively charged. Now the comb repels the foil ball, because they have like charges. See **Figure 8-26**.

Run the comb through your hair again to recharge it. You can push the foil balls around without touching them now, because of the electric fields. Of course if you try to push the balls too far to the side, the force of gravity will overcome the electric force. Then the balls will fall against the comb. Carefully bring the comb between the two balls and push one to the side until it touches the comb. Do the same with the other ball. You can add more charge to the balls by repeating this procedure a few times. (There is a limit to how much charge you can put on the foil balls, though.)

If you can find a piece of glass rod and some silk cloth, you can repeat the experiment with positive charges. Be careful with the glass rod, though.

Review Questions ――――――――――――――――

8.1 Where does the word electron come from?

8.2 What is the name of the instrument that has two thin gold leaves?

8.3 What is the name of the smallest particle of any material that has the properties of that material?

8.4 Explain why the north pole of the planet earth is a magnetic south pole.

8.5 Complete this sentence: Oppositely charged objects will always ...

8.6 Complete this sentence: In one molecule of water, there are _____ atoms of _____ and _____ atom of _____.

8.7 Compared to an electron, a proton:

a) has the same negative charge

b) has a much bigger positive charge

c) has a much larger mass

d) has a much smaller mass

Answers ――――――――――――――――

8.1 The Greek word for amber, which can be used to make a static electricity charge, is electron.

8.2 Electroscope.

8.3 Atom

8.4 The north pole of a compass points towards the geographic north pole of the earth. Since opposite magnetic poles attract, the geographic north pole of the earth must be a magnetic south pole.

8.5 Attract

8.6 In one molecule of water, there are two atoms of hydrogen and one atom of oxygen. The chemical symbol for water is H2O or H_2O.

8.7 c. The mass of a proton is about 1840 times the mass of an electron.

Chapter 9

Capacitors and Inductors

Capacitors like these are found in electronic circuits.

Contents

Stored Charge Produces an Electric Field

In this chapter you will learn about capacitors. Capacitor sounds a bit like *capacity*. You might want to look up capacity in a dictionary. Capacity is the ability to hold, receive or accommodate. A car's gas tank has a capacity of 16 gallons, while the car's capacity is five adult passengers and three big suitcases. A sign in a school auditorium may tell us that the capacity of the room is 250 people. This gives us a good beginning definition for a *capacitor*. Capacitors hold electrical energy. As you learned earlier, *energy* is the ability to do work.

You are familiar with several devices that store energy. Batteries store chemical energy. They produce electricity, or electrical energy, when the chemicals react under the proper conditions. A dam on a river stores water. The energy of that water pressure can run a generator to produce electricity. A coil spring on a screen door stores energy: open the door and the spring gets stretched, storing energy. Let go of the door, and the spring's energy pulls the door shut.

You may wonder how capacitors store electrical energy. **Figure 9-1** shows a circuit that stores electricity in a capacitor. Notice the capacitor schematic diagram looks like two parallel conductors with a space between them. This schematic symbol accurately pictures how a real capacitor is constructed: a metal plate

on top and bottom, with an insulator between the plates.

When you close the switch, electrons leave the negative battery terminal. The positive battery terminal attracts the electrons, and they move through the wires of the circuit. This current can't continue for long, however. The electrons reach the capacitor (the bottom plate), but they can't get through it because there is an insulating layer between the conductors. Two things happen here. First, electrons move onto the conductor surface of the bottom plate. These electrons exert an electric force to repel electrons from the opposite conductor (the top plate). Second, the positive battery terminal attracts electrons from the second conductor. As electrons move off the second conductor, it develops a positive charge.

Figure 9-2 shows the capacitor conductors, or plates, as the charge begins to accumulate. The negative charge on the first capacitor plate also repels any more electrons that try to reach it. At first there are few electrons and this repelling force is small. The battery pushes with a stronger force, so electrons continue to accumulate. As more electrons pile up, however, the repelling force becomes stronger. Eventually, the repelling force of electrons on the capacitor plate equals the battery force, and no more electrons flow onto the capacitor bottom plate.

While electrons are piling up on

one capacitor plate, the battery is pulling electrons off the other plate. Here, as the battery pulls electrons off that plate it becomes more difficult to pull electrons away. Again, the forces reach a balance, and the battery can't pull any more electrons off the top capacitor plate.

Notice that a rather amazing thing has happened here. Electrons flowed out of the battery's negative terminal and accumulated on the capacitor's bottom plate, which forced other electrons (not the same ones) to leave the capacitor's top plate and flow back to the battery. Not one electron flowed through the space between the bottom and top plates! Engineers refer to this flow (into one plate,

Figure 9-2 — One capacitor plate receives a negative charge and the other one receives a positive charge. Eventually no more electrons can flow onto the negative side and no more can leave the positive side.

Figure 9-1 — This circuit includes a battery, a switch, a resistor and a capacitor. The text explains how this circuit stores electrical energy in the capacitor. Notice the capacitor schematic diagram looks like two parallel conductors with a space between them. This schematic symbol accurately pictures capacitor construction.

and out of the other) as a *displacement current*.

Figure 9-3 shows a graph of the circuit current. When you first close the switch the current is 20 milliamps (mA, or 0.020 amp). Don't worry right now about why it's 20 mA. Later we'll learn about Ohm's law, and that the current is determined by the amount of voltage and resistance in a given circuit.

Almost immediately the current decreases, though. Figure 9-3 also has a graph of the voltage across the capacitor plates. When you first close the switch there is no voltage on the plates (the capacitor is said to be *uncharged*). As the electric charge builds up, there is a corresponding voltage building up between them, however. When that voltage becomes equal to the battery voltage, current no longer flows in the circuit, and the capacitor is fully charged.

The time, current and voltages shown in Figure 9-3 apply only to this circuit. These numbers depend on the battery voltage, circuit resistance and the capacitor used in the circuit. Other combinations result in different numbers on the graph. The graph

Figure 9-3 — This graph shows the current through the Figure 9-1 circuit. It also shows the voltage across the capacitor.

shapes don't change, however.

Do you remember there is an *electric field* between two electrically charged objects? This is similar to the magnetic field between two magnets. As charge builds up on the capacitor plates, then, there is an electric field between the plates.

This electric field between the capacitor plates represents stored electrical energy. The capacitor will store this energy as long as the charge remains on the capacitor plates.

Suppose we remove the capacitor

from the circuit. A perfect capacitor would not lose any charge. Of course no capacitor is perfect, so some of the charge will leak through the insulation between the capacitor plates. The capacitor must have wire leads to attach it to a circuit, so some charge always leaks off the capacitor into the air surrounding the capacitor leads.

You should be very careful with capacitors that are in circuits. They can hold a dangerous charge long after you turn off the circuit. If you accidentally touch the leads of such a capacitor, you can receive an electrical shock. A shock from a capacitor can be startling, painful, or even fatal.

An older television or a computer monitor with a picture tube uses high voltage to create the picture on the screen. The picture tube itself can act like a capacitor, storing a charge for hours, days, or even weeks in very dry weather. The voltage across this picture tube capacitor can be tens of thousands of volts, and can cause a very painful (and possibly dangerous) electric shock. Never open a TV or computer monitor containing a picture tube without knowing what you are doing.

A capacitor has two conducting surfaces separated by an insulator. A battery or other voltage source puts extra electrons on one surface, leaving a negative charge. The voltage source removes electrons from the other surface, leaving a positive charge. The electric charge on these surfaces, or plates, produces an electric field.

Suppose you connect a capacitor to a voltage source. The capacitor charges until the voltage across the plates equals the supply voltage. You can't put any more charge on the capacitor unless you increase the supply voltage. A larger voltage stores a larger charge, and thus more energy.

Do you keep a bottle of water in your refrigerator? Sometimes nothing quenches thirst better than a glass of ice-cold water. Have you ever reached for the water bottle only to find it nearly empty? That can be frustrating, especially on a hot summer day. Perhaps you need a water bottle that has a larger *capacity*. Instead of a 1 liter bottle you might want a 2 liter bottle or even a 4 liter bottle. Larger bottles hold more water.

Does this give you any ideas about how to store more energy in an electronic *capacitor*? What do you suppose would happen if the capacitor plates were larger? Yes, the negative plate could hold more electrons. The positive plate also would give up more electrons, to have a larger positive charge.

Figure 9-4 shows two capacitors made from aluminum plates. A layer of air separates the plates and insulates them so no electrons can flow between them. The capacitor shown at A has small plates and only stores a small charge. The electric field between the plates of this capacitor is weak. It doesn't store much electrical energy.

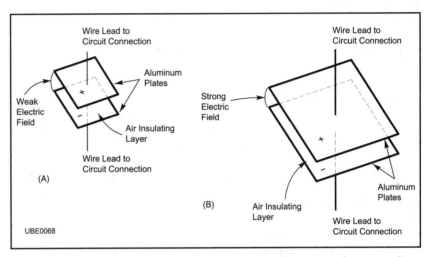

Figure 9-4 — The capacitor shown at A has a small plate surface area. It holds a small electric charge and there is a weak electric field between the capacitor plates. Capacitor B is much larger than capacitor A. When the same voltage connects to each capacitor, capacitor B holds a larger electric charge.

Figure 9-5 — This is a cut-away view of a ceramic disk capacitor. The metal plates have a thin ceramic insulating layer between them. A small wire lead attaches to each plate, so you can connect the capacitor to a circuit. This assembly then has a ceramic or plastic coating applied to protect the capacitor from moisture and other harmful effects.

Figure 9-4B shows a capacitor with much larger plates. Let's imagine they are 10 times larger than the plates of capacitor A. Capacitor B can hold 10 times more charge than capacitor A if they are charged to the same voltage.

One common type of capacitor is the *ceramic disk*. These capacitors have two metal plates with a thin ceramic insulating layer between them. Small wire leads attach to each plate, so you can connect the capacitor into a circuit. **Figure 9-5** shows how ceramic disk capacitors are constructed.

The insulating layer material and thickness determine the capacitor's highest safe operating voltage. If you connect a capacitor to a voltage that is too high for the insulating layer, a spark will jump through the insulation. This will destroy the capacitor.

Suppose you find two ceramic disk capacitors with the same voltage rating. One disk has a larger diameter than the other. Which capacitor is likely to have the higher capacitance rating? That's right. The capacitor with the larger diameter probably has a higher capacitance. It will hold a larger electric charge and will store more electrical energy.

Increasing the Number of Plates Increases Plate Surface Area

Larger capacitor plates hold more electric charge. This produces a stronger electric field and stores more energy. How large can we make the capacitor plates, though? Can you imagine capacitors made with plates 12 inches on a side? That sure would limit how small we could make electronic circuits.

We don't want a capacitor that takes up the area of a kitchen table top. How can we make a capacitor with more plate surface area? Suppose we fold the two plates in half. Fit one side of each plate between the two halves of the other plate. **Figure 9-6** shows a capacitor made this way.

It will be difficult to fold the plates more than once because there is no way to fit them together after you fold them. You can cut the large plates into smaller pieces, though. Then you can connect half the pieces along one edge and half along the other edge. You can put the two stacks together, then, like **Figure 9-7** shows.

This is a much more practical construction method than using two large plates. Many capacitor types use this stacked-plate construction. It is difficult to see the construction when you look at a capacitor, though. Most capacitors have a protective coating, so you can't see inside.

Many electronic circuits require adjustable capacitors. You may change the *capacitance*, or the amount of charge a capacitor can hold, when you tune a radio receiver, for example.

One common variable capacitor type uses one set of plates that rotates and another set of fixed plates. The rotating plates change the overlapping area. When the plates completely mesh, the capacitor has its maximum value. When the plates have no overlapping area, the capacitor has its minimum value.

Figure 9-6 — This capacitor has two plates folded in half to save space.

Capacitor plate folded in half.

Air space to insulate between capacitor plates.

Capacitor plate folded in half.

UBE0070

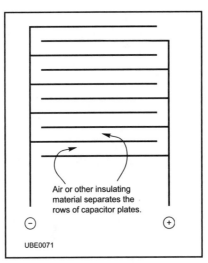

Air or other insulating material separates the rows of capacitor plates.

UBE0071

Figure 9-7 — This capacitor consists of two stacks of plates each connected along one edge. Air or another insulating material separates the two sets of plates.

UBE0072

Moveable Plates

Rotation

Shaft

Stationary Plates

Figure 9-8 — This variable capacitor has two sets of plates. One set can rotate, while the other set cannot move. The rotating plates turn in and out of the fixed plates, changing the overlapping surface area.

Figure 9-8 shows such a variable capacitor. A layer of air separates the rows of capacitor plates, preventing electrons from flowing between them.

You can find these "air variable capacitors" in many sizes. Some have a few small plates. Others have larger plates, and usually more of them.

There is another way to reduce the capacitor's package size. If you make the plates from a metal foil, you can roll the plates and insulating material into a cylinder. This only works if you use a solid material to insulate between the plates, of course.

You can make a capacitor using

this construction technique. See **Figure 9-9** to help visualize the steps described here. You'll need some aluminum foil and waxed paper. The size of the aluminum-foil capacitor plates isn't critical. Tear four square pieces of waxed paper. Make their length equal the roll's width. Then tear four pieces of aluminum foil. Make the foil about an inch smaller than the waxed paper in both dimensions. Leave a foil tab on each foil piece. These will connect alternate foil layers. When you assemble your capacitor, alternate the direction of the tabs, so the first and third layers connect on one side and the second and fourth layers connect on the other side.

Figure 9-9A shows a "sandwich" of several aluminum-foil and waxed paper layers. The odd-numbered foil layers connect to form one side of the capacitor. Even-numbered foil layers connect to form the other side. Waxed-paper layers separate each foil layer. "Alligator clip leads" connect to each side of the capacitor.

Now you can roll your capacitor, starting at the end opposite the clip leads. A few small pieces of tape will hold the capacitor in a cylindrical shape. Figure 9-9B shows the rolled capacitor.

If you wish, you can perform an experiment with your capacitor. Connect one lead to a 6- or 12-V battery's negative terminal and the other lead to the positive terminal. Now connect a voltmeter across the capacitor leads. The voltmeter should register the battery voltage.

Figure 9-9 — You can make an experimental capacitor. Part A shows a "sandwich" of aluminum-foil layers with waxed paper between them. Part B shows how to roll the capacitor into a cylinder.

Disconnect the battery and watch the voltmeter. The reading will gradually decrease. The voltmeter drains off the stored energy because it needs some current to register the voltage.

Charge your capacitor again, but don't connect the voltmeter. Disconnect the battery and wait a minute or two. Then connect the voltmeter. Remember which side went to the positive battery terminal, and connect the voltmeter the

same way. Otherwise the meter needle will try to swing the wrong way, and you could damage the meter.

Do not connect your capacitor across the ac mains (an electrical outlet in your home). This would be extremely dangerous because the voltage provided by an electrical outlet can be fatal. To be safe, connect your capacitor to batteries only. Don't use an ac-operated power supply.

Decreasing Plate Separation Strengthens the Electric Field

Figure 9-10 shows a single positive charge and a single negative charge. These charges are far apart, and there is a very weak electric field between them. Now let's move the charges closer together. As they move toward each other, the electric field becomes stronger. Remember that opposite electric charges attract. When the charges are closer together there is a stronger attraction force between them.

The capacitor plates in **Figure 9-11A** are far apart. The extra electrons on the negative plate exert a weak force to repel electrons from the positive plate. (The negative side also exerts a weak force to attract more positive charge onto the positive capacitor plate.)

Now let's move the capacitor plates closer together. Figure 9-11B shows a much stronger electric field between the plates. There are more electrons on the negative plate. There is more positive charge on the positive capacitor plate.

The plates are the same size for both capacitors. We connected the same voltage source to the capacitors in each case as well. The only variable for the two capacitors in Figure 9-11 is the plate spacing.

How close can we safely move our capacitor's plates? Remember that the insulation between the plates keeps the electrons from jumping across to the positive plate. Air is a good insulator, as long as the voltage doesn't become too large. Lightning is an example of an electric spark jumping through air, however. Even at low voltages, the electrons will jump across the gap when the plates move too close.

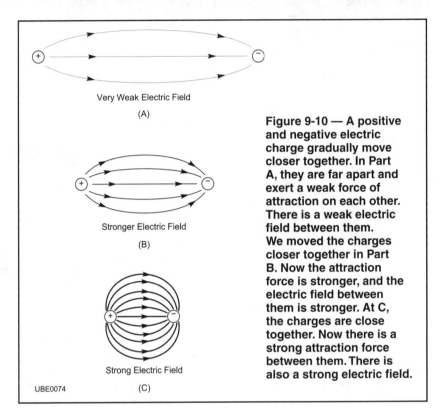

Very Weak Electric Field
(A)

Stronger Electric Field
(B)

Strong Electric Field
(C)

UBE0074

Figure 9-10 — A positive and negative electric charge gradually move closer together. In Part A, they are far apart and exert a weak force of attraction on each other. There is a weak electric field between them. We moved the charges closer together in Part B. Now the attraction force is stronger, and the electric field between them is stronger. At C, the charges are close together. Now there is a strong attraction force between them. There is also a strong electric field.

There is a trade-off between the safe operating voltage and increased capacitance achieved by moving the plates closer together. This is why most capacitors use insulators other than air. Many materials can withstand higher voltages than air. A thin layer of mica or ceramic material is a good capacitor insulator.

Figure 9-12 shows the construction of a mica compression variable capacitor. Several sets of plates have a thin mica wafer (an insulator) separating them. A screw passes through a hole in the center of the assembly and threads into the ceramic capacitor base. As you turn the screw into the base, it compresses the capacitor layers. This brings the plates closer together. As you learned earlier, the plates hold more charge when they are closer together. This produces a stronger electric field.

Other capacitors use a construction method similar to the one you used to make your experimental capacitor in the last section. Solid insulating materials allow the plates to be close together, increasing the amount of charge the capacitor can hold. Rolling the assembly into a cylinder reduces package size.

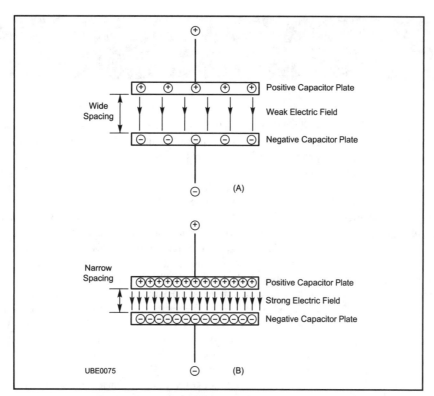

Figure 9-11 — The plates of capacitor A have a wide spacing. We charged this capacitor by connecting it to a battery, so there is some positive and negative charge on the plates. The plate spacing is wide, so the electric field between the plates is weak. At B, we move the capacitor plates closer together. The plates have the same dimensions. We connected the new capacitor to the same battery we used to charge the first capacitor. This time there are more electrons on the negative capacitor plate. The positive charge is also larger. We increased the electric-field strength by moving the plates closer together.

Figure 9-12 — A mica compression capacitor uses thin mica wafers as insulators between the capacitor plates. A screw passes through the plates and mica, threading into the ceramic base. As you turn the screw into the case it presses the capacitor plates closer together. This increases the capacitance, producing a stronger electric field between the plates.

Dielectric Constants and the Electric Field

A capacitor does not conduct direct-current electricity. The insulation between the capacitor plates blocks the flow of electrons. You learned earlier there is a short current pulse when you first connect the capacitor to a voltage source. The capacitor quickly charges to the supply voltage, and then the current stops.

We call the insulation used in a capacitor a *dielectric* because the capacitor does not conduct *direct electric* current. An *air dielectric capacitor* uses air to insulate the capacitor plates. Some common capacitor dielectrics are mica, polystyrene plastic, paper, ceramic and aluminum oxide.

Breakdown voltage is an important dielectric rating. You usually will see breakdown voltage expressed as a number of volts per mil of dielectric thickness. A *mil* is a thousandth of an inch (0.001 inch).

Air has a breakdown voltage of 21 V per mil. Suppose you plan to use the capacitor in a circuit that has a 20-V supply. That means you

will need at least 0.001-inch spacing between the capacitor plates. (You probably will want more spacing to allow a safety factor.) What if you want to use the capacitor in a circuit that has 200 V? You'll need a spacing of 10 mils, or 0.01 inch.

Most capacitor-*dielectric* materials have higher breakdown-voltage ratings than air. Mica, for example, has a breakdown-voltage rating of 3800 to 5600 V per mil. Obviously, a 1-mil thickness of mica is sufficient for most applications.

You should always check the voltage rating of a capacitor before you install it in a circuit. Normally, low-voltage capacitors are physically smaller than higher-voltage units with the same capacitance rating. If a capacitor cannot withstand the voltage applied to it, a spark probably will jump through the insulation, as shown in **Figure 9-13**. This will destroy the capacitor, and may damage other circuit components as well.

Another important dielectric rating is the *dielectric constant*. This is a

measure of how much energy you can store in the insulation between the capacitor plates. Another way to say this is that the dielectric constant indicates the electric-field strength.

Usually when you see a dielectric constant listed, it will be the *relative dielectric constant*. This means it is given in comparison to air. Engineers give air a relative dielectric constant of 1.0.

Porcelain is one type of ceramic used in capacitors. The relative dielectric constant for porcelain is between 5.1 and 5.9. What does this mean? Suppose you make a ceramic capacitor (using porcelain for the ceramic) and an air-dielectric capacitor. Both have the same plate size and spacing. The porcelain-dielectric capacitor will have a capacitance that is 5.1 to 5.9 times greater than the air-dielectric one.

Table 9-1 lists some common dielectric materials and their characteristics.

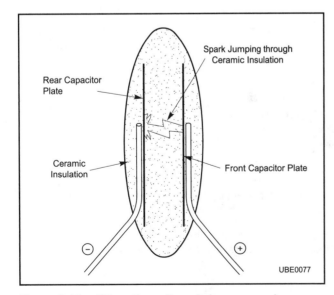

Figure 9-13 — When the voltage is large enough, a spark will jump through any insulating material. A thicker insulator requires a higher voltage to make the spark jump.

Table 9-1

Dielectric Constants and Breakdown Voltages

Material	Relative Dielectric Constant*	Breakdown Voltage**
Air	1.0	21
Bakelite	4.4-5.4	240
Bakelite, mica filled	4.7	325-375
Formica	4.6-4.9	450
Glass, window	7.6-8	200-250
Glass, Pyrex	4.8	335
Mica, ruby	5.4	3800-5600
Mycalex	7.4	250
Paper, Royalgrey	3.0	200
Polyethylene	2.3	1200
Polystyrene	2.6	500-700
Porcelain	5.1-5.9	40-100
Quartz, fused	3.8	1000
Teflon	2.1	1000-2000

*At 1 megahertz
**In volts per mil (0.001 inch)

Factors that Determine Capacitance

In this chapter you have been studying capacitors. When you connect a capacitor to a voltage source, an electric charge builds up on the capacitor plates. Extra electrons build up on one plate, giving it a negative charge. The other plate loses electrons, so it takes a positive charge. These opposite charges, separated by an insulating material, produce an electric field. Capacitors store electrical energy in the form of an electric field.

In this chapter's previous sections we discussed several ways to increase the amount of charge a capacitor holds. In this section we will summarize those factors. First, however, let's discuss the units we use to measure this stored charge. *Capacitance* is the measure of a capacitor's ability to store electric charge.

The basic unit of capacitance is the *farad*. Scientists named the farad for Michael Faraday. Faraday was a British scientist during the early 1800s. Faraday had an interest in static electric fields, such as the field in a charged capacitor. We use a capital letter F to abbreviate farad.

The farad is too large a unit for practical capacitor measurements. A capacitor with a 1-farad capacitance would be physically very large. Microfarads (10^{-6}), abbreviated µF, and picofarads (10^{-12}), abbreviated pF, are more practical measurement units. You also may see capacitance values given in nanofarads (10^{-9}), abbreviated nF. See **Appendix A** to learn more about micro, nano and pico.

Three main factors determine capacitance. The first of these is the plate surface area. Capacitance varies directly with plate surface area. You can double the capacitance value by doubling the capacitor's plate surface area. **Figure 9-14** shows a capacitor with a small surface area and another one with a large surface area.

Remember you can increase the plate surface area by adding more capacitor plates. **Figure 9-15** shows alternate plates connecting to opposite capacitor terminals. Many capacitors use this multiple-plate construction technique.

Larger plates produce physically larger capacitors. Stacking many smaller plates also increases a capacitor's size. Manufacturers roll the stack of plates and insulating material into a cylinder for some capacitor types.

The second important factor affecting capacitance rating is the distance between the plates. Capacitance varies inversely with the distance between plate surfaces. The capacitance increases when the plates are closer together. **Figure 9-16** shows capacitors with the same plate surface area, but with different plate spacing.

The third important factor determining capacitance is the dielectric constant of the insulating material. An insulating material with a higher dielectric constant produces a higher capacitance rating. (This assumes the same plate surface area and spacings.)

Figure 9-17 shows two capacitors. Both have the same plate surface area and spacing. Air is the dielectric in the first capacitor and mica is the dielectric in the second one. Mica's dielectric constant is 5.4 times greater

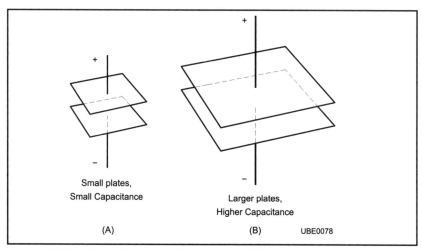

Figure 9-14 — Capacitance varies directly with plate surface area. If all other factors are the same, a capacitor with more plate surface area will have a larger capacitance.

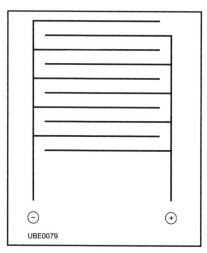

Figure 9-15 — You can connect several sets of plates to produce a capacitor with more surface area.

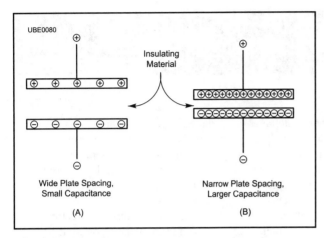

Figure 9-16 — Capacitance varies inversely with the distance between the plate surfaces. If all other factors are the same, a capacitor with plates closer together will have a larger capacitance.

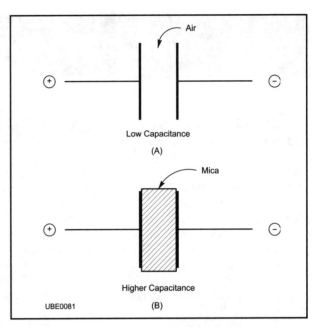

Figure 9-17 — Capacitance depends on the dielectric constant of the insulating material.

than air's dielectric constant. The mica capacitor will have 5.4 times more capacitance than the air-dielectric capacitor. In addition, the mica capacitor can withstand much higher voltages.

To summarize, there are three ways to increase capacitance. You can increase the plate surface area, either by increasing the size of one pair of plates or by increasing the number of plates. You can reduce the spacing between the capacitor plates, by using a thinner layer of insulating material. You can use a better insulator (with a bigger dielectric constant) between the capacitor plates.

Practical Capacitors

You can buy capacitors made with a variety of dielectrics. Each dielectric lends itself to certain construction techniques. There are many trade-offs with regard to cost, breakdown-voltage rating and size. Some dielectric materials are less effective at higher operating frequencies, so you want to avoid those for radio-frequency (RF) circuits. Operating-temperature changes have a significant effect on the capacitance value of some capacitor types.

Selecting the proper capacitor for a specific job isn't difficult. You do have to understand the effects of some trade-offs, however. For example, an inexpensive ceramic capacitor may do fine as a bypass or coupling capacitor in an audio amplifier circuit (audio frequencies are those from about 20 Hz to 20,000 Hz). You would not use a normal ceramic capacitor in an RF oscillator circuit, as radio frequencies are typically from hundreds of thousands of hertz (hundreds of kilohertz) all the way up to billions of

> ## Three main factors that determine capacitance:
> ✔ *plate surface area*
> ✔ *distance between plates*
> ✔ *dielectric constant of the insulating material*

hertz (gigahertz). Ceramic capacitors don't perform well at these high frequencies (RF).

This section is an introduction to common capacitor construction methods and dielectric materials. It will help you understand why a 10 µF paper capacitor may not be a good substitute for a 10 µF tantalum capacitor.

You may see the breakdown-voltage rating given as working-volts dc (WVDC). This is the highest direct (dc) voltage you can safely connect to the capacitor. It is wise to select a capacitor with a breakdown voltage at least two times larger than the highest voltage you expect it to endure. This provides a safety margin. Recall that once the insulating dielectric material in a capacitor is punctured by excessive voltage, the capacitor is ruined. It may even explode in some cases.

Mica Capacitors

Mica capacitors consist of metal-foil strips separated by thin mica layers. **Figure 9-18** shows this construction. Alternate plates connect to each electrode. A plastic or ceramic coating seals the capacitor.

Mica has a breakdown-voltage rating between 3800 and 5600 V per mil (a mil is one-thousandth of an inch). This is why we use mica capacitors in transmitters and high-power amplifiers. Their ability to

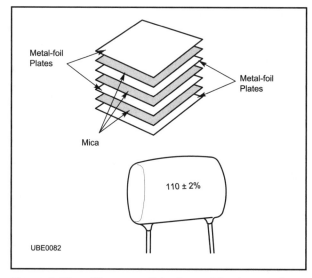

Figure 9-18 — Mica capacitors have thin sheets of mica separating metal-foil capacitor plates. Alternate foil layers connect to the capacitor leads. A ceramic coating protects the assembly from dirt and moisture.

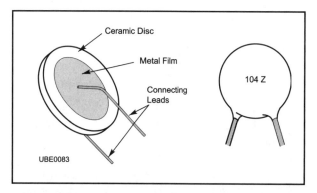

Figure 9-19 — This drawing shows the construction of a disc ceramic capacitor. A metal film deposited on both sides of a small ceramic disc forms the electrodes. Wires attach to the metal, and the assembly gets a protective plastic or ceramic coating.

withstand high voltages is important.

Mica capacitors have good temperature stability. Their capacitance does not change much as the temperature changes.

Typical capacitance values for mica capacitors range from 1 pF to 0.1 µF. Breakdown-voltage ratings as high as 35,000 volts are possible.

Ceramic Capacitors

Ceramic capacitors have a metal film on both sides of a thin ceramic disc. Wire leads attach to the metal film. **Figure 9-19** shows this construction. The capacitor has a protective plastic or ceramic covering.

Ceramic capacitors are inexpensive and easy to make. Many electronics circuits use ceramic capacitors. You can't use them in every application, however.

The capacitance of ordinary ceramic capacitors changes when the temperature changes. It would be unwise to use them in a circuit requiring a capacitance that doesn't change with temperature, such as an oscillator for a receiver or transmitter. You would have to adjust the frequency of the oscillator many times as the circuit warmed up.

Some capacitors have a *negative temperature coefficient*. This means their value decreases when the temperature goes up. Others have a *positive temperature coefficient*. Their capacitance increases when the temperature goes up.

There are special ceramic capacitors that don't change value with temperature changes. These *C0G capacitors* have a zero temperature coefficient. A C0G capacitor has neither a negative temperature coefficient nor a positive one. The capacitance of a C0G capacitor remains nearly unchanged over a wide temperature range. You can buy ceramic capacitors with values from 1 picofarad (1 pF) to 0.1 microfarad (0.1 µF). Ceramic capacitors with breakdown-voltage ratings up to 1000 V are common.

Paper and Plastic Film Capacitors

Paper capacitors consist of

Figure 9-20 — Several capacitor types use the same construction method as the paper capacitor. An insulating material between metal-foil plates forms the capacitor. Roll the assembly into a cylinder and finish it with a protective coating. Paper capacitors use an insulating paper as the dielectric. Plastic-film capacitors use mylar or polystyrene. Chemical-soaked paper goes between the aluminum-foil layers of an aluminum electrolytic capacitor.

Inner Foil

Outer Foil

Insulating Material

UBE0084

alternate layers of metal foil and insulating paper. Wire leads attach to the two sets of metal-foil plates. Then the manufacturer rolls the layers into a cylinder, as **Figure 9-20** shows.

The capacitor may have a plastic covering. This outer layer protects the capacitor from dirt and moisture.

The capacitor may have a stripe around one end. This shows the lead that attaches to the outer metal-foil plate. You can connect this end to the circuit ground, so the outer foil shields the capacitor from radio-frequency energy.

Capacitance values of paper capacitors range from about 500 pF to about 50 µF. They come with voltage ratings up to about 600 WVDC. Paper capacitors are generally inexpensive. They have a larger size for a given value than other capacitor types, and this makes them impractical for some uses.

Plastic-film capacitors are similar in construction to paper capacitors. Thin sheets of mylar or polystyrene serve as the insulating layers. The plastic material gives the capacitors a high voltage rating in a physically small package. Mylar and polystyrene capacitors have good temperature

Figure 9-21 — Tantalum capacitors, sometimes called "tear-drop capacitors" use a small tantalum pellet as the positive plate. This drawing shows the construction of these capacitors.

Dipped Epoxy Coating

Tantalum Pentoxide (Dielectric)

Manganese Dioxide (solid electrolyte)

Silver

Graphite

Tantalum Pellet (Anode)

Positive Lead

Negative Lead

UBE0085

stability. Typical values range from 5 pF to 0.47 µF.

Electrolytic Capacitors

Aluminum electrolytic capacitors also use a similar construction technique. Sheets of aluminum foil have a layer of paper soaked in a chemical solution between them. The rolled assembly goes into a protective casing, usually a metal can.

The chemical causes a reaction when you apply electricity, so we call the chemical an *electrolyte*. This is where we get the name *electrolytic*.

When you apply a voltage to the capacitor it causes a chemical reaction on the positive plate surface. This produces a thin aluminum-oxide layer, which forms the capacitor dielectric. Electrolytic capacitors have a high capacitance value in a small package because of this thin dielectric layer.

One lead of an electrolytic capacitor always has a + or a − sign clearly marked. You must observe this polarity when you connect the capacitor into a circuit. If you connect an aluminum electrolytic capacitor with the wrong polarity, a gas will form inside the capacitor. This may cause the capacitor to explode. At the very least, you are likely to destroy an electrolytic capacitor by connecting it with reverse polarity. Another problem with connecting an electrolytic capacitor backwards is that it behaves like a resistor instead of behaving like a capacitor.

Electrolytic capacitors are available in capacitance values from 1 µF to 100,000 µF (0.1 farad). Some of them have voltage ratings of 400 V or more. Electrolytic capacitors with high capacitance values and/or high voltage ratings are physically large.

Tantalum capacitors are another form of electrolytic capacitor. These are much smaller than aluminum electrolytic capacitors for a given value. They usually have the shape of a water drop.

The *anode*, or positive capacitor plate, is a small tantalum pellet. A layer of manganese dioxide forms the solid electrolyte, or chemical, which produces an oxide layer on the outside of the tantalum pellet. This oxide layer serves as the dielectric. Layers of carbon and silver form the *cathode* or negative capacitor plate.

An epoxy coating gives the capacitor its characteristic shape. This is why we often call them "tear-drop capacitors." **Figure 9-21** shows the construction of a tantalum electrolytic capacitor.

Inductors — Electric Current Produces a Magnetic Field

When electrons move they produce a magnetic field. An electric current flowing through a wire produces a magnetic field. The magnetic field extends outward from the wire. It is stronger close to the wire and gets weaker as you move away from the wire. **Figure 9-22A** pictures this magnetic field around a wire as a series of concentric circles. Each larger circle represents a weaker part of the field. Figure 9-22B shows the magnetic field as tiny bar magnets around the wire.

You can't see a magnetic field, but you can observe its effects. One way to observe a magnetic field is with a compass. Strip the insulation from the ends of a piece of wire that is about 1 meter long. Set a D-cell battery on one end of the wire. Lay a compass on the edge of a table and hold the wire close to it. Touch the other end briefly to the battery top. Watch the compass closely. You should see the needle move slightly when you touch the wire to the battery. The compass needle will move back to North when you remove the wire.

Don't hold the wire on the battery for more than a few seconds at a time. Otherwise the battery may overheat. Then there is a danger that it could explode. You will quickly kill the battery with this experiment, so only touch the wire to the battery a few times.

If the compass does not seem to move, you may need a new battery. It also is possible that you don't have the compass close enough to the wire. **Figure 9-23** shows how the compass needle moves when you touch the wire to the battery.

This relationship between electricity and magnetism is very important. You may have built a simple electromagnet. Most electrical meters operate because

Figure 9-22 — Electrons produce a magnetic field when they move. Part A shows a series of circles surrounding the wire to represent the magnetic field. Part B represents this magnetic field with several small bar magnets around the wire.

Figure 9-23 — These drawings show a D-cell battery, a wire and a compass. The compass needle moves slightly when you touch the wire ends to the battery.

a small electric current creates an electromagnet. This electromagnet turns because there is a permanent magnet around it. A pointer attached to the electromagnet moves across a scale. Voltmeters, ammeters and ohmmeters all operate on this principle.

Electric motors turn because of the magnetic field produced when an electric current moves through the motor's wires. Even the existence of radio signals depends on the relationship between an electric field and a magnetic field.

In the last section you learned that an electric current produces a magnetic field around the wire. The magnetic force surrounding a straight wire is usually weak.

Larger currents produce stronger magnetic fields. It takes a current of many amperes to produce a strong magnetic field with a straight wire.

What if you bend the wire into a circle, and then make several turns next to each other? The weak magnetic field around each piece of wire adds to the force of the pieces on either side of it. **Figure 9-24** shows a piece of wire wound into several turns. The magnetic-force lines wrap through the center of the cylinder, and around the outside. The magnetic field through the coil is much stronger than the individual field of a straight wire.

You probably remember building an electromagnet using a big nail, some wire and a flashlight battery. If you have never made an electromagnet, this is a good time to try it.

For this electromagnet you will need a pencil or plastic stick-type

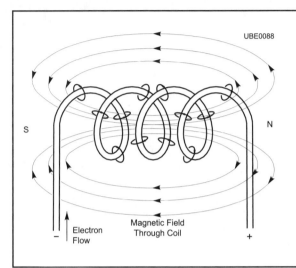

Figure 9-24 — Electric current through a wire coil produces a stronger magnetic field than the same current through a straight wire. The lines of force around each turn reinforce the field around the other turns.

pen. You also will need a coil of small-diameter, enamel-coated copper wire. Leave about 20 cm of wire free on one end. Begin winding wire around the pencil, as **Figure 9-25** shows. Wind each turn against the previous one, but don't overlap the wire. Continue winding until you have covered about 10 cm of the pencil. Leave another 20 cm of wire at the end, cut the wire, and then

remove the pencil. That leaves an open coil of wire, as shown in **Figure 9-26**. Clean the enamel insulation off both ends of your magnet's wire.

To complete your magnet, touch the wire ends to opposite sides of a D-cell battery. Now try to pick up some paper clips by bringing one coil end close to a pile of paper clips. You may have to place one paper clip into the coil center at first. That paper

Figure 9-25 — You can make a simple electromagnet by winding a coil of wire around a pencil or other cylindrical form. The text explains how to wind the wire.

Figure 9-26 — A paper clip held into the wire coil becomes magnetized. Then it picks up more paper clips.

clip becomes magnetized, and it will attract other clips. See Figure 9-26.

How many paper clips will your magnet hold? Do you think your magnet would be stronger if you connected it to a 3-V battery instead of the 1.5-V battery? What do you think would happen if you wound a longer coil of wire?

Increasing the battery voltage increases the current through the wire. This makes a stronger magnetic field. Increasing the number of wire turns on the pencil also makes a stronger magnet. You must be careful to wind the coil in only one direction, however. If you wind back over the top of your first layer, the direction of the magnetic field reverses. In that case, the two layers oppose each other. Your magnet would seem weaker instead of stronger.

We call a coil of wire used in an electronic circuit an *inductor*. An electric current through an inductor creates a magnetic field. You will learn more about inductors and the magnetic fields they create in the rest of this chapter and in Unit 3.

Winding the Conductor Around a Magnetic Material Strengthens the Magnetic Field

In the last section we described how to make an electromagnet by winding some wire around a pencil. Have you ever made an electromagnet like that? Chances are, you used a nail or an iron bar inside the coil of wire in an electromagnetic project.

You might want to make such an electromagnet now like the one shown in **Figure 9-27**. Use a large nail or iron rod. Wind the enamel-coated copper wire around the nail as you did with the pencil in the previous section. Then connect your new magnet to a D-cell battery. How many paper clips will this magnet pick up? Probably many more than the coil without a nail in the last section.

You just learned one way to increase an inductor's magnetic field strength. Winding the coil around

an iron core produces a stronger magnetic field.

What other materials can we use for the center of an inductor or coil? There are many choices. There are many materials made especially for use as inductor cores. Iron powder mixed with clay and other compounds forms one type of core. The manufacturer forms the material into rods or other shapes, and then bakes them to harden the material. Manufacturers prepare special mixtures for different applications. Two general categories of these products are the *powdered iron* and *ferrite* materials. *Ferrite* comes from the Latin word for iron. Chemists often refer to iron compounds as *ferrous* materials.

Ferrite materials have other metal alloys mixed with the iron.

Manufacturers select various alloys for the mixture to provide specific characteristics. You can select a mixture to provide the best performance over a certain frequency range. Iron and powdered iron materials normally cover the audio-frequency range. Various ferrite mixtures cover certain portions of the radio-frequency range.

Figure 9-28 shows two common inductor types. You will find the air-core inductors in many radio transmitters and power amplifiers. There are iron-core inductors in many electronic circuits. Figure 9-28 also includes the schematic-diagram symbols used for these inductors.

Many transmitter and receiver circuits use a special type of inductor core. A toroid is an inductor wound on a core that curves into a donut

Figure 9-27 — A coil wound around a nail or iron rod produces a strong electromagnet.

Figure 9-28 — Plastic strips hold the wires securely in place on one common type of air-core inductor. Iron-core inductors take many forms. The one shown at B has a wire wound on a powdered-iron rod. Heavier wires embedded into the core form leads to connect the inductor into a circuit.

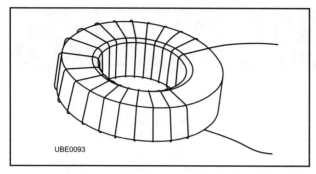

Figure 9-29 — This coil has a toroid (donut-shaped) core. This coil produces a magnetic field that remains completely inside the core.

Figure 9-30 — Part A shows how you can attach a lead to an air core inductor. This allows you to select the number of turns required for your application. Part B shows another type of adjustable inductor. A form of ceramic or other material holds the wire coil. A core of powdered iron or ferrite material threads into the form. You can set the position of the ferrite material inside the coil to adjust the magnetic field.

shape. *Toroid* cores are available in many powdered-iron and ferrite core materials. **Figure 9-29** shows a coil wound on a *toroid* core.

Remember the magnetic field produced by an inductor goes through the center of the coil. The magnetic field from a straight coil curves back around outside the core, because magnetic-field lines form a closed loop.

A magnetic field inside a toroid core doesn't have to loop around outside the core, however. Since the toroid forms a donut (it's a closed circle), the field stays completely inside the core. This is one big advantage of toroid inductors.

Many electronic circuits require an inductor with a magnetic field that you can change. There are several ways to make a *variable* or *adjustable* inductor. One method is to attach a lead to an air-core inductor. See **Figure 9-30A**. You can attach this lead to any point in the coil, selecting the proper number of turns for an application. Radio frequency power amplifier circuits often use a switch with several positions to select coil tap points. You select a different tap point for each frequency band on which the amplifier is to operate.

You also can make an adjustable inductor with a powdered-iron or ferrite core that moves into or out of the coil. You can wind the coil on a form made of ceramic or other material. Then a *slug* or piece of ferrite core material threads into the ceramic form. A screw adjustment allows you to adjust the position of the material in the coil. This changes the magnetic-field strength. Figure 9-30B shows this type of variable inductor.

Factors that Determine Inductance

In this chapter you have been studying inductors. You learned that when electrons move through a conductor they produce a magnetic field. By winding the conductor into a coil, we produced a stronger magnetic field. You also learned that you can wind coils on iron and other magnetic materials. Magnetic materials placed in the center of an inductor also increase the magnetic-field strength.

In Unit 3 you will discover why we use the name *inductor* to describe a coil in an electronic circuit. The *inductance* of a coil is a property that relates to the magnetic-field strength produced by the coil. We use a capital L to represent inductance. A coil with more inductance will produce a stronger magnetic field than one with less inductance.

The basic unit of inductance is the *henry*, abbreviated *H*. This name is in honor of the American physicist Joseph Henry. He discovered a relationship between electricity and magnetism during the early 1800s.

The *henry* is usually too large for practical inductance measurements. A 1-henry inductor is physically very large. We use millihenrys (mH, 10^{-3}) and microhenrys (μH, 10^{-6}) for most measurements. You should be familiar with these metric prefixes.

Four main factors help determine a coil's inductance. Changing any of these factors changes the coil's inductance.

Inductance depends on *the number*

> ## *Factors that determine inductance:*
>
> 1. *number of turns*
> 2. *spacing between turns*
> 3. *coil diameter*
> 4. *type of core material*

---

of wire turns used to wind the coil. Wind more turns to increase the inductance. Take off turns to decrease the inductance. **Figure 9-31** compares the inductance of two coils made with different numbers of turns.

Inductance also depends on *the inductor's length*, and the spacing between turns. **Figure 9-32** shows two inductors with the same number of turns. The first inductor's turns have a wide spacing. This coil is 5 cm long. The second inductor's turns are close together. The second coil is only 1 cm long. Which one do you think has more inductance? Yes, the close-spaced inductor has a larger inductance value.

The third factor that helps determine inductance is the *coil diameter*. You may see coil diameter called *cross-sectional area*. It may

surprise you to learn that larger-diameter inductors have more inductance. **Figure 9-33** shows two inductors. They have the same number of turns, and the spacing between turns is the same. The first inductor has a small diameter and the second one has a larger diameter. The second inductor has more inductance than the first one.

The fourth factor affecting inductance is *the type of core material* in the center of the coil. *Permeability* is a measure of how easily a magnetic field goes through a material. Permeability also tells us how much stronger the magnetic field will be with that material inside the coil.

Permeability is usually given as *relative permeability*. This means the value compares the material with the permeability of air.

One ferrite material has a relative permeability of 75. How much more inductance will a coil wound on this material have than an identical air-core coil? Did you say 75 times more? That's right! Another core material with a relative permeability of 25 will produce an inductance 25 times larger than the same air-core coil.

Figure 9-34 shows three identical coils. One has an air core, one has a powdered-iron rod in the center and the other has a soft iron rod. (*Soft* means the iron hasn't been tempered to harden it. Most nails are soft iron.) This figure illustrates the effects of core material on inductance.

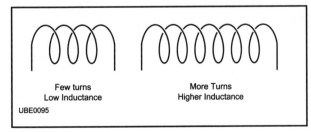

| Few turns
Low Inductance | More Turns
Higher Inductance |

UBE0095

Figure 9-31 — Coil's inductance depends on the number of turns used to make the coil.

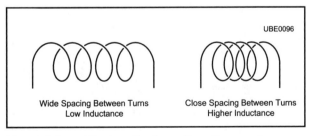

UBE0096

| Wide Spacing Between Turns
Low Inductance | Close Spacing Between Turns
Higher Inductance |

Figure 9-32 — The length of a coil, or the spacing between turns, affects the inductance.

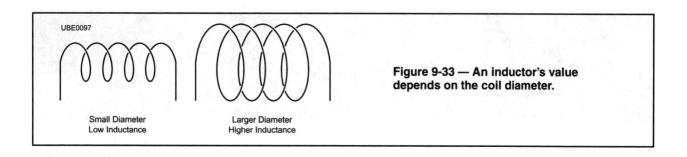

UBE0097

Small Diameter
Low Inductance

Larger Diameter
Higher Inductance

Figure 9-33 — An inductor's value depends on the coil diameter.

Air Core
Low Inductance

Powdered-iron Core
Higher Inductance

Soft-iron Core
Highest Inductance

UBE0098

Figure 9-34 — The core material, or material in the center of the inductor, helps determine the inductance value.

Inductors Store Electrical Energy in a Magnetic Field

What purpose does a magnetic field have in an electronic circuit? You may be wondering about this. It is a good question. After all, we haven't discussed any other effects that an inductor might have on a circuit. An inductor's primary purpose results from a changing current rather than from a steady, direct current. This section gives a partial answer to the question. The next few chapters will give you a clearer picture of the role inductors play in electronics.

A piece of wire does not produce a magnetic field by itself. An electric current flowing through it does produce a magnetic field, though. There is no magnetic field before you connect the wire to a voltage source. When you do connect it to a voltage, electrons begin to flow. The magnetic field gradually increases. (Well, okay, the magnetic field is there almost immediately. If you could study it in slow motion, however, you would see the magnetic field increase gradually.)

Figure 9-35 shows an inductor connected to a battery. The battery supplies a direct voltage that doesn't change. This voltage produces a steady, direct current. The magnetic field reaches a strength determined by the amount of current and the coil's inductance. This magnetic field represents stored energy. Once the magnetic field reaches the strength set by the current and inductance, it doesn't change, as long as the steady current continues.

Imagine you are watching the electrons move through the wire. We can make an interesting observation here. Let's open the switch, breaking the circuit.

When you disconnect the voltage source, the magnetic field collapses. This happens quickly, but again, if you could watch it slowly, you would see the field decrease gradually.

The electrons don't stop immediately when you remove the voltage. Instead, the number of moving electrons gradually decreases as the magnetic field collapses. The magnetic field returns the energy stored in it by continuing to move electrons through the wire.

If the electrons continue to flow, even for a short time, there must be a voltage to push them. (This conclusion results from Ohm's Law, which we'll discuss in a later chapter.) We removed the battery from the circuit, so it doesn't provide a voltage any longer. The inductor is the only part left in the circuit, so it must produce a voltage that keeps the electrons moving while the magnetic field collapses.

The collapsing magnetic field *induces* a voltage across the inductor, trying to maintain the current. The dictionary definition of *induce* is "to move by persuasion or influence." The collapsing magnetic field persuades some electrons to continue moving through the coil (**Figure 9-36**).

You might ask, "If a collapsing magnetic field induces a voltage across an inductor, does an increasing field also induce a voltage?" Yes, it does. In that case the voltage tries to oppose the current, however. So the induced voltage has the opposite polarity to the applied voltage when the magnetic-field strength is increasing. This is why the current increases gradually when you first connect the battery.

The magnitude of the induced voltage depends on how rapidly the current changes. Suppose you have a strong magnetic field built up in a

Figure 9-35 — The magnetic field around an inductor increases from zero when you first connect it to a voltage source. The field strength depends on the current and inductance value. The magnetic field reaches a steady strength with a steady direct current through the inductor.

Figure 9-36 — When we open the switch, the magnetic field begins to collapse. The field returns the energy stored in it by inducing a voltage across the coil, which tries to keep the electrons flowing.

Figure 9-37 — A gasoline engine depends on a large induced voltage to create a spark that explodes the gasoline. There is a strong magnetic field through the induction coil before the circuit is broken. This creates a large induced voltage across the coil, and that voltage causes a spark to jump across the spark plug.

coil. If you suddenly break the circuit, there is a large induced voltage across the coil. This large voltage tries to maintain the current through the coil. The voltage can be many times larger than the original applied voltage. It is common to have a spark jump across the switch contacts as they open.

This is exactly the principle used in the induction coil (or spark coil) of older gasoline engines. A large current flows through the coil. At the proper instant a set of contacts (a switch) opens, inducing a much larger voltage than the battery applies. This induced voltage causes a spark to jump across the gap in the spark plug. The spark ignites the gasoline in the cylinder, and this explosion drives the piston to turn the engine. See **Figure 9-37**. Of course modern electronics has influenced engine design too. The latest systems replace the mechanical distributor and coil with

Figure 9-38 — The magnetic field from one inductor can induce a voltage across other inductors.

individual coils for each spark plug, all operating under the control of an engine management computer.

Figure 9-38 shows two inductors. A battery connects to the first one, but the second one has only a resistor connected across its terminals. The second inductor is close to the first one. Now suppose we open the switch, disconnecting the first inductor from its circuit. A sensitive

ammeter will show a small current in the second circuit when we open the switch.

This experiment is another example of a collapsing magnetic field inducing a voltage. This time the induced voltage was across another coil, however. The magnetic field of one inductor can induce a voltage across other inductors positioned close to the first one.

Review Questions ――――――

9.1 An electrical component that stores energy in its electric field is a:
a) inductor
b) capacitor
c) resistor
d) magnet

9.2 The insulating layer between the plates of a capacitor is called the:
a) dielectric
b) conductor
c) resistor
d) memristor

9.3 In order to increase the capacitance of a parallel-plate capacitor, we can decrease the spacing between the plates. This change will:
a) increase the breakdown voltage of the capacitor
b) cause the plates to reverse polarity
c) make the area of the plates become larger
d) decrease the breakdown voltage of the capacitor

9.4 One dielectric material that can withstand high voltages is:
a) water
b) copper
c) mica
d) aluminum

9.5 To increase the capacitance of a capacitor, which of the following will work?
a) increase the spacing between the plates
b) increase the area of the plates
c) change the dielectric material to air
d) use copper instead of aluminum for the plates

9.6 A capacitor that is an electrolytic capacitor:
a) has a very small capacitance
b) is variable, allowing the capacitance to be changed
c) always behaves as a resistor
d) is polarized, and can be used only with + on one side and – on the other

9.7 An inductor:
a) is a capacitor with magnetic enhancements
b) is a type of permanent magnet
c) is part of a battery
d) stores energy in a magnetic field when current flows through it

9.8 The core of an inductor is frequently made of:
a) iron or a ferrite material
b) an electrolyte
c) copper
d) porcelain

9.9 The unit by which inductance is measured is the:
a) farad
b) ohm
c) henry
d) ampere

9.10 Permeability is the term used to express:
a)   how well a capacitor will dissolve in water
b)   how easily a magnetic field goes through a material
c)   the length of wire in an inductor
d)   the diameter of a toroid

9.11 If you change the current flowing through an inductor:
a)   the inductor will create an induced voltage
b)   you can't change the current; it must be held constant
c)   the inductor will become, for a short time, a capacitor
d)   nothing happens

Answers

9.1   b
9.2   a
9.3   d
9.4   c
9.5   b
9.6   d
9.7   d
9.8   a
9.9   c
9.10 b
9.11 a

Chapter 10

Electrical Circuits — Series And Parallel

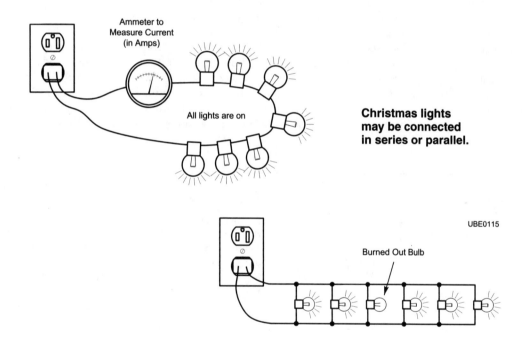

Ammeter to Measure Current (in Amps)

All lights are on

Christmas lights may be connected in series or parallel.

UBE0115

Burned Out Bulb

Contents

Series Circuits

In Chapter 7, we described the use of conductors, insulators and resistors in electronic circuits. Just what is an *electronic circuit*, anyway? One simple definition is that an electronic circuit is a path that electrons follow. An electronic circuit usually includes more than a wire from the negative to the positive side of the voltage source, however. Other parts help the circuit do something useful. The flashlight in **Figure 10-1** is a simple electronic circuit.

Figure 10-2 shows this flashlight circuit drawn as a schematic diagram. Two D cells provide the voltage to make electrons flow in our circuit. The label on Figure 10-2 identifies the schematic symbol for any battery. Notice that the long and short bars on the battery symbol identify the positive and negative ends of the voltage source. The schematic symbol shown for an ON/OFF switch is one of several symbols used to represent switches. As you become more familiar with electronic circuits, you will learn the symbols for other types of switches. The lamp symbol shown in the figure can represent just about any type of light bulb.

In Figure 10-2, the switch is *open*, and the light bulb is off. With the switch in this position, we have an *open circuit*. No electrons can flow in an open circuit. Let's close the switch, as shown in **Figure 10-3**. Now there is a complete path for electrons to move from the negative side of the battery to the positive side. The light bulb glows brightly when electrons flow through it. With the switch in the closed position, we have a *closed circuit*, also sometimes called a *complete circuit*. Electrons can only flow in a closed circuit.

Now let's review what we need to make a useful electronic circuit. First we need a voltage source, the electrical pressure to move electrons through the circuit. Next we need some wire or other conductor for the electrons. Finally, there should be some purpose for the circuit. The light bulb provides the purpose for our flashlight circuit. We often refer to the part that gives a purpose to the circuit as the *load*. So we say the light bulb in our flashlight is the load for the circuit. Any useful electronic circuit has at least these three parts.

We often draw a resistor to represent the load in a circuit. Sometimes a resistor also represents the combined resistance of all the other parts of a circuit. This resistor can include the resistance of the wire that connects the various parts. Even batteries, often used as the voltage source for circuits, have some resistance to the flow of electrons. These resistances are not commercially manufactured resistors placed in the circuit. They represent the unavoidable natural resistance of the materials. **Figure 10-4** shows a simple circuit that includes resistors to represent the load and the other circuit resistances.

All the circuits shown in this section have one other important feature. Any electrons that leave

Figure 10-1 — A flashlight is one example of a very simple electronic circuit.

UBE0108

UBE0109

Figure 10-2 — This drawing shows the schematic diagram representing the flashlight of Figure 10-1. The diagram labels explain the meaning of each special symbol. These symbols represent parts of the circuit. In this diagram the switch is open, so we have an open circuit, and the lamp is off.

UBE0110

Figure 10-3 — This schematic diagram of a flashlight shows the switch in a closed position. This time we have a closed, or complete circuit, and the lamp is on.

Figure 10-4 — All parts of an electronic circuit have some resistance to current flowing through them. This includes batteries, wires and other parts, along with resistors. The diagram shown here includes resistors to represent the natural resistances of the circuit, as well as the resistance of the load.

Figure 10-5 — The bulbs for some Christmas tree lights connect in series. When one bulb burns out, none of the bulbs will light.

the negative battery terminal must flow through every part of the circuit to reach the positive battery terminal. There is no place in the circuit where the electrons have a choice of directions. This is a bit like getting on an interstate highway and finding there are no exits to get off the highway. You just have to keep going until you reach the end of your journey.

We have a special name for electronic circuits that provide no alternate paths for electrons to follow. A *series circuit* is one in which all electrons must follow the same path, going through every part of the circuit. The current in one part of a series circuit is the same as in every

other part. If you measure the current at any place in a series circuit, you'll know the current everywhere in the circuit.

You can have more than one load in an electronic circuit. If you connect several loads so the same current must flow through each load, you have a series circuit. Christmas tree lights give us a common example of a series circuit with several loads. The light strings with small bulbs are often connected in series, as shown in **Figure 10-5**.

If you are familiar with these lights, you also know there is one big disadvantage to such series circuits. If there is a break in the circuit at any point, it becomes an open circuit, and no electrons can flow. So if one bulb burns out, all the lights go out. It can be quite a problem to find the bad bulb in a case like this. Often you have to change one bulb at a time, until you change one and the lights all come on again! If more than one bulb burned out at the same time, you can have a real problem.

Parallel Circuits

Many electronic circuits include alternate paths for the current to follow. **Figure 10-6** is an example of such a circuit. The electrons can follow one of two different paths to move from the negative to the positive side of the voltage supply. *Parallel circuits* are electronic circuits that have alternate paths, so all the electrons don't follow the same path. Each possible electron path forms a *branch* of the parallel circuit.

The current that flows through each individual path may be different. Each branch of the circuit shown in **Figure 10-7** has an ammeter to measure the current in that branch. In this example, in branch 1 the current is 2 amps. In branch 2 the current is 3 amps. In a parallel circuit, the branch currents add up to the total current from the voltage supply. At the negative or positive battery terminal, we should measure a total of 5 amps for the circuit of Figure 10-7. (Remember, in a *series circuit* the current in every part of the circuit is the same as in every other part.)

It's often helpful to compare an electronic circuit and water flowing through a pipe. A garden hose is like a series circuit. The faucet that you connect the hose to is like a voltage source, providing pressure to push the water through the hose. The other end of the hose is like the circuit load, where the circuit does something useful. It doesn't matter if you are using the hose to water your lawn, wash a car or fill a swimming pool. All the water flowing into the hose must come out the other end. There is no other way for the water to get out of the hose — at least if you don't have a leaky hose!

Similarly, we can compare the water pipes through your house to a parallel circuit. Some of the water coming into your house goes to the water heater. Some water goes to the kitchen sink, some to the bathtub and some to an outside faucet. There are many paths for the water to follow. There may be water running from several faucets at the same time, or there may only be one running. This is much the same as a parallel electronic circuit.

Look at the circuit shown in **Figure 10-8**. Here, we've connected several light bulbs in parallel. Notice that one of those bulbs has burned out, but the others remain lit. This is an important characteristic of parallel circuits. An open circuit in one part may not stop current from flowing in other parts of the circuit. A switch placed in one parallel branch can turn the current in that branch on or off. Having one branch turned off won't affect the current in other branches.

Even with a parallel circuit, there are parts of the circuit through which all the current must flow. The battery and wires connecting it to the rest of the circuit, for example, must carry all the current. **Figure 10-9** also includes a resistor that must carry all the current. We wire those parts of a circuit that must carry all the current in series. Those parts that carry only some of the current are in *parallel*.

You may sometimes see a reference to a *series/parallel circuit*. This simply means that the circuit has some parts wired in series and other parts wired in parallel. **Figure 10-10** shows another example of a series/parallel circuit. Notice that you can have some parts connected in series as a part of a parallel branch.

Some electronic circuits

Figure 10-7 — Ammeters measure current in a circuit. There is an ammeter in each branch of the circuit shown in this diagram. Add the current in each branch. This total current is equal to the current out of the battery. In this example, there is a current of 5 amps from the battery.

Figure 10-6 — Here is a simple example of a *parallel circuit.* There are at least two paths that the electrons can follow to move from the negative to the positive battery terminal.

Figure 10-8 — These light bulbs are in parallel. If one bulb bums out, current can still flow in other branches of the circuit.

Figure 10-9 — This is an example of a *series/parallel* circuit. There are some parts of the circuit through which all the current must flow. In other parts of the circuit, the current has a choice. Switches in the parallel branches can add or remove that branch from the circuit. Switch S1, in series with the entire circuit, can turn off all the current.

Figure 10-10 — Parallel circuit branches can include parts wired in series.

Figure 10-11 — If a conductor provides a current path around the circuit load, there is a *short circuit*. A short circuit can damage other electronic parts in a circuit and may produce enough heat to start a fire

Figure 10-12 — A *fuse* protects a circuit from accidental shorts. The wire in the fuse melts if there is more current than its rating allows. In this way, the fuse produces an *open circuit*, stopping all current. Part B shows another symbol sometimes used to represent a fuse on schematic diagrams.

look very complicated. Just remember that all the parts connect either in series or in parallel with the parts around them. With this idea, you can always simplify a circuit to make it easier to understand.

There is one other special type of parallel circuit that you should know about. Suppose that a bare wire or other conductor falls across the circuit, as shown in **Figure 10-11**. The alternate electron path provided by this wire will have very little resistance and a large current will flow from the battery. We say the bare wire *shorts* the circuit, because it conducts the electrons around the desired path. This is a *short circuit*.

There are many possible causes for short circuits. Frayed insulation

on an electrical power cord is one common cause. A situation like this is dangerous. First is the danger of someone touching the bare wires and receiving a shock or being electrocuted. When the bare wires touch, there will be sparks, and they may cause a fire. The large current flowing in a short circuit can cause the wires to become hot. That heat also can start a fire.

Many circuits include *fuses* to protect against short circuits. A fuse

has a thin piece of wire that will get hot and melt if a large current goes through it. Fuses have a rating for how much current they can carry. If the current is larger than the rated amount, the fuse wire melts, and opens the circuit. (No current can flow in an open circuit.) After you correct the cause of the short circuit, you can replace the fuse with a new one. **Figure 10-12** shows a circuit that has a fuse to protect it from short circuits.

Review Questions ———

10.1 The name of the circuit in which the same current flows through every element of the circuit is a:

a) parallel circuit

b) open circuit

c) series circuit

d) resonant circuit

10.2 A circuit in which the current can divide and flow through different loads is a:

a) parallel circuit

b) open circuit

c) series circuit

d) resonant circuit

10.3 If the insulation is worn on two wires, and they touch, creating sparks until the battery is completely discharged (if you're lucky) or a fire starts (if you're not), that is called:

a) an open circuit

b) a really bad day

c) a short circuit

d) series-parallel failure

10.4 Water flow through a garden hose is an analogy for a:

a) parallel circuit

b) series circuit

c) series-parallel circuit

d) kitchen sink

10.5 The device in a circuit that can protect against too much current flowing is:

a) good insulation

b) parallel circuit branches

c) a current limiter

d) a fuse

Answers ———

10.1 c

10.2 a

10.3 c

10.4 b

10.5 d

Chapter 11

Ohm's Law

ARRL0005

This simple diagram will help you remember the Ohm's Law relationships.

Contents

Voltage, Current and Resistance are Related

Let's review a few definitions before getting into the details of Ohm's Law. *Voltage* is the force or pressure that causes electrons to move. *Current* is the movement of electrons through a wire or other conductor. *Resistance* is the opposition to electron movement that any material has. In our earlier discussions, we mentioned that if there is more electrical pressure, more electrons will move in a circuit. We also mentioned that if a conductor presents more resistance to the flow of electrons, there will not be as much current. Obviously, there is some relationship between these three quantities.

In the late 1820s, Georg Simon Ohm, a German scientist, conducted some experiments with simple electric circuits. Ohm discovered a simple mathematical relationship between the voltage applied to a circuit, the resistance of the circuit conductor and the current through the circuit. Other scientists did not accept Ohm's work at first. By the 1840s they began to understand the importance of his discovery, however. Today, *Ohm's Law*, as we call it, is perhaps the most important key to understanding modern electronics.

Look at the simple electronic circuit shown in **Figure 11-1**. There is a voltage source and some resistance in the conductor between the positive and negative voltage terminals. A voltmeter in the circuit gives us a convenient way to measure the voltage. An ammeter indicates circuit current.

Let's assume that the resistance in the circuit is a constant value, but we can change the voltage over a range from 0 to 20 V. We can read the circuit current from the ammeter as we change the voltage. **Table 11-1** shows a series of measurements that we could make with such a circuit. Take a look at the numbers in that table. Do you recognize a pattern? For one thing, you should notice that as the voltage increases, the current also increases. There is also another pattern that may not be so obvious. Every time we double the voltage, the current also doubles.

The graph of **Figure 11-2**, which is based on the data from Table 11-1, may help you recognize these patterns. There is a direct relationship between the voltage applied to the circuit and the current through the circuit. In mathematical terms, we would say that the voltage and current

Figure 11-1 — This simple electronic circuit will help us study the relationship between voltage, current and resistance. The voltmeter and ammeter provide a convenient way to measure conditions in the circuit. The text describes some measurements that we can make with such a circuit. Tables 11-1 and 11-2 list the results of these measurements for two values of circuit resistance.

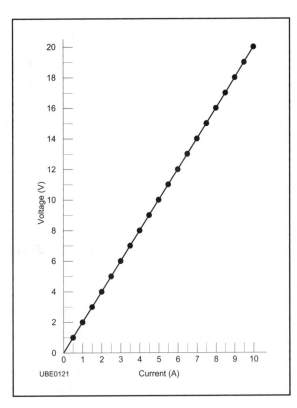

Figure 11-2 — This graph presents the data from Table 11-1 to illustrate the straight-line, direct-proportion relationship between voltage and current. The values in Table 11-1 represent an ideal set of data. Actual measured values would vary somewhat from these ideal values.

Table 11-1

Voltage and Current Measurements

These measurements are from the circuit of Figure 11-1 as the voltage changes from 0 to 20 V.

Voltage (V)	Current (A)
0	0
1	0.5
2	1.0
3	1.5
4	2.0
5	2.5
6	3.0
7	3.5
8	4.0
9	4.5
10	5.0
11	5.5
12	6.0
13	6.5
14	7.0
15	7.5
16	8.0
17	8.5
18	9.0
19	9.5
20	10.0

Table 11-2

Voltage and Current Measurements

These measurements are from the circuit of Figure 11-1 as the voltage changes from 0 to 20 volts. The resistance (R) has been changed to be twice that used for the measurements in Table 11-1.

Voltage (V)	Current (A)
0	0
1	0.25
2	0.50
3	0.75
4	1.00
5	1.25
6	1.50
7	1.75
8	2.00
9	2.25
10	2.50
11	2.75
12	3.00
13	3.25
14	3.50
15	3.75
16	4.00
17	4.25
18	4.50
19	4.75
20	5.00

are *directly proportional* to each other. Another way to say this is that there is a *linear relationship* between voltage and current.

When two quantities are *directly proportional*, you can write a simple mathematical equation. For any value of one quantity (let's use current for our example), you can find the value of the other quantity (voltage) by multiplying by some number. So to find the value of voltage for any value of current, we just have to know the correct number, or constant. We can write this direct proportion as an equation:

voltage = current × constant

(Equation 11-1)

From the data shown in Table 11-1, you can tell that the correct constant for our example is 2. If you

multiply any of the listed current values by 2 you will get the voltage value which produced that current.

What Happens When We Change Resistance?

Now let's suppose there is twice as much resistance in the circuit of Figure 11-1. **Table 11-2** shows a new set of values for the current as the voltage varies from 0 to 20 V. Again, you should notice that the current increases as the voltage increases. Also, again, the current doubles every time the voltage doubles. You might try plotting a graph of voltage and current similar to the graph of Figure 11-2. You will get a straight line graph, proving that voltage and current are still directly proportional. This time, however, you must multiply the current values by

4 to get the corresponding voltages.

We are making the same discovery here that Georg Simon Ohm made in his experiments! We define the amount of resistance in a circuit as the constant that you must multiply current by in order to find the voltage. So in our first example, the circuit had 2 *ohms* of resistance and in the second example it had 4 *ohms* of resistance. With the constant in Equation 11-1 defined as the circuit resistance, we can rewrite that equation as:

voltage = current × resistance

(Equation 11-2)

We use the letter E to represent voltage (or electromotive force). The letter I represents current (from the French word for current, *intensite*) and R represents resistance. Using these letters instead of the words in Equation 11-2, we can write:

$E = I \times R$ (Equation 11-3)

Here we have Ohm's Law expressed in its most common form.

The equation for Ohm's Law defines a unit for measuring resistance. The name given to this unit, the *ohm*, is in honor of Georg Simon Ohm and his experiments. We often use the upper case Greek letter omega (Ω) to represent ohms. If a certain resistor has 200 ohms of resistance, we might write this as 200 Ω. We can write 1000 ohms as 1 kΩ (kilohm) and 1,000,000 ohms as 1 MΩ (megohm).

If we know any two of the three quantities in Equation 11-3, we can calculate the other one. For example, given current and resistance, we can calculate voltage. If we know the voltage and resistance we should be able to calculate the circuit current. If we know the circuit current and voltage, we can calculate the resistance of the circuit. In the next section, we will discuss the variations on the basic Ohm's Law equation, and ways to help you remember those variations.

Finding the Unknown —
The Ohm's Law Circle

Ohm's Law is a tool you will use to study most electronic circuits. There are other important rules and conditions that you will study as you learn more about modern electronics. Most of those rules will require an understanding of Ohm's Law, however.

We usually write Ohm's Law as an equation.

$$E = I \times R \qquad \text{(Equation 11-4)}$$

We often omit the multiplication sign in such equations, simply writing the letters of quantities to be multiplied next to each other:

$$E = I\,R \qquad \text{(Equation 11-5)}$$

When you know any two of the three quantities in a circuit (voltage, current and resistance) you can calculate the third quantity.

Suppose the voltmeter in the circuit of **Figure 11-3** reads 10 V and the ammeter reads 0.5 amps. How can we calculate the circuit resistance? With Ohm's Law, of course. It's not too difficult to *solve* Equation 11-5 for R, if you remember how to work with such equations. Some of you may have already written a new equation:

$$R = E / I \qquad \text{(Equation 11-6)}$$

and calculated the circuit resistance.

$$R = 10 \text{ V} / 0.5 \text{ A} = 20 \text{ }\Omega$$

If you're not familiar with solving equations, you're probably wondering what sort of magic we used here! You can look at the end of this chapter for a review of the steps involved in solving equations. **Figure 11-4** also shows a very helpful memory device for working with Ohm's Law. Let's take a closer look at how this *Ohm's Law Circle* works.

The basic operation of such a diagram is rather simple. First decide which piece of information you want to calculate and which two you already know. (You may have to examine the circuit or diagram to find this information.) **Figure 11-5** shows another problem that we'll use as an example. We're trying to find the voltage, and the diagram gives us the circuit current and resistance. In

Figure 11-3 — This circuit presents a simple Ohm's Law problem. You want to find the circuit resistance, and are given the voltage and current.

Figure 11-4 — The Ohm's Law Circle is a memory aid, or mnemonic, to help you solve the Ohm's Law equation for voltage, current or resistance.

Figure 11-5 — Here is another circuit that presents an Ohm's Law problem. This time you are given the current and resistance, and have to find the circuit voltage.

Figure 11-6 — Here's how to use the Ohm's Law Circle to solve a problem that asks us to calculate a circuit voltage. By covering the letter of the quantity we want to find, the remaining letters show us what calculation to perform. Here, we must multiply current (I) and resistance (R) to calculate voltage (E).

Figure 11-7 — This diagram shows an electronic circuit in which we know the voltage and current, but not the resistance. Ohm's Law will help us calculate that resistance using the other information about the circuit.

Figure 11-8 — In this drawing the Ohm's Law Circle helps to find the equation needed to solve the problem given in Figure 11-7.

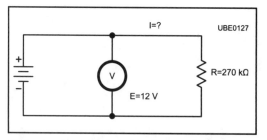

Figure 11-9 — Here is another electronic circuit. In this one, we know the voltage and resistance, but not the current. Again, Ohm's Law will rescue us with an equation to calculate current.

Figure 11-10 — Find an equation that will solve the problem of Figure 11-9 by covering the I on the Ohm's Law Circle.

this case, cover the E on the Ohm's Law Circle, as shown in **Figure 11-6**. Notice that you can still see the I and R on the diagram. They are next to each other, indicating multiplication.

Now it is time to write an equation. The letter you covered goes on the left side of an equals sign, and the other two letters go on the right side:

E = I R

Next substitute the values from the problem into the equation and do the arithmetic.

E = 5 mA × 2.2 kΩ

E = 5 × 10⁻³ A × 2.2 × 10³ Ω = 11 V

(Do you remember how to write numbers using powers of 10 instead of metric prefixes? If not, this is a good time to review the metric prefix discussion in Appendix A.)

Shall we try another example? Look at **Figure 11-7**. This problem tells us the circuit voltage and current, and asks us to find the resistance. We'll use the Ohm's Law Circle again. This time we have to cover the R (see **Figure 11-8**). The rest of the diagram shows E in the top of the circle and I on the bottom. This represents a division problem, and the equation is the same as Equation 11-6:

R = E / I

R = 15 V / 2 mA = 15 V / (2 × 10⁻³A)

R = 7.5 × 10³ = 7.5 kΩ

Let's work one more example problem using Ohm's Law. **Figure 11-9** presents a problem in which you know the circuit voltage and resistance, and you are to calculate the current. **Figure 11-10** shows how to use the Ohm's Law Circle to find

the equation:

I = E / R   (Equation 11-7)

I = 12 V / 270 kΩ
I = 12 V / (270 × 10³ Ω)

I = 4.44 × 10⁻⁵ A
I = 0.0444 × 10⁻³ A
I = 0.0444 mA

or

I = 4.44 × 10⁻⁵ A
I = 44.4 × 10⁻⁶ A
I = 44.4 µA

Notice that the current in the problem above can be expressed two ways — as 0.0444 milliamps (a small part of one milliamp), or as 44.4 microamps (quite a few microamps). Recall that one milliamp (1 mA) is one thousandth of an ampere, while a microamp (1 µA) is one thousandth of a milliamp, or one millionth of an ampere. Alternatively, we can say there are 1000 µA in 1 mA. Both mA and µA are commonly used measures of current found in electronic circuits.

Through these examples, you worked one of each type of Ohm's Law problem. You calculated a voltage in one circuit, a resistance in another and a current in the third example. Remember the Ohm's Law Circle, because it shows you the proper equation for each type of problem. After awhile, you probably will remember the three ways of writing the equation. While you are learning about Ohm's Law, you won't have to worry about remembering these equations. Just picture this diagram each time you work a problem.

In Chapter 12 you will learn how to solve circuit problems.

Some Practice Problems and Their Solutions

You will become more confident in your ability to solve Ohm's Law problems as you get more practice solving them. It's very important that you improve your skill at solving Ohm's Law problems and gain some confidence before we proceed much further. The practice problems in this section should help you meet those goals.

Each problem is presented using

Figure 11-11 — The Ohm's Law Circle provides a simple way to write the Ohm's Law equation for any particular problem.

a schematic diagram, with circuit values labeled on the diagram. There is also a brief description of each problem. **Figure 11-11** shows the Ohm's Law Circle for your convenience in solving these problems. After you have completed this exercise you can check your work with the solutions shown after the six sample problems have been presented.

PRACTICE PROBLEMS

Practice Problem 1

The schematic diagram shows a circuit with a 33-kΩ resistor connected to a battery. There is an ammeter in the circuit to measure current. It indicates 5 mA of current in the circuit. What is the battery voltage?

Practice Problem 2

We use a voltmeter to measure the voltage of a battery, and find it to be 24 V. How much current will flow through a 1.5-MΩ resistor connected across the battery terminals?

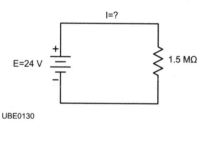

Practice Problem 3

This schematic diagram shows an unknown value of resistance connected to a voltage supply. By connecting meters in the circuit, we are able to measure the circuit voltage and current. The voltage supply is 50 V and there is 125 mA of current in the circuit. What is the resistance of the resistor in this circuit?

Practice Problem 4

What voltage must you apply to a 250-Ω resistor to force 1 amp of current through it?

Practice Problem 5

How much current will there be in a circuit that applies 120 V to a 4700-Ω (4.7 kΩ) resistor?

Practice Problem 6

A 6-volt battery connects to a complicated mixture of resistors connected in series and parallel with each other. An ammeter in the circuit indicates that a current of 75 mA flows out of the battery. What is the total effective resistance of this complicated resistor maze?

SOLUTIONS TO PRACTICE PROBLEMS

Solution to Problem 1

Use the Ohm's Law Circle to find the equation to calculate voltage. From this, write the equation, E = I R.

$E = I\,R$

$E = 5\ mA \times 33\ k\Omega$

$E = 5 \times 10^{-3}\ A \times 33 \times 10^{3}\ \Omega$

UBE0135

$E = 165\ V$

Solution to Problem 2

Using the Ohm's Law Circle, we write the equation to solve this problem.

$I = \dfrac{E}{R}$

$I = \dfrac{24\ V}{1.5\ M\Omega}$

$I = \dfrac{24\ V}{1.5 \times 10^{6}\ \Omega}$

UBE0136

$I = 1.6 \times 10^{-5}\ A$

$I = 16 \times 10^{-6}\ A = 16\ \mu A$

or

$I = 0.016 \times 10^{-3}\ A = 0.016\ mA$

Solution to Problem 3

Use the Ohm's Law Circle to solve Ohm's Law for resistance.

$R = \dfrac{E}{I}$

$R = \dfrac{50\ V}{125\ mA}$

$R = \dfrac{50\ V}{125 \times 10^{-3}\ A}$

UBE0137

$R = 400\ \Omega$

Solution to Problem 4

By now you probably remember the basic Ohm's Law equation, solved for voltage. If not, use the Ohm's Law Circle.

$E = I\,R$

$E = 1\ A \times 250\ \Omega$

$E = 250\ V$

Solution to Problem 5

If you need to, use the Ohm's Law Circle to find the Ohm's Law equation solved for current.

$I = \dfrac{E}{R}$

$I = \dfrac{120\ V}{4.7\ k\Omega}$

$I = \dfrac{120\ V}{4.7 \times 10^{3}\ \Omega}$

$I = 0.0255\ A$

or

$I = 25.5 \times 10^{-3}\ A = 25.5\ mA$

Solution to Problem 6

Don't think of this as a trick question. The problem illustrates one important practical use for Ohm's Law. We can find the total effective resistance of a complicated maze of resistors simply by measuring the applied voltage and the current from the voltage supply. Then we use the Ohm's Law equation R = E/I to solve for resistance, using that voltage and current.

$R = \dfrac{E}{I}$

$R = \dfrac{6\ V}{75\ mA}$

$R = \dfrac{6\ V}{75 \times 10^{-3}\ A}$

$R = 80\ \Omega$

Ohm's Law Applies to Circuits and Components

We have been working example problems showing how to use Ohm's Law to calculate voltage, current or resistance of an entire circuit, usually a simple circuit. Can this important rule of electronics help us calculate information about more complex circuits as well? The answer is an enthusiastic YES!

Look at the circuit of **Figure 11-12**. Here we have three resistors connected in series with the battery. The voltmeter shows that the battery applies 12 V to the circuit. The ammeter tells us that the current is 2 mA.

It takes some battery voltage to push electrons through each resistor in the circuit. This is similar to a water pipe that is blocked in several places. **Figure 11-13** shows a water

pipe with high water pressure at the left end. The blockage at point A prevents the full amount of water from flowing through the pipe. After forcing its way through that blockage, there is not as much pressure when the water comes to point B. Here there is another blockage, which restricts the water even more. By the time the water gets through the blockage at point C, there is only a trickle of water coming out of the pipe!

Each resistor in an electronic circuit is similar to a blockage in a water pipe. There is a voltage across each resistor, usually called a *voltage drop*. The voltage drop across a resistor represents the force or electrical potential needed to push the electrons through the resistor. (If

you want a larger current — more electrons — it will take a larger voltage.)

For example, if you connect a voltmeter into the circuit, as shown in **Figure 11-14A**, the meter will read the full 12 V of the battery. When you connect the voltmeter across R1 (in parallel with R1), as shown in Part B, the meter will read less than the full battery voltage. Part C shows that the meter also reads less than the battery voltage when you connect it between points B and C, in parallel with R2. Of course, the meter also reads something less than 12 V when you connect it between points C and D. Part D shows the meter connected across R3 to make this measurement.

Our question now is, just how much does the voltage drop as we

Figure 11-12 — Ohm's Law will help us calculate the voltage drop across each resistor in this series circuit. The voltmeter measures the supply voltage applied to the entire circuit. The ammeter measures the amount of current flowing in each part of the circuit.

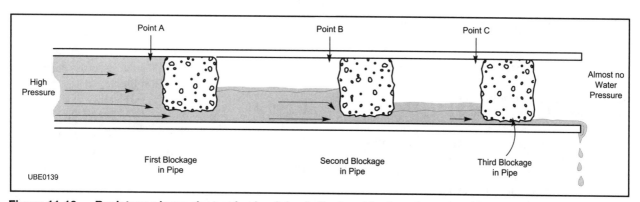

Figure 11-13 — Resistance in an electronic circuit is similar to a blockage in a water pipe. The water forced past each blockage produces less pressure than there was before the blockage. Here we see that by the time the water gets past the blockage at point C, there is little pressure left. The water only drips out of the pipe.

Figure 11-14 — Part A shows a simple series circuit. A voltmeter measures the battery voltage and an ammeter measures the current through the circuit. If we connect the voltmeter between points A and B, as shown in Part B, we can measure the voltage drop across R1. (Notice that the voltmeter is in parallel with the resistor. You should always connect a voltmeter in parallel with the part of the circuit you want to measure.) In Part C, the voltmeter connects between points B and C, in parallel with R2. We are measuring the voltage drop across R2 in this example. To measure the voltage drop across R3, we connect the voltmeter between points C and D, as shown in Part D.

Figure 11-15 — Here is a circuit with three resistors connected in parallel with a voltage source. Ohm's Law can help calculate the current through each branch of a parallel circuit.

move across each resistor? Is the voltage drop the same across each resistor? Well, let's see how Ohm's Law can answer those questions for us. We know the value of resistance for each resistor because the diagram shows those values. We also know the current through each resistor because the same current must flow through every part of a series circuit. The ammeter also shows that the circuit current is 2 mA.

We use Ohm's Law to find the voltage drop across resistor R1:

$$E_1 = I\,R_1 \qquad \text{(Equation 11-8)}$$

$$E_1 = 2\ \text{mA} \times 1\ \text{k}\Omega$$

$$E_1 = 2 \times 10^{-3}\ \text{A} \times 1 \times 10^3\ \Omega$$

$$E_1 = 2\ \text{V}$$

The voltmeter connected as shown in

Figure 11-14B reads 2 V, so it agrees with our calculation!

How about the voltage drop across resistor R2?

$$E_2 = I\,R_2 \qquad \text{(Equation 11-9)}$$

$$E_2 = 2\ \text{mA} \times 2\ \text{k}\Omega$$

$$E_2 = 2 \times 10^{-3}\ \text{A} \times 2 \times 10^3\ \Omega$$

$$E_2 = 4\ \text{V}$$

So the voltage drop across R2 is 4 V, as the voltmeter in Figure 11-14C shows.

What is the voltage drop across resistor R3?

$$E_3 = I\,R_3 \qquad \text{(Equation 11-10)}$$

$$E_3 = 2\ \text{mA} \times 3\ \text{k}\Omega$$

$$E_3 = 2 \times 10^{-3}\ \text{A} \times 3 \times 10^3\ \Omega$$

$$E_3 = 6\ \text{V}$$

We can use Ohm's Law to calculate the voltage drop across any resistor in a series circuit. The only requirement is that we know the resistance and the current through the series circuit.

You may have noticed that the voltages across the three resistors in Figure 11-12 are 2 V, 4 V and 6 V, and these *just happen* to add up to 12 V, which is the voltage of the battery. Well, it turns out this isn't a coincidence at all. It's a very important concept known as *Kirchhoff's Voltage Law*. We will look at Kirchhoff's laws in the next chapter.

Now take a look at **Figure 11-15**. This parallel circuit presents a slightly different problem. The current through each branch of the circuit is different. If you examine the circuit carefully, however, you will realize that it applies the full battery voltage to each parallel branch. Can we then use Ohm's Law to calculate the amount of current through each branch? Of course!

Draw an Ohm's Law Circle and write the Ohm's Law equation solved for current.

$$I = E / R \qquad \text{(Equation 11-11)}$$

Let's find the current through R1 first.

$$I_1 = 15 \text{ V} / 6 \text{ k}\Omega$$

$$I_1 = 15 \text{ V} / (6 \times 10^3 \text{ }\Omega)$$

$$I_1 = 2.5 \times 10^{-3} \text{ A} = 2.5 \text{ mA}$$

Now calculate the current through R2.
$$I_2 = 15 \text{ V} / 5 \text{ k}\Omega$$

$$I_2 = 15 \text{ V} / (5 \times 10^3 \text{ }\Omega)$$

$$I_2 = 3.0 \times 10^{-3} \text{ A} = 3.0 \text{ mA}$$

Finally, we'll calculate the current through R3.

$$I_3 = 15 \text{ V} / 10 \text{ k}\Omega$$

$$I_3 = 15 \text{ V} / (10 \times 10^3 \text{ }\Omega)$$

$$I_3 = 1.5 \times 10^{-3} \text{ A} = 1.5 \text{ mA}$$

Ohm's Law is important to us in our study of electronics not just because it will help us learn something about the conditions of an entire circuit. Ohm's Law is also important because we can apply it to individual components in the circuit. Later in your studies you will have to expand your understanding of Ohm's Law a bit. When we begin to study more complex circuits we'll have to add a bit more to the definition of this important rule. The bottom line, however, is that every electronic circuit obeys Ohm's Law.

Math and Calculator Hints

MATH HINTS

For more background on math, refer to **Appendix A — Scientific and Engineering Notation**.

How to Solve Equations

When it comes time to solve an equation for some unknown quantity, you'll have to follow a few basic rules. There are a few simple procedures that you should follow in working with equations. It doesn't hurt to know a couple of little tricks, either.

What does it mean to solve an equation? When you solve an equation, you normally want to have the unknown quantity by itself on one side of the equal sign. The other equation terms (the known values used to calculate the unknown) are on the opposite side of the equal sign.

The branch of mathematics that involves solving equations has its own name: *algebra*. That word may remind some readers of complicated procedures and difficult computations. The equations we'll be using in basic electronics are quite simple, however, and you'll be able to solve them easily. In this section we'll explain a few rules that you should follow when working with electronics equations. Also, we'll discuss the most common techniques that you'll use to solve these simple equations. You'll even learn a few tricks to make your task a bit easier.

"The first rule is to be neat!"

The first rule is to be neat! Start with an organized work area, and have the materials you'll need within easy reach. Write carefully, being especially careful to form your numbers and letters properly. Don't crowd your work, and if you make a mistake be sure to erase completely.

Do only one or two steps at a time, carefully copying the equation on a new line with each step. Later you can do more of the work mentally, and you won't have to write as many steps. Until you've gained more experience, though, you should follow this step-by-step technique carefully.

Always keep your final goal in mind. You want the unknown term on one side of the equal sign and all other terms on the other side. Each step of simplifying the equation should help you work toward this goal. In general, you can add, subtract, multiply or divide the equation by just about any quantity that helps you meet that goal. (Never divide by 0. Also, it doesn't help to multiply by 0! Multiplying by 1, or adding or subtracting 0, don't help much either.)

"Any operation you do to one side of the equation you also must do to the other side."

Any operation you do to one side of the equation you also must do to the other side. Perform these operations on one side of the equation as a group rather than to individual terms. A couple of examples should help explain this process.

Let's use the letter I to represent the current in an electronic circuit. Then suppose we have an equation that relates the current with some other circuit conditions. We want to solve the equation for the circuit current.

$$2I + 5 - 3I = 10 - 16I$$

The first step here is to add 16I to both sides of the equation.

$$(2I + 5 - 3I) + 16I = (10 - 16I) + 16I$$

Since we are adding all these terms, we don't really need the parentheses. We can combine similar terms, simplifying the equation a bit.

$$15I + 5 = 10$$

The next step is to subtract 5 from both sides of the equation.

$$15I + 5 - 5 = 10 - 5$$

Then combine like terms again.

$$15I = 5$$

We have one more step to go before we have the solution to our equation. Divide both sides of the equation by 15, and we'll have the unknown by itself on the left side of the equation!

$$\frac{15I}{15} = \frac{5}{15} = 0.333$$

$$I = 0.333$$

Here we have the solution to our equation. Since we measure electrical current in units called amperes, the current in our circuit must be 0.333 amp.

"One time-saving trick is to transpose terms across the equal sign."

What tricks could we use to save some time and a few steps in this solution? Well, you probably got a few ideas from the examples shown so far. Adding a term to both sides of the equation cancels the term on one side and moves it to the other. (Adding a negative value is the same as subtracting. So you can add or subtract a term to both sides of the equation.) On the opposite side of the equal sign, however, positive terms become negative and negative terms become positive. One time-saving trick, then, is to transpose such terms across the equal sign.

Suppose we have the equation:

I + 25 = 30

Instead of writing a step that shows 25 being subtracted from both sides of the equation, we can simply transpose the term, and write:

I = 30 − 25 = 5

> ## "Cross multiplication provides a quick way to multiply or divide both sides of an equation by some term."

Another trick involves a technique known as *cross multiplication*. This technique provides a quick way of multiplying or dividing both sides of the equation by some term.

Suppose you have an equation like the one shown here.

$$\frac{44Z}{10} = \frac{80}{9}$$

where Z is some unknown quantity

We could multiply both sides by 9 and then multiply both sides by 10. Instead, let's cross multiply. Move the denominator of both fractions diagonally across the equal sign. (The *denominator* of a fraction is the bottom part.)

$$\frac{44Z}{10} = \frac{80}{9}$$

$$44Z \times 9 = 80 \times 10$$

$$396Z = 800$$

Now, we can cross multiply again by moving the 396 diagonally across the equal sign. (Leave the unknown, Z, where it is.) Or, perhaps simpler, we can divide both sides of the equation by 396.

$$\frac{396Z}{396} = \frac{800}{396} = 2.02$$

Z = 2.02

Each type of problem is a little different from other types, so it's impossible to give you an exact procedure to follow. It's also possible to solve a problem by following several slightly different procedures. You'll have to study each problem to find a way to solve it. Follow the guidelines described in the examples of this section. With practice you'll soon gain the confidence to tackle problems that are even more difficult.

CALCULATOR HINTS

The following examples show how to use your TI-30X IIS calculator to solve equations like those in this chapter on Ohm's Law. For more information on using a calculator to work these examples, refer to **Appendix B — Understanding and Using Your TI-30X IIS Scientific Calculator**.

Example 1

E = I × R

E = 5 mA × 2 kΩ

E= 5 × 10⁻³ A × 2 × 10³ Ω = 10 V

Calculator keystrokes:

5 2nd EE – 3 × 2 2nd EE 3 =

[Note that the – (minus sign) key in the equation above is the *white key* under the 3 key. There is a – (subtract) key above the + (add) key. *Do NOT use the blue subtract key* when you mean to use the white minus sign key.]

The calculator's second display line shows: **10 × 10⁰⁰**

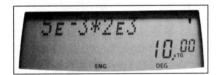

[Note that $10^{00} = 10^0 = 1$, so 10×10^{00} = 10 × 1 = 10 (V).]

Example 2

R = E / I

R = 15 V / 2 mA = 15 V / (2 × 10⁻³ A)

R = 7.5 × 10³ = 7.5 kΩ

Calculator keystrokes:

1 5 ÷ 2 2nd EE – 3 =

The calculator's second display line shows: **7.5 × 10⁰³**

Example 3

I = E / R

I = 12 V / 270 kΩ
I = 12 V / (270 × 10³ Ω)

I = 4.44 × 10⁻⁵ A
I = 0.0444 × 10⁻³ A
I = 0.0444 mA

or

I = 4.44 × 10⁻⁵ A
I = 44.4 × 10⁻⁶A
I = 44.4 µA

Calculator keystrokes:

1 2 ÷ 2 7 0 2nd EE 3 =

The calculator's second display line shows: **44.4 × 10⁻⁰⁶**

[The calculator display shows 44.44444444, but the first one or two decimal places provides plenty of precision for our examples.]

Review Questions

11.1 **The mathematical formula that describes the relationship between voltage, current and resistance is called:**
a) Ampere's Law
b) Ohm's Law
c) Maxwell's Equation
d) Inverse Square Law

11.2 **The measuring instrument that tells us how much current is flowing in a circuit is the:**
a) electron meter
b) electroscope
c) wattmeter
d) ammeter

11.3 **The letter used to represent voltage in equations is:**
a) I
b) P
c) E
d) R

11.4 **The letter used to represent electrical current in equations is:**
a) I
b) R
c) E
d) C

11.5 **Describe, in words, the relationship between voltage, current and resistance. See if you can do this in three different sentences.**

11.6 **If a circuit has a fixed voltage (perhaps a 12 V battery), what happens to the circuit current if the resistance is doubled?**
a) current stays the same
b) current doubles
c) current is halved
d) current drops to zero

11.7 **The symbol for the ohm is:**
a) O
b) Ω
c) π
d) λ

11.8 **How much current flows through a 100 ohm resistor when a voltage of 9 volts is across it?**

11.9 **What value of resistor, when placed across a 12 volt battery, will cause 2 mA to flow through it?**

11.10 **If a current of 50 mA flows through a 400 ohm resistor, what voltage appears across the resistor?**

Answers

11.1 b

11.2 d

11.3 c

11.4 a

11.5 *Voltage* is the product of current and resistance ($E = I R$).
   Current is voltage divided by resistance ($I = E/R$).
   Resistance is voltage divided by current ($R = E/I$).

11.6 c

11.7 b

11.8 $I = E / R$, so $I = 9$ V $/ 100 \, \Omega = 0.09$ A $= 90$ mA

11.9 $R = E / I$ so
   $R = 12$ V $/ 2$ mA
   $R = 12$ V $/ (2 \times 10^{-3}$ A$)$
   $R = 6 \times 10^{3} \, \Omega = 6$ kΩ

11.10 $E = I R$ so
   $E = 50$ mA $(400 \, \Omega)$
   $E = (50 \times 10^{-3}$ A$) (400 \, \Omega)$
   $E = 20,000 \times 10^{-3}$ V
   $E = 20$ V

Chapter 12

How to Solve Circuit Problems — Some Techniques and Tricks

Follow the arrow
around the loop to write the
Kirchhoff's Voltage Law Equation

UBE0143

In this chapter you'll learn how to evaluate voltage and current in a complicated circuit.

Contents

Kirchhoff's Voltage Law

Ohm's Law can help us calculate voltage, current or resistance. You are familiar with this important electronics principle and can use it to calculate information about a circuit. There are times, however, when you can save yourself work if you know a few other rules.

Kirchhoff's Voltage Law, sometimes called *Kirchhoff's First Law*, is one of these rules. Gustav Kirchhoff, like Georg Simon Ohm, was a German scientist. In 1857, just three years after Ohm's death, Kirchhoff stated his two rules of electric circuits.

According to Kirchhoff's Voltage Law, *all voltage drops must equal all voltage rises around a closed loop*. There is a *voltage drop* across any circuit resistance when there is a current through it. We use Ohm's Law to calculate the amount of these voltage drops. A *voltage rise* normally refers to a voltage source, such as a battery. We add all the voltage rises and all the voltage drops. If you think the statement of Kirchhoff's First Law sounds like a mathematical equation, you are exactly right! We might write

this rule as:

$$\Sigma\, E_{RISES} = \Sigma\, E_{DROPS} \quad \text{(Equation 12-1)}$$

The uppercase Greek sigma (Σ) represents the summation, or addition, of all related terms. To use Kirchhoff's Law, you must first identify the voltage rises around the loop you are working with, and add them. Then you must identify the voltage drops around the loop, and add them. Do you remember how to use Ohm's Law to calculate the voltage drops?

Figure 12-1 shows a simple circuit with one voltage rise and four voltage drops. You must go around a complete loop of the circuit to use Kirchhoff's Voltage Law. Let's write the Kirchhoff's First Law equation for this circuit.

$$\Sigma\, E_{RISES} = \Sigma\, E_{DROPS} \quad \text{(Equation 12-1)}$$

$$30\ V = I\,R1 + I\,R2 + I\,R3 + I\,R4$$

$$30\ V = 1.5\ mA \times 4\ k\Omega + $$
$$1.5\ mA \times 6\ k\Omega + 1.5\ mA \times 2\ k\Omega + $$
$$1.5\ mA \times 8\ k\Omega$$

$$30\ V = 6\ V + 9\ V + 3\ V + 12\ V$$

$$30\ V = 30\ V$$

This example shows the meaning of Kirchhoff's Voltage Law. Often, we use this law to calculate the current through a circuit. **Figure 12-2** shows another circuit. This one has three voltage sources to include in the equation. Let's use Kirchhoff's Voltage Law to calculate the current through this circuit.

Figure 12-2 will help illustrate another important point about using Kirchhoff's Voltage Law. When you go around the loop, there are two possible directions, clockwise (↻) or counterclockwise (↺). Normally, go in a direction that takes you through the voltage sources from the negative to the positive terminal. Notice this is the direction we followed in the example of Figure 12-1. Going through a voltage source from negative to positive results in a voltage increase, or voltage rise. If you go through a voltage source from positive to negative, you have a voltage drop! The common practice is to assign a

Figure 12-1 — A simple series circuit, which forms a closed loop. We can write a Kirchhoff's Voltage Law equation by going around that loop adding all voltage drops and all voltage rises.

Follow the arrow around the loop to write the Kirchhoff's Voltage Law Equation

UBE0143

Figure 12-2 — This diagram shows a more complicated series circuit, including three voltage sources and four resistors. With Kirchhoff's Voltage Law, we can write an equation and calculate the current in this circuit.

negative value to any voltage source that you go through "backward" around the loop. The example of Figure 12-2 will make this easier to understand.

First, we'll write the equation for Kirchhoff's Voltage Law.

$$\Sigma\ E_{RISES} = \Sigma\ E_{DROPS} \quad \text{(Equation 12-1)}$$

To add the voltage rises, proceed around the loop in the direction indicated by the arrow. Notice that when you come to E3, you go through the battery from positive to negative. That results in a voltage decrease at this point. Give E3 a negative sign in the equation.

$$\Sigma\ E_{RISES} = E1 + E2 + E3$$
$$\text{(Equation 12-2A)}$$

$$\Sigma\ E_{RISES} = 20\ V + 5\ V + (-\ 10\ V)$$

$$\Sigma\ E_{RISES} = 15\ V \quad \text{(Equation 12-2B)}$$

To add the voltage drops, we'll use Ohm's Law to calculate the voltage drop across each resistor. (E = IR)

$$\Sigma\ E_{DROPS} = I\ R1 + I\ R2 + I\ R3 + I\ R4$$
$$\text{(Equation 12-3A)}$$

We don't know the current in the circuit (that's what we are trying to find), but we do know each of the resistances.

$$\Sigma\ E_{DROPS} = I \times 200\ \Omega + I \times 800\ \Omega + I \times 900\ \Omega + I \times 500\ \Omega$$

Did you notice that we multiply each resistance value by the current, I? When you multiply each value in a group by some constant value, you simplify the problem. First you can add all the numbers, and then multiply that sum by the constant value. We can rewrite Equation 12-3A as:

$$\Sigma\ E_{DROPS} = I \times (R1 + R2 + R3 + R4)$$

$$\Sigma\ E_{DROPS} = I \times (200\ \Omega + 800\ \Omega + 900\ \Omega + 500\ \Omega)$$

$$\Sigma\ E_{DROPS} = I \times (2400\ \Omega)$$
$$\text{(Equation 12-3B)}$$

Now we combine Equations 12-2B and 12-3B into a single Kirchhoff's Law equation (like Equation 12-1).

(We could have built both sides of the equation at the same time. It's often more convenient to work with one side at a time, though, and then combine them for the final solution.)

$$\Sigma\ E_{RISES} = \Sigma\ E_{DROPS}$$

$$15\ V = I \times 2400\ \Omega$$

$$\text{(Equation 12-4)}$$

To solve this equation for I, divide both sides of the equation by 2400 Ω.

$$\frac{15\ V}{2400\ \Omega} = \frac{I \times 2400\ \Omega}{2400\ \Omega}$$

$$I = \frac{15\ V}{2400\ \Omega} = 6.25 \times 10^{-3}\ A = 6.25\ mA$$
$$\text{(Equation 12-5)}$$

You can use Kirchhoff's Voltage Law to solve problems even more complicated than this. In the next section you'll learn several ways this important electronics principle can help you simplify a complex series circuit.

Simplifying Series Circuits

Kirchhoff's Voltage Law gives us several ideas for ways to simplify series electronic circuits. Look at the circuit shown in **Figure 12-3**. It includes some voltage sources, such as batteries, connected in series, along with a string of resistors. Sometimes we might like to redraw a circuit like this to show an *equivalent circuit*. An equivalent circuit has the same voltage and current as the original. The equivalent circuit uses one voltage source and one resistor, however. **Figure 12-4** shows the simplified circuit, but without values for the voltage and resistance.

We'll use Kirchhoff's Voltage Law to find these component values. Start with the basic Voltage Law equation:

$$\Sigma E_{RISES} = \Sigma E_{DROPS}$$

Remember that we worked with each half of this equation separately at first, to make the job easier. To add the voltage rises, go around the circuit in a direction that takes you through most of the voltage sources from negative to positive. Notice that the order of connecting the voltages doesn't really matter. The order in which we add them doesn't make a difference, either. It doesn't even matter if there are a few resistors between some of them. Just remember to give a negative sign to any voltage source that you go through from positive to negative along the way. (These voltages subtract from the others.)

From Kirchhoff's Voltage Law you can see that voltage sources either help or restrict electrons flowing through the circuit. Sometimes you might hear the terms *aiding* and *bucking* (or *opposing*) in relation to how we connect the voltage sources. Aiding sources connect positive to negative, so the voltages add. Bucking sources connect negative to negative (or positive to positive), so the voltages subtract. You can find the total voltage of a circuit like the one shown in Figure 12-3 with some simple arithmetic.

$$E_{TOTAL} = E1 + E2 + E3 + (-E4) + (-E5) \quad \text{(Equation 12-6)}$$

$$E_{TOTAL} = 20\ V + 30\ V + 10\ V + (-15\ V) + (-15\ V)$$

$$E_{TOTAL} = 30\ V$$

This is the equivalent voltage for the single source of Figure 12-4.

Now let's calculate the equivalent resistance of the single resistor for Figure 12-4. Write an equation using Kirchhoff's Voltage Law again, adding the voltage drops around the circuit loop. Let I represent the circuit current, since we don't know the actual value.

$$\Sigma E_{DROPS} = I \times R1 + I \times R2 + I \times R3 + I \times R4 + I \times R5 + I \times R6 \quad \text{(Equation 12-7)}$$

Since we are multiplying the same current, I, times each resistor value, we can rewrite this equation.

$$\Sigma E_{DROPS} = I\ (R1 + R2 + R3 + R4 + R5 + R6) \quad \text{(Equation 12-8)}$$

All we are really trying to do here is find the total equivalent resistance of the resistors in Figure 12-3. That one equivalent resistor must produce the same voltage drop as all the others combined. The current, I, times the equivalent resistance must equal the right side of Equation 12-8, then

$$I\ (R_{TOTAL}) = I\ (R1 + R2 + R3 + R4 + R5 + R6) \quad \text{(Equation 12-9)}$$

Divide both sides of this equation by I to cancel current out of the equation. Then we have a simple equation to calculate the total resistance of a string of resistors connected in series.

Figure 12-3 — This circuit is a rather complex combination of resistors and voltage sources connected in series. Kirchhoff's Voltage Law can help us find a simple equivalent circuit that includes one voltage source and one resistor. (An equivalent circuit means that both circuits produce the same external effects. In this example, it means the same current will flow in both circuits.)

Figure 12-4 — This diagram represents a simple circuit that is equivalent to the complex circuit of Figure 12-3. The text explains how to calculate the voltage and resistance values for the new circuit.

$R_{TOTAL} = R1 + R2 + R3 + R4 + R5 + R6$ (Equation 12-10)

This result shows us that the total equivalent resistance of series-connected resistors is equal to the sum of the individual resistor values. A general equation that you can apply to any combination of series resistors is:

$R_{TOTAL} = R1 + R2 + R3 + \ldots + R_N$

(Equation 12-11)

where R_N represents the last resistor in the string. This equation works if there are two resistors in series or two hundred (or more) in series. This equation does not work for resistors connected in parallel, however. (We'll come to that case later.)

For the example of Figure 12-3, the total resistance is:

$R_{TOTAL} = 2\ k\Omega + 2.5\ k\Omega + 5\ k\Omega + 10\ k\Omega + 1.5\ k\Omega + 4\ k\Omega$

$R_{TOTAL} = 25\ k\Omega$

Going back to Equation 12-9, we can write the equation as:

$I\ (R_{TOTAL}) = I \times 25\ k\Omega$

We can also write Equation 12-8 as:

$\Sigma\ E_{DROPS} = I \times 25\ k\Omega$

Now we can write Equation 12-1 with all of the additional information we have calculated.

$\Sigma\ E_{RISES} = \Sigma\ E_{DROPS}$

$30\ V = I \times 25\ k\Omega$

Does this look like an Ohm's Law equation? It should. The only unknown quantity here is the current, I. Now we can solve the equation for current, I.

$I = \dfrac{30\ V}{25\ k\Omega}$

$I = \dfrac{30\ V}{25 \times 10^3\ \Omega}$

$I = 1.2 \times 10^{-3}\ A = 1.2\ mA$

With the help of Kirchhoff's Voltage Law, we calculated the total circuit current. In fact, there is only one circuit current, since in a series circuit the same current flows through all the circuit elements (voltage sources, resistors and so on). You can use this method to calculate unknown information about circuits with even more voltage sources and resistances.

Kirchhoff's Current Law

Kirchhoff's Current Law, sometimes also called Kirchhoff's Second Law, is an important electronics principle. Kirchhoff's Current Law provides us with a very powerful tool for studying an electronic circuit and calculating conditions in that circuit.

Before you learn what this law says, you must learn another term sometimes used to describe part of an electronic circuit. A circuit node is any point in a circuit where two or more conductors connect. A node is the point where two resistors connect. The point where a wire connects to a battery is also a node. Most of the time we look for nodes that are branch points in the circuit. At least three conductors connect at that point. **Figure 12-5** points out several nodes on a circuit diagram.

Kirchhoff's Current Law states that *all currents into a circuit node equal all currents out of that node.* If you think about it, this rule should seem just as obvious as Kirchhoff's Voltage Law. After all, the current has to go somewhere. You can't just lose electrons as they flow around a circuit. No matter how obvious it is, however, this law is very important and extremely powerful in helping us solve electronic circuit problems.

Kirchhoff's Current Law indicates that we could write an equation for

the current at any circuit node. Again, we use the Greek letter sigma (Σ) to represent a summation of similar values.

$$\Sigma I_{IN} = \Sigma I_{OUT} \qquad \text{(Equation 12-12)}$$

Figure 12-6 shows a simple parallel circuit. Ammeters measure the current in the two branches, but we want to know the total battery current. Kirchhoff's Current Law will help us make that calculation. There is one current flowing into node A, I_{TOTAL} and two currents flowing out, I_1 and I_2.

Remember that engineers define the direction of current to be from the positive side of the voltage source to the negative side. We normally use this *conventional current* direction when dealing with Kirchhoff's Current Law. This is just a matter of convenience, because when you divide a positive voltage (a voltage rise) by a resistance, the positive number indicates a positive current. A negative value would mean the current flows in the opposite direction.

We can write a Kirchhoff's Current Law equation at node A of Figure 12-6, using Equation 12-12. This will allow us to calculate the total current out of the battery.

$$\Sigma I_{IN} = \Sigma I_{OUT} \qquad \text{(Equation 12-12)}$$

$$I_{TOTAL} = I_1 + I_2 \qquad \text{(Equation 12-13)}$$

$$I_{TOTAL} = 5.5 \text{ mA} + 4.4 \text{ mA} = 9.9 \text{ mA}$$

You also might want to write an equation for node B, just to prove that the results are the same.

$$\Sigma I_{IN} = \Sigma I_{OUT} \qquad \text{(Equation 12-12)}$$

$$I_1 + I_2 = I_{TOTAL} \qquad \text{(Equation 12-14)}$$

$$5.5 \text{ mA} + 4.4 \text{ mA} = I_{TOTAL} = 9.9 \text{ mA}$$

This example is almost too easy. The real usefulness of Kirchhoff's Current Law is for much more complicated circuits than this. For these more complicated problems, we often have to use both of Kirchhoff's Laws. Most of the time there are several circuit conditions we want to calculate. The solution involves the technique of solving *simultaneous equations*. That term simply means that if there is more than one variable or unknown in a circuit, you will need more than one equation about circuit conditions. You'll need one equation for each unknown, and those equations must all apply to the circuit at the same time. (That's what *simultaneous* means.)

Most problems like that are beyond the beginner's level of this

Figure 12-5 — This circuit diagram shows several circuit nodes. A node is the point where two or more conductors meet. Most of the time our interest is in nodes that occur at circuit branch points. In those cases, there will be three or more conductors, such as at nodes B and C on this diagram.

Figure 12-6 — This simple parallel circuit includes ammeters to measure the current in each branch. There is no ammeter to measure the total battery current, however. We must use Kirchhoff's Current Law to find the total current.

Figure 12-7 — This diagram will help illustrate the technique of using *simultaneous equations* to solve a problem that has more than one unknown. We want to calculate the total battery current and the current in each branch of this circuit. The text explains the procedure.

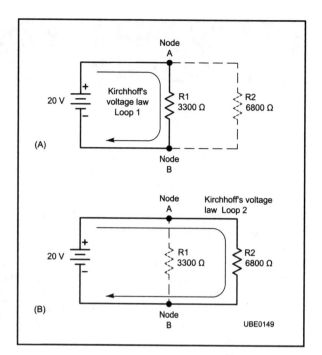

Figure 12-8 — The two parts of this drawing duplicate the diagram of Figure 12-7. Part A shows one loop that we can use to write a Kirchhoff's Voltage Law equation and Part B shows a second loop. The two equations from these loops, along with a Kirchhoff's Current Law Equation, allow us to calculate the three currents in the circuit.

book. Let's work through one easy example, though, just so you can see the steps involved.

Figure 12-7 shows a parallel circuit. We know the battery voltage and resistance values as shown on the diagram. We want to calculate the current through each branch of the circuit, and the total current drawn from the battery. That amounts to three currents that we want to calculate. We might start by writing a Kirchhoff's Current Law equation at node A.

$$\Sigma I_{IN} = \Sigma I_{OUT} \qquad \text{(Equation 12-12)}$$

$$\Sigma I_{TOTAL} = I_1 + I_2 \qquad \text{(Equation 12-15)}$$

This equation represents the three quantities we want to find, so you might wonder how it can help. Remember, with three unknowns, we'll need three simultaneous equations about this circuit. What other equations can we possibly write? There are at least two Kirchhoff's Voltage Law equations for this circuit. **Figure 12-8** shows the same circuit as Figure 12-7, with two loops identified to write these equations.

$$\Sigma E_{RISES} = \Sigma E_{DROPS} \quad \text{(Equation 12-16)}$$

For loop 1:

$$20 \text{ V} = I_1 \times R_1 \qquad \text{(Equation 12-17)}$$

For loop 2:

$$20 \text{ V} = I_2 \times R_2 \qquad \text{(Equation 12-18)}$$

Now we have three different equations that represent our three unknown quantities in this circuit. There are several mathematical techniques for solving simultaneous equations. One of those, which works well with simple equations like these, is *substitution*. To use this method, we solve one or more of the equations for known quantities or in terms of the other variables, and substitute that value into the remaining equations. (This method is easier than it sounds! Let's continue with the example, to see how it's done.)

First, we'll solve Equation 12-17 for I_1 by dividing both sides of the equation by R_1.

$$\frac{20 \text{ V}}{R_1} = \frac{I_1 \times R_1}{R_1} \qquad \text{(Equation 12-17)}$$

$$\frac{20 \text{ V}}{R_1} = I_1 \qquad \text{(Equation 12-19)}$$

Since the value for R_1 is given on the diagram, we can substitute that into the equation, and calculate I_1.

$$\frac{20 \text{ V}}{3300 \text{ } \Omega} = I_1$$

$$6.06 \times 10^{-3} \text{ A} = 6.06 \text{ mA} = I_1$$

Then we'll solve Equation 12-18 for I_2 in the same way.

$$\frac{20 \text{ V}}{R_2} = \frac{I_1 \times R_2}{R_2} \qquad \text{(Equation 12-18)}$$

$$\frac{20 \text{ V}}{R_2} = I_2 \qquad \text{(Equation 12-20)}$$

We also know the value for R_2 from Figure 12-7, so we can complete this calculation.

$$\frac{20 \text{ V}}{6800 \text{ } \Omega} = I_2$$

$$2.94 \times 10^{-3} \text{ A} = 2.94 \text{ mA} = I_2$$

Now we have expressions for I_1 and I_2 that we can substitute into Equation 12-15.

$$I_{TOTAL} = I_1 + I_2 \qquad \text{(Equation 12-15)}$$

$$I_{TOTAL} = 6.06 \text{ mA} + 2.94 \text{ mA} \qquad \text{(Equation 12-21)}$$

$$I_{TOTAL} = 9.00 \text{ mA}$$

This example shows you that Kirchhoff's Laws can solve complex circuit problems. You can solve problems with circuits that have many parallel branches, although the math can be tricky.

Simplifying Parallel Circuits

When we studied Kirchhoff's Voltage Law, we discovered that it could help us simplify series circuits. For example, if there were several voltage sources connected in series, we could replace them with one equivalent source. We also discovered a simple equation for calculating the value of a single resistor to replace several resistors connected in series.

You might be wondering if Kirchhoff's Current Law provides a similar way to simplify parallel circuits. The answer is a very definite *yes*.

Figure 12-9 shows a circuit that has two batteries connected in parallel as a voltage source. What effect will this have on the circuit? Each battery supplies some current to the circuit. Without writing an equation, let's think about how Kirchhoff's Current Law applies to this circuit. Each battery supplies a current that flows into node A. The total circuit current flows out of node A. Connecting the batteries in parallel helps them last longer. It's similar to using a bigger battery when the circuit needs more current than a smaller one can supply. For example, compare a 1.5 volt AAA cell with a 1.5 volt D cell, as shown in **Figure 12-10**. They all produce the same voltage, but the bigger batteries can supply a lot more current.

You wouldn't normally connect batteries of different voltages in parallel. That might lead to a large current flowing between the batteries, overheating them and possibly causing other damage or dangerous conditions. There are times, however, when you may want to connect several batteries of the same voltage in parallel.

Take another look at Figure 12-9. There are two voltage sources, each having the same voltage, connected in parallel. We can simplify this circuit by replacing the two voltage sources with one that can supply the same current. Pretty simple, isn't it?

Can Kirchhoff's Current Law help us combine several resistors connected in parallel and replace them with a single equivalent resistor? Again, *yes*! Let's start with the circuit of **Figure 12-11**. What is the resistance of a single resistor that could replace the three parallel resistors shown? The same total current flows from the battery. First, we'll write a Kirchhoff's Current Law equation at node A.

$$\Sigma I_{IN} = \Sigma I_{OUT} \qquad \text{(Equation 12-12)}$$

$$I_{TOTAL} = I_1 + I_2 + I_3 \quad \text{(Equation 12-23)}$$

We also can write Kirchhoff's Voltage Law equations for three loops around this circuit. See **Figure 12-12**. Since each of these loops involves the battery voltage and a single resistor, the full battery voltage appears across each resistor. We can use Ohm's Law to write equations for the voltage across each resistor. Then we can solve these equations for the branch currents.

$$E = I_1 \times R_1 \qquad \text{(Equation 12-24)}$$

Solving for I_1:

$$\frac{E}{R_1} = \frac{I_1 \times R_1}{R_1} \qquad \text{(Equation 12-25)}$$

$$I_1 = \frac{E}{R_1} \qquad \text{(Equation 12-26)}$$

Next, we'll find I_2.

$$E = I_2 \times R_2 \qquad \text{(Equation 12-27)}$$

$$I_2 = \frac{E}{R_2} \qquad \text{(Equation 12-28)}$$

Finally, the third branch current.

$$E = I_3 \times R_3 \qquad \text{(Equation 12-29)}$$

$$I_3 = \frac{E}{R_3} \qquad \text{(Equation 12-30)}$$

Now we can substitute these branch current values into Kirchhoff's Current Law, Equation 12-23.

$$I_{TOTAL} = I_1 + I_2 + I_3 \quad \text{(Equation 12-23)}$$

$$I_{TOTAL} = \frac{E}{R_1} + \frac{E}{R_2} + \frac{E}{R_3}$$
$$\text{(Equation 12-31)}$$

Figure 12-9 — We can connect batteries in parallel if they have equal voltage. This increases battery life because the circuit draws less current from each battery.

Figure 12-10 — A watch battery, an AAA cell and a D cell all produce 1.5 V. The larger the battery size, however, the more current it can supply before it goes dead.

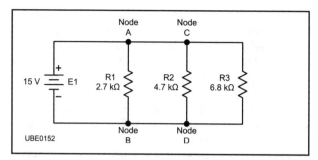

Figure 12-11 —This simple parallel circuit has three resistors connected in parallel with the battery. We want to replace these three resistors with a single one that will have the same effect in the circuit. The text describes the procedure to follow.

The total current in this circuit is the same as the current through a single resistor equivalent to the three in parallel. With this piece of information, we can solve an Ohm's Law equation for TOTAL:

$$I_{TOTAL} = \frac{E}{R_{TOTAL}}$$

(Equation 12-32)

Substituting into Equation 12-31, we have:

$$\frac{E}{R_{TOTAL}} = \frac{E}{R_1} + \frac{E}{R_2} + \frac{E}{R_3}$$

(Equation 12-33)

By dividing every term on both sides of this equation by E, we can eliminate the voltage from our equation. Then we are left with an equation to calculate the total resistance of a string of parallel-connected resistors.

$$\frac{1}{R_{TOTAL}} = \frac{1}{R_1} + \frac{1}{R_2} + \frac{1}{R_3}$$

(Equation 12-34)

It's pretty easy to find reciprocals (one divided by a number) on a scientific calculator. You can solve this whole equation in a few simple steps.

$$\frac{1}{R_{TOTAL}} = \frac{1}{2.7\ k\Omega} + \frac{1}{4.7\ k\Omega} + \frac{1}{6.8\ k\Omega}$$

$$\frac{1}{R_{TOTAL}} =$$

$$\frac{3.7 \times 10^{-4} + 2.1 \times 10^{-4} + 1.5 \times 10^{-4}}{\Omega}$$

Figure 12-12 —The three parts of this figure each shows the circuit of Figure 12-11. Each part shows a circuit loop that we can use with Kirchhoff's Voltage Law, to write an equation about the circuit.

Notice that the ohm unit in the right side of this equation, (Ω), is in the denominator (bottom). This is the unit of the final answer, R_{TOTAL}. Makes sense; resistance is measured in ohms.

Next step, add
$3.7 \times 10^{-4} + 2.1 \times 10^{-4} + 1.5 \times 10^{-4}$
$= 7.3 \times 10^{-4}$

$$\frac{1}{R_{TOTAL}} = \frac{7.3 \times 10^{-4}}{\Omega}$$

There are several ways to solve the equation above for R_{TOTAL}. One way is to take the reciprocal of each side of the equation:

$$R_{TOTAL} = \frac{1}{7.3 \times 10^{-4}}\ \Omega = 1400\ \Omega$$

(Equation 12-35)

(Your calculator probably will read something like 1369.49, but we've rounded the answer off to show only two significant figures.)

If you have a string of resistors connected in parallel (N of them), you find the value of one resistor that is equivalent to the string. Just add the reciprocal of each resistor in the string, and then take the reciprocal of that result.

$$\frac{1}{R_{TOTAL}} = \frac{1}{R_1} + \frac{1}{R_2} + \frac{1}{R_3} + \cdots \frac{1}{R_N}$$

(Equation 12-36)

For example, if four resistors were in parallel: 10 Ω, 20 Ω, 50 Ω, and 100 Ω, the total resistance would be calculated as follows:

$$\frac{1}{R_{TOTAL}} = \frac{1}{10\ \Omega} + \frac{1}{20\ \Omega} + \frac{1}{50\ \Omega} + \frac{1}{100\ \Omega}$$

$$= (0.1 + 0.05 + 0.02 + 0.01)\frac{1}{\Omega}$$

$$= (0.18)\frac{1}{\Omega}$$

$$R_{TOTAL} = \left(\frac{1}{0.18}\right)\Omega = 5.56\ \Omega$$

It's very important for you to realize that you must add the *reciprocal values* of the resistances.

This is *not* the same as adding the resistance values themselves! With your scientific calculator in hand, you can easily add the *reciprocals* of the resistances.

There are a couple of other important observations that we should make about resistors connected in parallel. Notice the answer given in Equation 12-35. The combined resistance of the parallel resistors in Figure 12-11 is only 1.4 kΩ. That's less than any resistor in the circuit! Whenever you have some resistors connected in parallel, the equivalent resistance of the combination is always less than any of the individual resistors.

Equal value resistors connected in parallel present another interesting condition. Connect two equal resistors in parallel. The total resistance will be ½ the resistance of either one by itself. Connect three equal resistors in parallel and the total will be ⅓ the value of any one resistor. You can find the equivalent resistance of any number of equal-value resistors connected in parallel. Divide the value of a single resistor by the number of resistors in the string. This gives you a quick way to calculate the equivalent resistance of a parallel string of equal resistors.

Simplifying Series-Parallel Circuits

Kirchhoff's Voltage and Current Laws provide us with the tools to simplify electronic circuits. If a circuit includes a string of resistors connected in series, we can find a single equivalent resistor to replace the string. Likewise, if a circuit includes a string of resistors connected in parallel, we can find a single equivalent resistor to replace that string. To combine *series resistors*, we simply add the individual resistor values.

$$R_{TOTAL} = R_1 + R_2 + R_3 + ...+ R_N$$

(Equation 12-37)

To combine *parallel resistors*, we must add the reciprocals of the individual resistor values, and then take the reciprocal of that sum.

$$\frac{1}{R_{TOTAL}} = \frac{1}{R_1} + \frac{1}{R_2} + \frac{1}{R_3} + ... \frac{1}{R_N}$$

(Equation 12-38)

The best way to learn how to use these equations is through practice, so let's try a couple of examples. **Figure 12-13** shows a circuit with five resistors connected in series. What is the equivalent resistance of a single resistor that can replace them?

Since this is a series circuit, we'll have to use Equation 12-37. Simply add the five resistance values to find the equivalent resistance. Sounds easy, doesn't it?

$$R_{TOTAL} = R_1 + R_2 + R_3 + ... + R_N$$

(Equation 12-37)

$$R_{TOTAL} = 1 \text{ k}\Omega + 3.3 \text{ k}\Omega + 5.6 \text{ k}\Omega + 4.7 \text{ k}\Omega + 1.5 \text{ k}\Omega$$

$$R_{TOTAL} = 16.1 \text{ k}\Omega$$

Now let's try a parallel-circuit problem. **Figure 12-14** shows a circuit that includes three resistors connected in parallel. What is the value of a single resistor that can replace these three? This one requires us to use Equation 12-38.

$$\frac{1}{R_{TOTAL}} = \frac{1}{R_1} + \frac{1}{R_2} + \frac{1}{R_3} + ... \frac{1}{R_N}$$

(Equation 12-38)

$$\frac{1}{R_{TOTAL}} = \frac{1}{R_1} + \frac{1}{R_2} + \frac{1}{R_3} + ... \frac{1}{R_N}$$

$$\frac{1}{R_{TOTAL}} = \frac{1}{2.2 \text{ k}\Omega} + \frac{1}{1.5 \text{ k}\Omega} + \frac{1}{2.7 \text{ k}\Omega}$$

$$\frac{1}{R_{TOTAL}} = \frac{4.5 \times 10^{-4} + 6.7 \times 10^{-4} + 3.7 \times 10^{-4}}{\Omega}$$

$$\frac{1}{R_{TOTAL}} = \frac{14.9 \times 10^{-4}}{\Omega}$$

Now solve this equation for R_{TOTAL} by cross multiplying the terms.

$$R_{TOTAL} = \frac{1 \Omega}{14.9 \times 10^{-4}} = 670 \Omega$$

This took a bit more work than the previous problem. With the help of your scientific calculator, it shouldn't have given you too much trouble, though. You'll get plenty of additional practice adding series and parallel resistors as you learn more about electronics.

You will find electronic circuits that look much more complicated than these simple series or parallel circuits. Most circuits include some combination of series and parallel connections. You'll have to use your knowledge of the simple circuits to solve these problems. Take them one step at a time, and work with part of the circuit at each step. This way, you can solve some difficult problems.

Let's look at **Figure 12-15**. Here is a network of series and parallel resistors. Your job is to find the value of a single resistor that can replace the entire network. Why would you want to do that? Well, one practical reason would be to calculate the total current flowing in the circuit. Now, you could write Kirchhoff's Voltage and Current equations and solve them for the total circuit current. This is a difficult task for even a circuit like the one of Figure 12-15, however. You would have up to seven variables, and need seven simultaneous equations to solve this problem! That's an exercise better left for an advanced student.

How will we find the equivalent resistance of this circuit? Start working at the point farthest from the voltage source. Study the circuit

Figure 12-13 — Find a single resistor to replace this string of resistors connected in series. The text explains how to do this problem.

Figure 12-14 — Find a single resistor to replace this string of resistors connected in parallel. The text explains the steps involved in solving this problem.

Figure 12-16 — The parts of this figure show the steps involved in simplifying the circuit of Figure 12-15. Each part shows a further reduction in the number of resistors in the circuit, until, in Part E, there is only one left. This one resistor draws the same current from the voltage source as the entire circuit of Figure 12-15.

diagram to determine if the resistors at that point connect in series or parallel. When you look at Figure 12-15, you'll notice that R6, R7 and R8 are in series. The first step is to combine these three resistors into one. We'll rewrite Equation 12-37 a bit to fit this problem.

$R_{6-8} = R_6 + R_7 + R_8$

(Equation 12-39)

where R_{6-8} means the equivalent resistor that replaces resistors numbered from 6 to 8.

$R_{6-8} = 680\ \Omega + 180\ \Omega + 820\ \Omega$

$R_{6-8} = 1680\ \Omega = 1.68\ k\Omega$

Figure 12-16A shows the circuit of Figure 12-15 with this resistor replacing resistors R6, R7 and R8. Take a close look at this new circuit of Figure 12-16A. You should immediately notice that the three resistors farthest from the voltage source connect in parallel. Our next step, then, is to combine these three

into a single equivalent resistance. Using Equation 12-38, we have:

$$\frac{1}{R_{4-8}} = \frac{1}{R_4} + \frac{1}{R_5} + \frac{1}{R_{6-8}}$$

(Equation 12-40)

where R_{4-8} represents a single resistor that is equivalent to resistors R_4 through R_8 in the original circuit.

$$\frac{1}{R_{4-8}} = \frac{1}{R_4} + \frac{1}{R_5} + \frac{1}{R_{6-8}}$$

$$\frac{1}{R_{4-8}} =$$

$$\frac{1}{4.7 \times 10^3\Omega} + \frac{1}{8.2 \times 10^3\Omega} + \frac{1}{1.68 \times 10^3\Omega}$$

$$\frac{1}{R_{4-8}} =$$

$$\frac{2.13 \times 10^{-4} + 1.22 \times 10^{-4} + 5.95 \times 10^{-4}}{\Omega}$$

$$\frac{1}{R_{4-8}} = \frac{9.30 \times 10^{-4}}{\Omega}$$

To solve this equation for R_{4-8} cross multiply the terms.

$$R_{4-8} = \frac{1\ \Omega}{9.30 \times 10^{-4}} = 1075\ \Omega$$

Figure 12-16B shows the circuit redrawn with this new equivalent resistor. Notice that R_3 and R_{4-8} are in series. We can replace those two resistors with a single value found by adding them.

$R_{3-8} = 390\ \Omega + 1075\ \Omega$

$R_{3-8} = 1465\ \Omega$

Figure 12-16C includes this substitution in our circuit. It's beginning to look much simpler, isn't it? How do R_2 and R_{3-8} connect? How will you find an equivalent value for them? That's right, they connect in parallel, so you'll have to add the reciprocals of their values, using Equation 12-38.

$$\frac{1}{R_{2\text{-}8}} = \frac{1}{R_2} + \frac{1}{R_{3\text{-}8}}$$

(Equation 12-41)

$$\frac{1}{R_{2\text{-}8}} = \frac{1}{100 \text{ k}\Omega} + \frac{1}{1465 \text{ }\Omega}$$

$$\frac{1}{R_{2\text{-}8}} = \frac{1.00 \times 10^{-5} + 6.826 \times 10^{-4}}{\Omega}$$

$$\frac{1}{R_{2\text{-}8}} = \frac{6.926 \times 10^{-4}}{\Omega}$$

Cross multiply the terms to solve for $R_{2\text{-}8}$.

$$R_{2\text{-}8} = \frac{1 \text{ }\Omega}{6.926 \times 10^{-4}} = 1444 \text{ }\Omega$$

Figure 12-16D shows this newest circuit, one step from completion. All that's left is to combine R_1 with $R_{2\text{-}8}$. Since they connect in series, you probably don't even need to write an equation. Just add the values.

$$R_{TOTAL} = R_1 + R_{2\text{-}8} \quad \text{(Equation 12-42)}$$

$$R_{TOTAL} = 560 \text{ }\Omega + 1444 \text{ }\Omega$$

$$R_{TOTAL} = 2004 \text{ }\Omega$$

Part E of Figure 12-16 shows this final equivalent circuit.

By simplifying this circuit in steps, we found a single resistor (R_{TOTAL} = 2004 Ω) that is equivalent to the whole circuit. You could now calculate the total current that flows from the voltage supply using this equivalent resistor. Ohm's Law will help you with that calculation.

$$E = I \times R \quad \text{(Equation 12-43)}$$

Solve this equation for I (or use an Ohm's Law Circle to find the new equation).

$$I = E / R \quad \text{(Equation 12-44)}$$

$$I = 10 \text{ V} / 2004 \text{ }\Omega = 4.99 \times 10^{-3} \text{ A}$$

$$I = 4.99 \text{ mA}$$

We won't go through any more calculations here. It's not difficult to work back through the original circuit, calculating all the branch currents. Kirchhoff's Current and Voltage Laws will be a big help. Even though it was lots of work to simplify this circuit, it was the easiest way to calculate the total circuit current.

Remember, when you want to simplify a complicated electronic circuit, begin at the farthest point from the voltage source. Replace series and parallel resistor combinations one step at a time. Eventually you will find a single resistor to take the place of all those in the original circuit.

Math and Calculator Hints

MATH HINTS

For more background on math, refer to **Appendix A — Scientific and Engineering Notation.**

CALCULATOR HINTS

The following examples show how to use your TI-30X IIS calculator to solve equations like those in Chapter 12. Simpler numbers are used, so they will all be visible in the display of the calculator at the same time. For more information on using a calculator to work these examples, refer to **Appendix B — Understanding and Using Your TI-30X IIS Scientific Calculator**

Example 1

If three resistors were in parallel: 5 Ω, 8 Ω, and 10 Ω, the total resistance would be calculated as follows:

$$\frac{1}{R_{TOTAL}} = \frac{1}{5\ \Omega} + \frac{1}{8\ \Omega} + \frac{1}{10\ \Omega}$$

$$= (0.20 + 0.125 + 0.10)\frac{1}{\Omega}$$

$$= (0.425)\frac{1}{\Omega}$$

$$R_{TOTAL} = \left(\frac{1}{0.425}\right)\Omega = 2.3529\ \Omega$$

Calculator keystrokes:

5 x⁻¹ + 8 x⁻¹ + 10 x⁻¹ =

The calculator's second display line shows the result: **425 × 10⁻⁰³**

[Note that $10^{-03} = 10^{-3} = 0.001$, so $425 \times 10^{-03} = 425 \times 0.001 = 0.425$]

But we're not done; 425×10^{-03} is $1/R_{TOTAL}$, and is not the final answer. In order to get R_{TOTAL} we must invert (or take the reciprocal of) 425×10^{-03}.

There are two ways to do this. The easy way is to press the **x⁻¹** key, which will invert the ANS (the answer of 425×10^{-03}). So with 425×10^{-03} showing in the bottom line of the display, press the **x⁻¹** key, and the total resistance, R_{TOTAL}, will be displayed ($R_{TOTAL} = 2.3529\ \Omega$).

The almost-as-easy way is to re-enter the value of $1/R_{TOTAL}$, which is 0.425 (or 425×10^{-03}), and then to press the **x⁻¹** key. The total resistance, R_{TOTAL}, will be displayed

($R_{TOTAL} = 2.3529\ \Omega$).

Note that the calculator keystrokes shown above:

5 x⁻¹ + 8 x⁻¹ + 1 0 x⁻¹ =

are adding the reciprocals of the three resistors, which is the first step to finding the total resistance of 5 Ω, 8 Ω, and 10 Ω resistors in parallel. Your calculator is doing the following mathematical operation:

$(1/5) + (1/8) + (1/10) =$

You can revisit some of the examples in this chapter, such as finding the total resistance of 2.2 kΩ, 1.5 kΩ, and 2.7 kΩ resistors in parallel.

$$\frac{1}{R_{TOTAL}} = \frac{1}{2.2\ k\Omega} + \frac{1}{1.5\ k\Omega} + \frac{1}{2.7\ k\Omega}$$

As shown in this chapter, the answer you get should be:

$$R_{TOTAL} = \frac{1}{1.49158 \times 10^3}\ \Omega = 670\ \Omega$$

(Your calculator probably will read something like 670.429, but we've rounded the answer off to show only two significant figures.)

Review Questions

12.1 Kirchhoff's Voltage Law (KVL) is a powerful tool to be used when solving circuit problems. Express KVL in your own words.

12.2 Kirchhoff's Current Law (KCL) is a powerful tool to be used when solving circuit problems. Express KCL in your own words.

12.3 Four resistors are in series: 10 Ω, 30 Ω, 50 Ω and Rx. Their total resistance is 150 Ω. What is the value of Rx?

12.4 Three resistors are in parallel. Their values are 10 Ω, 40 Ω and 32 Ω. What is their combined resistance?

12.5 (Warning – tricky question) Four equal resistors R1, R2, R3 and R4 (each has the same resistance) are connected as follows: R1 is placed in series with R2, and R3 is placed in parallel with R4. Then the series resistors (R1 and R2) are placed in series with the parallel combination of R3 and R4. The total resistance of the combination is 15 Ω. What is the value, in ohms, of each resistor? *Hint: guessing a value, and "seeing if it works", is a good way to get the answer quickly.*

Answers

12.1 According to Kirchhoff's Voltage Law, *all voltage drops must equal all voltage rises around a closed loop*. There is a *voltage drop* across any circuit resistance when there is a current through it. We use Ohm's Law to calculate the amount of these voltage drops. A *voltage rise* normally refers to a voltage source, such as a battery. We add all the voltage rises and all the voltage drops. If you think the statement of Kirchhoff's First Law sounds like a mathematical equation, you are exactly right! We might write this rule as: $\Sigma E_{rises} = \Sigma E_{drops}$

12.2 Kirchhoff's Current Law states that *all currents into a circuit node equal all currents out of that node*. This may seem obvious, since the current has to go somewhere. You can't just lose electrons as they flow around a circuit. No matter how obvious it is, however, this law is very important and extremely powerful in helping us solve electronics circuit problems. We might write this rule as: $\Sigma I_{IN} = \Sigma I_{OUT}$

12.3 Resistors in series.

$R_{Total} = R1 + R2 + R3 + R4 = 10\,\Omega + 30\,\Omega + 50\,\Omega + Rx = 150\,\Omega$

$Rx = 150\,\Omega - (10\,\Omega + 30\,\Omega + 50\,\Omega) = 150\,\Omega - 90\,\Omega = 60\,\Omega$

12.4 Resistors in parallel.

$$\frac{1}{R_{TOTAL}} = \frac{1}{R_1} + \frac{1}{R_2} + \frac{1}{R_3}$$

$$\frac{1}{R_{TOTAL}} = \frac{1}{10\,\Omega} + \frac{1}{40\,\Omega} + \frac{1}{32\,\Omega}$$

$$\frac{1}{R_{TOTAL}} = 0.10 + 0.025 + 0.03125 = 0.15625$$

$$R_{TOTAL} = \frac{1}{0.15625}\,\Omega = 6.4\,\Omega$$

12.5 Recall that two equal resistors in parallel (R3 and R4 for this question) have a combined resistance of ½ the value of each resistor.

Guess 1 Ω: $1\,\Omega + 1\,\Omega + 1\,\Omega/2 = 2\,\Omega + 0.5\,\Omega = 2.5\,\Omega$; too low a combined resistance.

Guess 10 Ω: $10\,\Omega + 10\,\Omega + 10\,\Omega/2 = 20\,\Omega + 5\,\Omega = 25\,\Omega$; too high a combined resistance.

The correct answer is R1 = R2 = R3 = R4 = 6 Ω.

$6\,\Omega + 6\,\Omega + 6\,\Omega/2$
$= 12\,\Omega + 3\,\Omega$
$= 15\,\Omega$

Chapter 13

Energy and Power

This diagram is similar to the Ohm's Law circle, but is for power calculations.

Contents

Energy is the Ability to Do Work

What can electricity do for us? It gives light when electrons flow through a light bulb. Electricity can warm our home, run a motor to turn a drill, spin a saw blade or run an electric hair dryer. The heating elements in an oven or stove use electricity to produce the heat needed to cook our food. Electrons flowing through the circuits inside our radios and TV sets convert radio signals into sounds and pictures. The list could go on and on.

Electric companies sell us this electricity, and the amount they charge us depends on how much electricity we use each month. So how do they decide how much to charge? They measure the electricity we use during the month. This is more than just measuring the current or voltage, since those quantities change from moment to moment. The electric company uses a meter that measures the amount of *electrical energy* you use. (A kilowatt-hour meter measures this energy.)

What is *electrical energy*, and how do we measure it? Well, as the title for this module says, *energy* is the ability to do *work*. The amount of work to be done determines how much energy is required. Since you may not be familiar with these terms, let's go over some basic definitions. We'll also look at a few examples that will help you understand the terms a little better.

To do some work, there are two requirements. There must be a force acting on an object, and that force must move the object some distance. To calculate how much work was done, multiply the amount of the force and the distance the object moves. In the metric system, the unit for work is the *joule*. (Pronounce that jool, which rhymes with pool.) Energy is a measure of how much work something can do. It takes one joule of energy to do one joule of work. The common abbreviation for joule is J.

Figure 13-1 shows a simple example of work and energy — picking up a football and holding it above your head. To lift the ball, you had to exert a force equal to the force of gravity pulling down on the ball. In metric units, let's say that took a force of 1 newton. If you lift the ball 1 meter, you do 1 joule of work. We also can say the ball has 1 joule of *potential energy* now. If you let go, gravity will pull the ball back to the earth. *Potential energy* is energy stored in an object for later release. As the ball falls back to the ground it loses some of its potential energy because it doesn't have as far to fall anymore. (Remember, it's force times distance.) But, the ball now has *kinetic energy*, which is energy of motion.

What does all this have to do with electronics? Well, electrons can have potential energy stored in them. For example, the electrons at the negative side of a battery have potential energy. This is because the battery voltage will push and pull the electrons through a circuit when we connect it to one. (Remember, voltage is the force that moves electrons through a circuit.) Electrons also have kinetic energy, because each is in constant motion around the

UBE0158

Figure 13-1 — Here's a simple illustration of work and energy. Imagine lifting a football and holding it above your head. When you do work on the football to lift it, you also store some energy in it, which we call potential energy. Later, when you drop the football, the football's potential energy changes into kinetic energy, the energy of motion.

Electrons here have only one quarter of their maximum potential energy left. Three quarters of the original energy was converted to heat energy and light energy.

Electrons have no potential energy left at this point.

Electrons have maximum potential energy here.

Electrons have less than maximum potential energy. Some energy was converted to heat in the resistor.

UBE0159

Figure 13-2 — As we move away from the negative battery terminal, electrons have less potential energy after passing through any circuit resistance. Electrons at the negative terminal have the most potential energy and electrons at the positive terminal have zero potential energy. (Don't confuse *conventional current* direction with *electron flow* here. With conventional current, we would say the positive battery terminal has the highest potential, just the opposite of looking at the electrons.)

Figure 13-3 — This simple electronic circuit shows a battery doing 1 joule of work every second. A joule is the amount of work done on a coulomb of electrons to move them through a voltage drop of 1 volt.

nucleus of an atom. After an electron goes through a resistor, there is less voltage pushing and pulling it the rest of the way through the circuit. Ohm's Law tells us there is a voltage drop across the resistor, and that drop depends on the amount of current and the resistance (E = I R). The electron has less potential energy as it gets closer to the positive battery terminal. This is similar to the football, which has less potential energy as it gets closer to the ground. Some of the electron's energy changes to heat

energy in the resistor. When electrons move through a light bulb, some of their energy changes into light energy. (Some of it also changes to heat energy in a light bulb.)

We start with a certain amount of energy stored in the electrons at the negative battery terminal. As we move around the circuit, we find that the electrons have less and less potential energy (see **Figure 13-2**). We also find that the electricity has given us other forms of energy. This is an important idea. The total amount of energy doesn't change. Some energy changes from one form to another, but we still have the same total amount. Scientists call this principle *conservation of energy*. Work is done when one form of energy changes to another. The amount of work done is equal to the amount of energy converted.

Earlier, we mentioned that electric companies measure the amount of electric energy we use, so they can charge us for this electricity. Remember that we often measure the amount of electric charge (or the

number of electrons) in *coulombs*. There are 6.24×10^{18} electrons in one *coulomb* of charge. If one coulomb of electrons flows past a point in a circuit in one second, there is a *one ampere* current in that circuit. Now that we've reminded you of those important definitions, we can explain what a joule of electrical energy means.

Suppose you have a circuit like the one shown in **Figure 13-3**. A 1-ampere current flows through the circuit. There is a voltage drop of 1 volt across the 1-ohm resistor. The battery does 1 joule of work every second as it pushes the 1-amp current through the resistor. From this you can guess that 1 joule of electrical energy is a small amount. Too small, in fact, for the electrical companies to use. They use a larger unit, the *kilowatt-hour* (equal to 1000 watt-hours), to calculate our monthly electricity bills. We'll define that unit in more detail in the next section, but for now you can recognize the metric prefix kilo (meaning thousand) and the time unit *hour*.

Power is the Rate of Doing Work or the Rate of Using Energy

The circuit of **Figure 13-4** uses 2 joules of energy every second. We also could say the voltage supply in this circuit does 2 joules of work every second. If we just measure the amount of energy in joules, it doesn't tell us as much about the circuit. That's why we also include a time.

Suppose we just said that the battery in the circuit of Figure 13-4 does 2 joules of work. We also can say that the battery in **Figure 13-5** does 2 joules of work. Of course these circuits are much different from each other. In fact, it takes eight seconds for the battery in the circuit of Figure 13-5 to do 2 joules of work. (That's eight times as long as it takes the battery of Figure 13-4!) We might

even draw a circuit that would take an hour or more to do 2 joules of work. The point is that different circuits will use energy (or do work) at different rates. The time rate of doing work provides us with some important information about a circuit.

A special term defines this rate of doing work or using energy. *Power* is the rate of doing work. If something uses energy at the rate of 1 joule per second, the power is 1 *watt* (abbreviated W). Most readers have at least heard of this term. This basic power unit is named in honor of James Watt, a scientist and inventor who built the first successful steam engine. A watt is a small unit of power, so we use the *kilowatt* (1000 W, or 1 kW) to measure large amounts of power. When you are talking about electric generating plants, you might even measure the power output in *megawatts* (MW).

By now you are probably wondering how we measure energy and power in a practical way. The joule represents the energy used to move one coulomb of electrons through a 1 volt change in *potential* (or *voltage*). A coulomb of electrons per second gives us the definition of an *ampere*. Without going through a lot of mathematics, you should begin to realize that we can define the *watt* in terms of current and voltage. We multiply the current through a circuit times the voltage drop across that circuit to get the power in the circuit. Since we can measure current and voltage easily, this gives us a good, practical way to measure power.

We can write an equation to calculate power.

$$P = I\,E \qquad \text{(Equation 13-1)}$$

where

P = power in watts
I = current in amperes
E = voltage in volts

This may be the easiest electronics equation to remember. Just look at the letters. Don't they spell one of your favorite kinds of dessert? Whether it's lemon meringue, apple or pumpkin, most people like some type of PIE. Once you've made that association, you will always remember the equation to calculate power.

Take a look at **Figure 13-6**. How much power does the battery in this circuit provide? The battery voltage is 15 V, and the circuit current is 25 mA. Since Equation 13-1 calls for current in amps, we'll have to convert the 25 mA to 0.025 A. Then, using Equation 13-1, we have:

$$P = I\,E \qquad \text{(Equation 13-1)}$$

$$P = 0.025\ \text{A} \times 15\ \text{V} = 0.375\ \text{W}$$
$$\text{(or 375 mW)}$$

Figure 13-7 shows a radio transmitter and amplifier tuned to 14.030 megahertz (MHz) in the amateur 20-meter band. A meter in the feed line to the antenna measures the radio frequency current from the transmitter. The current in the feed line is 5 amps. A voltmeter measures the amplifier output as 270 V. What is the power output from this transmitter and amplifier combination?

Figure 13-4 — This simple electronic circuit uses energy at the rate of 2 joules every second.

Figure 13-5 — The voltage of this battery is much larger than the voltage of the battery shown in Figure 13-4. This battery supplies energy to its circuit at a much slower rate, because the resistance is much larger. In fact, this circuit only uses ¼ J of energy every second.

Figure 13-6 — You can calculate the rate that a circuit uses energy (its power) by multiplying the circuit voltage times the total current.

Figure 13-7 — This Amateur Radio station includes a transmitter and power amplifier. It also includes meters to measure the radio frequency current and voltage in the antenna feed line. You can determine the output power of the amplifier by multiplying the current and voltage readings. This amplifier feeds energy to the antenna at the rate of 1350 watts.

Figure 13-8 — This "Power Circle" provides a way to solve the basic power equation for any of the three quantities in the equation. As with the Ohm's Law Circle, simply cover the part you want to calculate. The other two sections show you how to calculate it. Practice writing equations to calculate power, current and voltage from this circle.

$$P = I \, E \qquad \text{(Equation 13-1)}$$

$$P = 5 \text{ A} \times 270 \text{ V} = 1350 \text{ W}$$

You also can express this in kilowatts. The amplifier is feeding 1.35 kW to the antenna in this amateur station.

If you know power and either current or voltage in a circuit, the power equation will help you calculate the third quantity. You can solve Equation 13-1 for current and voltage in much the same way we solved Ohm's Law for current or resistance. We also can draw a "Power Equation Circle," as shown in **Figure 13-8**. Use the Power Circle by covering the quantity you want to find. Write the equation from the remaining parts. Be sure you can write Equations 13-2 and 13-3 from the Power Circle.

$$I = \frac{P}{E} \qquad \text{(Equation 13-2)}$$

$$E = \frac{P}{I} \qquad \text{(Equation 13-3)}$$

Let's use a simple flashlight circuit as an example. Our flashlight uses a 6-V battery and a bulb rated at 2 W. How much current will this bulb draw from the battery? From the Power Circle, we write Equation 13-2.

$$I = \frac{P}{E} \qquad \text{(Equation 13-2)}$$

$$I = \frac{P}{E} = \frac{2 \text{ W}}{6 \text{ V}} = 0.33 \text{ A}$$

You could use a similar procedure to find the circuit voltage if you knew power and current.

The power rating on a light bulb (or any electric appliance) describes the rate that it uses electric energy. In an incandescent light bulb, some of that energy gets converted to light energy and some gets converted to heat energy. The power rating helps you calculate the current or voltage that the bulb requires. Of course it also gives you an idea how much light the bulb will produce. Don't expect a 75-W bulb to produce 75 joules of *light* energy every second, though! Some of that energy will be heat energy. Fluorescent lights produce less heat than incandescent bulbs, so there is a lot less "wasted" energy for a given power rating.

More Power Calculations

It's an easy task to calculate the power in a circuit if you know the voltage and current. Equation 13-3 shows how to do this calculation.

$$P = I E \qquad \text{(Equation 13-3)}$$

Many times, you won't know both of those quantities directly, though. You may know some circuit conditions that will help you calculate power, however. Remember, Ohm's Law gives us a relationship between voltage, current and resistance. If you know the circuit voltage and resistance, you can calculate the current using Ohm's Law. Then you can calculate power from those values.

We don't have to use numbers to solve Ohm's Law for current. We can use the letter symbols, and then substitute those symbols into the power equation. By doing that there'll only be one calculation step to find power. That will save time and reduce the number of possible errors.

First, let's assume we know the voltage applied to a circuit, and the circuit resistance. From Ohm's Law, we can calculate the current.

$$E = I R \qquad \text{(Equation 13-4)}$$

so

$$I = \frac{E}{R} \qquad \text{(Equation 13-5)}$$

If we substitute this expression for current into the power equation, we'll get a single equation to calculate power under these conditions.

$$P = I \times E = \frac{E}{R} \times E = \frac{E^2}{R}$$

$$\text{(Equation 13-6)}$$

Figure 13-9 shows a simple parallel circuit that includes a voltage source connected to two parallel resistors. How much power does the voltage source supply to this circuit? The voltage source applies 25 volts and the two resistors have a combined equivalent resistance of 50 ohms. (Be sure you can calculate that equivalent resistance. If you need some help, refer to the How to Solve Circuit Problems chapter of this book.)

Calculate the power for this circuit by using Equation 13-6.

$$P = \frac{E^2}{R} \qquad \text{(Equation 13-6)}$$

$$P = \frac{(25 \text{ V})^2}{50 \; \Omega} = \frac{625 \text{ V}^2}{50 \; \Omega}$$

$$P = 12.5 \text{ W}$$

Suppose we knew the current in a circuit, but not the voltage. If we also know the resistance, can we still calculate the power? Sure. Take a look at **Figure 13-10**. Here is a

series circuit in which we know the current and resistance (at least we can calculate the equivalent resistance easily). The ammeter indicates 700 mA of current, and when we combine the series resistors into one equivalent value we have 300 ohms. First, we'll find a single equation to solve for power. Using Ohm's Law, we can find the circuit voltage.

$$E = I R \qquad \text{(Equation 13-4)}$$

Next, we can substitute this expression for voltage into the power equation.

$$P = I E \qquad \text{(Equation 13-3)}$$

$$P = I \times I R = I^2 R \qquad \text{(Equation 13-7)}$$

$$P = (0.700 \text{ A})^2 \times 300 \; \Omega$$

$$P = 0.490 \text{ A}^2 \times 300 \; \Omega = 147 \text{ W}$$

Equations 13-6 and 13-7 are very important variations of the power equation. As you have learned here, you can combine Ohm's Law and the basic power equation to find these equations. They are important enough that you should memorize them along with the basic power equation, though.

Let's try a few more practice problems. **Figure 13-11** shows another circuit with a voltage source and three resistors connected in series. The voltage supply is a 12-V

Figure 13-9 — Find the power that this battery supplies to the circuit. You'll have to find a single equivalent resistor to replace the parallel pair first. The text explains the steps to follow to calculate power.

Figure 13-10 — How much power does the battery supply to this series circuit? You should have little trouble calculating an equivalent resistance to replace these series resistors.

Figure 13-11 — In this series circuit, the diagram shows the battery voltage and the values for three resistors. We must combine the resistors into a single equivalent resistance. Then we can calculate the power supplied by the battery.

battery, but the diagram doesn't give the current. The resistor values are 8200 ohms, 1500 ohms and 1200 ohms. How much power does the battery supply to the circuit? First, you'll have to calculate the equivalent resistance of the circuit. That works out to be 10.9 kΩ (10,900 Ω). Now, since we know the resistance and voltage, we can use Equation 13-6 to calculate the battery power.

$$P = \frac{E^2}{R} \qquad \text{(Equation 13-6)}$$

$$P = \frac{(12\ V)^2}{10.9 \times 10^3\ \Omega} = 0.0132 W$$

This is a pretty small amount of power. Since the watt is a unit in the metric system, we could write the value with a common metric prefix. We can write this power as 13.2×10^{-3} W. That should help you recognize the metric prefix that we often use for small power levels.

UBE0168

Figure 13-12 — Find the value of a single equivalent resistor to replace the two parallel resistors in this circuit. Then calculate the power that the battery supplies to the circuit.

$P = 13.2 \times 10^{-3}$ W = 13.2 mW

Figure 13-12 shows one more example for you to solve. There is an ammeter to measure the circuit current, which turns out to be 1.5 milliamperes. If the resistor values are 390 kilohms and 0.150 megohms, what is the equivalent circuit resistance? What is the power, in milliwatts, of this circuit?

Since these resistors are in parallel, we'll have to add their reciprocals, and then take the reciprocal of the result. Again, be sure you can do that

calculation. Round off your answer to include only three digits. You should get 108 kΩ. Now you are ready to use Equation 13-7 to calculate the circuit power.

$$P = I^2 R \qquad \text{(Equation 13-7)}$$

$$P = (1.5 \times 10^{-3}\ A)^2 \times 108\ k\Omega$$

$$P = 2.25 \times 10^{-6}\ A^2 \times 108 \times 10^3\ \Omega$$

$$P = 0.243\ W = 243 \times 10^{-3}\ W$$
$$\quad = 243\ mW$$

Math and Calculator Hints

MATH HINTS

For more background on math, refer to **Appendix A — Scientific and Engineering Notation.**

CALCULATOR HINTS

The following examples show how to use your TI-30X IIS calculator to solve equations like those in Chapter 13. Simpler numbers are used, so they will all be visible in the display of the calculator at the same time. For more information on using a calculator to work these examples, refer to **Appendix B — Understanding and Using Your TI-30X IIS Scientific Calculator.**

Example 1

$I = P / E$ (Equation 13-2)

$I = 2\ W / 6\ V = 0.33\ A$

Calculator keystrokes:

2 ÷ 6 =

The calculator's second display line shows the result: **333.333 × 10⁻⁰³**

[Note that $10^{-03} = 10^{-3} = 0.001$, so $333 \times 10^{-03} = 333 \times 0.001 = 0.333$]

Example 2

$$P = \frac{E^2}{R}$$ (Equation 13-6)

$$P = \frac{(25\ V)^2}{50\ \Omega} = \frac{625\ V^2}{50\ \Omega}$$

$P = 12.5\ W$

Calculator keystrokes:

2 5 x² ÷ 50 =

The calculator's second display line shows the result: **12.5 × 10⁰⁰**

[Note that $10^{00} = 10^{0} = 1$, so $12.5 \times 10^{00} = 12.5 \times 1 = 12.5$ (watts)]

Example 3

$P = I \times E$

$P = I \times I\ R = I^2\ R$ (Equation 13-7)

$P = (0.700\ A)^2 \times 300\ \Omega$

$P = 0.490\ A^2 \times 300\ \Omega = 147\ W$

Calculator keystrokes:

.7 x² X 3 0 0 =

The calculator's second display line shows the result: **147 × 10⁰⁰** or 147 (watts)

Review Questions ————

13.1 **The unit of energy is the:**

a)   watt

b)   volt

c)   ampere

d)   joule

13.2 **Explain the difference between *energy* and *power* in your own words.**

13.3 **A heater is designed to operate on 120 volts, and converts 1500 watts of electrical power into heat power (to warm your toes on a winter night). How much current flows through this heater?**

13.4 **Elwood, who is just learning about electronics, takes a 10 Ω, ½ watt resistor (that's the *maximum* power this resistor can safely dissipate) and places it across the terminals of a 12 volt battery. Using your knowledge of power, predict what will happen.**

13.5 **Elwood, having learned very little from his experience with a 10 Ω, ½ watt resistor (see the question above), brings the heater designed to operate on 120 volts and convert 1500 watts of electrical power, to Europe (where most countries have 240 volt electricity). Elwood plugs this heater into a 240 volt outlet, and turns it on. What happens?**

Answers

13.1 d

13.2 *Energy* is the ability to do work. A "D" cell contains energy in its chemicals which can produce a certain total amount of electrical energy. A "D" cell can light a flashlight bulb for a certain amount of time, perhaps 24 hours. If two flashlight bulbs were placed across a "D" cell, they would drain the cell in half the time, or 12 hours. Ten flashlight bulbs would drain the cell in 2.4 hours. So *power* is the rate at which energy is used. A 100 watt lamp could be lit for 10 hours for the same cost (in kilowatt-hours) as a 500 watt heater running for 2 hours, or a 1000 watt iron running for 1 hour. In this case, power is measured in watts, and energy is measured in kilowatt-hours.

13.3 Well, when the heater is turned off, zero current flows through it. But then your toes are cold. When it's turned on, we can calculate the current as follows: $P = E \times I$, so $I = P/E = 1500$ W / 120 V = 12.5 amperes.

13.4 $P = E^2/R$, so Elwood's resistor will dissipate (that means convert to heat) a power of $P = (12 \text{ V})^2 / (10 \ \Omega) = 144/10 = 14.4$ watts. This poor ½ watt resistor will very quickly turn into an LER (light-emitting resistor) and SER (smoke-emitting resistor), since it is converting to heat about 29 times (14.4 W /0.5 W) more power than it can safely handle.

13.5 The heater was designed to work properly on 120 volts (and produce 1500 watts of heat power), by using 12.5 amperes of current ($P = E \times I = 120$ V × 12.5 A = 1500 W); see question 13.3 and its answer. When Elwood plugs it in to a 240 volt outlet, since the voltage is twice what it's designed for, the heater draws a current twice what it did when used with 120 volts. The new power is $P = E \times I = (2 \times 120 \text{ V}) \times (2 \times 12.5 \text{ A}) = 240$ V × 25 A = 6000 W! With luck, this heater will blow a fuse. Until it does, it will glow really bright and might start a fire. *Thought question:* what would happen if a European heater, designed to operate on 240 volts and put out a heat power of 1500 watts, was plugged in to a 120 volt outlet in the US?

UNIT 3

AC Electrical
Circuit Concepts

In the last unit we studied steady, unchanging voltages and currents. We learned to use electronics principles to calculate circuit conditions with these steady voltages applied. Now we are ready to consider the effects of changing voltages and currents.

When we studied dc electronics in the last unit, we learned about circuit resistance. Resistance is an important circuit condition when all signals are steady, unchanging ones. Most electronic circuits include some signals that are changing, however. Circuit currents may increase and decrease over time even if their direction doesn't change. Other circuits include currents that change direction continuously. Signals that change direction are called *alternating current (ac) signals*.

Inductors and *capacitors* are components with a special purpose in circuits that have varying signals. They help guide dc and ac signals to the proper parts of a circuit. These components oppose changes in the current going through them. We call this opposition *reactance*. Reactance provides a way to control the amount of

Inductors and capacitors are components with a special purpose in circuits that have varying signals. We'll study them in this unit.

"AC electronics is a study of the effects various circuit components have on sine-wave signals"

alternating current in a circuit.

It is important to understand electric and magnetic fields in order to understand how capacitors and inductors work. These components store energy in electric and magnetic fields. The fields change when the signal going into an inductor or capacitor changes.

Most of the signals we study in this unit will change in a regular way over time. Such signals are easier to consider than ones that vary in an irregular way. We call regularly varying ac signals *sine* waves. AC electronics is a study of the effects various circuit components have on sine-wave signals.

In This Unit You Will Learn

✓ that all ac signals have a certain wavelength and frequency
✓ what capacitors are and how they affect various types of signals
✓ that capacitors present a special opposition to ac signals. We call this special opposition *reactance*
✓ about inductors and how they affect various types of signals
✓ that inductors also present opposition, or reactance, to ac signals. You also will learn the difference between inductive reactance and capacitive reactance
✓ about the quality factor of capacitors and inductors, *circuit Q*
✓ how transformers change the voltage and current of an input signal to larger or smaller output values
✓ about the combined effects of circuit resistance and reactance, called impedance
✓ that when a circuit's inductive reactance and capacitive reactance are equal, we say the circuit is *resonant*

Chapter 14

What is Alternating Current (AC)?

We use
alternating
current (ac)
every day.

Contents

Current Goes in Only One Direction in a DC Signal

"AC electronics is a study of the effects various circuit components have on sine-wave signals."

In Unit 2 you learned about many important electronics principles. You studied voltage, current and resistance. You learned there are two basic circuit types: series and parallel. Ohm's Law and Kirchhoff's Voltage and Current Laws helped you learn about conditions in those circuits.

We used steady, unchanging voltage sources to supply the current for those circuits. The current through the circuits didn't vary. Steady, unchanging currents make it easy for you to learn electronics principles. *Direct-current* (*dc*) supplies produce circuit currents that don't vary.

Batteries are common direct-current supplies. **Figure 14-1** is the schematic diagram of a simple circuit. There is a battery, a switch and two resistors. *Conventional current* flows from the positive battery terminal, through the resistors

and back to the negative battery terminal. The electrons move in the opposite direction through the circuit.

Imagine the electric circuit is like one side of a four-lane superhighway (**Figure 14-2**). All the traffic is going the same direction

UBE0170

Figure 14-2 — You can think of a simple dc circuit as being similar to one side of a superhighway. All the cars go in one direction, at nearly the same speed.

as your car. Most of the cars are traveling at the speed limit, so you move along at a steady speed.

This superhighway is like a direct-current circuit. The cars are like the electrons moving through the circuit. All the electrons move in the same direction at nearly the same speed.

It is easy to study traffic patterns on our superhighway. It is also easy to study electrons moving through a simple dc circuit.

Most roads are not like our superhighway, though. Traffic speeds up and slows down depending on the amount of traffic and the road conditions. Few electronic circuits are simple dc circuits, either. To understand more complex circuits, we will use the basic principles we learned to study what happens when circuit voltage and current change. In the next several sections we will study circuits with changing voltages and currents.

Figure 14-1 — This simple direct-current circuit has a steady, unchanging current. Electrons flow from the negative battery terminal, through the circuit, to the positive battery terminal.

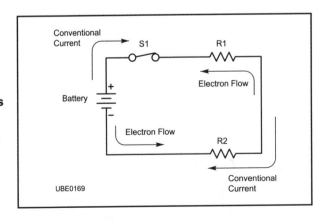

UBE0169

Current Can Be Constant or Changing

All the circuits we studied so far had constant currents. Most circuits have currents that do change with certain conditions, however. The simplest kind of change is to have a circuit with a switch. When we close the switch, there is current through the circuit. When we open the switch, there is no current.

Figure 14-3 shows a simple circuit with a switch to connect or disconnect the battery. There is a voltmeter to measure the voltage across the resistor, and an ammeter measures the current through the resistor.

With the switch in the open position, there is no voltage across the resistor. When we close the switch, the voltage across the resistor jumps to 12 volts. When the switch is open there is no current through the circuit and when we close it the current jumps to 10 mA. This circuit has a changing current and voltage.

Now suppose we change the switch position every 10 seconds. **Figure 14-4** graphs the voltage across the resistor and the current through the circuit. Notice the vertical axis on the left side indicates voltage and the vertical axis on the right side indicates current. Voltage and current both change each time the switch opens or closes, so this one graph shows both quantities.

When we refer to the *waveform* of a current or voltage, we mean the shape of the signal voltage or current. The Figure 14-4 graph shows a *square-wave* signal.

Have you ever had a ride on a highway with toll booths? On some toll roads you have to stop at a toll booth every few miles to pay a small fee. You can think of such roads as similar to the Figure 14-3 circuit. Between toll booths, the circuit is complete, and you drive down the highway. When you come to a toll booth, though, the switch opens and traffic must stop.

Figure 14-3 — This circuit's current and voltage change every time you change the switch position. The voltmeter measures the voltage across the resistor and the ammeter measures the current through the resistor.

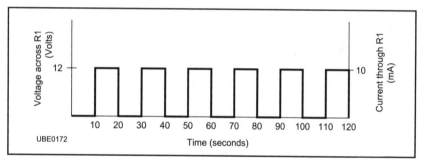

Figure 14-4 — Suppose we change the switch position in Figure 14-3 every 10 seconds. The horizontal or X axis shows time, marked off in 10-second intervals. The left-side vertical or Y axis shows the voltage across R1, which the voltmeter indicates. The right-side Y axis shows the current through R1, which the ammeter indicates.

Figure 14-5 — Part A shows a circuit that has a voltage source that gradually increases and decreases at regular intervals. This voltage source produces a triangle waveform. Part B shows the voltage and current of this triangle waveform.

Unlike the electrical current, your car won't stop instantly, however. You need some time to apply the brakes and slow the car. Neither will it go from 0 to 65 miles per hour in an instant. It will take at least a few seconds to get back up to travel speed.

Some circuits increase the voltage and current gradually. The voltage and current also may decrease gradually. **Figure 14-5A** shows a circuit with a voltage source that increases and decreases gradually. We drew this voltage source as a block instead of using the common battery symbol. Part B shows the output voltage and current from this voltage source. The output signal looks like a series of triangles. Are you surprised to learn that we call this type of signal a *triangle waveform*?

There are many ways that a voltage or current can change. Some waveforms are simple, like those we studied here. Others may be complex, following no apparent pattern. As long as the electrons move in one direction through the circuit, we say it is a direct-current signal.

Review Questions ———————————

14.1 "AC" is the abbreviation for:

a) All Clear

b) Alternating Current

c) Anti-Clockwise

d) Albert Camus

14.2 The name for a circuit component's opposition to a change in current or voltage is called:

a) resonance

b) reluctance

c) refusal

d) reactance

14.3 A signal generator creates a voltage that jumps up to +5 volts, then jumps down to –5 volts, and this repeats over and over. If the time spent at +5 volts is equal to the time spent at –5 volts, this signal is called a:

a) triangle wave

b) sine wave

c) square wave

d) exponential wave

14.4 If the electrons in a circuit move in one direction only, the current is known as:

a) DC

b) LC

c) AC

d) RC

Answers ———————————

14.1 b

14.2 d

14.3 c

14.4 a

Chapter 15

Frequency, Period and Examples of AC Voltages

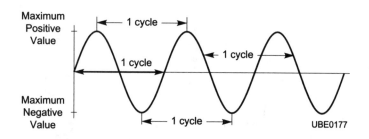

This sine-wave alternating current (ac) waveform shows several cycles.

Contents

If Current Changes Direction, It Becomes an AC Signal

In the two previous sections we used examples of a superhighway to study dc electronic circuits. We'll use another highway example in this section to study electric currents that change *direction*.

Instead of riding in a car, imagine you are the toll collector on a bridge. Your toll plaza stands at the eastern end of the bridge. There are three lanes going each direction to cross your bridge.

Figure 15-1 shows your toll plaza. There are nine toll booths and 10 lanes through the plaza. As a toll collector, you control a red X or a green O above the lanes at your booth. Figure 15-1 shows the plaza with four lanes open coming from the West. (This is from the bottom of the picture.) There are six lanes open coming from the East. Most of the traffic is from the East now, so the center lanes are open from that direction.

A few hours later most of the traffic comes from the West. You suddenly realize that traffic is backed up on the bridge because the cars can't get through the four open lanes fast enough. There is almost no traffic coming from the East, though, so those six lanes are empty.

You are in the center toll booth, so you decide to change the lights over the two lanes on either side of your booth. First you change the green Os to red Xs on the westbound side. Then you change the red Xs to green Os on the eastbound side. Immediately, some cars move out of the crowded lanes and toward the two

UBE0174

Figure 15-1 — The operation of this toll plaza at a bridge will help you understand electronic circuits with voltage and current that change direction. Cars approach the toll plaza from the bottom when they are driving East. Those cars just crossed the bridge. As they approach the toll plaza they see red Xs and green Os. They can go through the lanes with green Os. Those lanes with red Xs are open to traffic from the opposite direction. Cars approach the toll plaza from the top when they are driving West. As shown, there are six lanes open for cars driving West. There are only four lanes open for cars driving East. Later in the day, the center two lanes close to westbound traffic and open to eastbound traffic. Cars go through those lanes in the opposite direction. The direction of traffic through those two lanes reverses, depending on how much traffic there is going each way.

new lanes you just opened. Now there are six lanes open for the eastbound direction and only four open lanes for those heading West.

Traffic in the two center lanes changed direction when you switched the lights. Cars can move through the lane in only one direction at a time. You were able to change the traffic flow direction by switching the lights.

Some electronic circuits are like this. Electrons can move through the circuit in one direction. A very short time later they can change direction and move through the circuit the other way. When electrons flow first in one direction and then in the other, we say there is an *alternating current*. We abbreviate alternating current as *ac*.

Figure 15-2A shows a circuit with an alternating current signal. This is a simple circuit that includes a voltage source and two resistors. We connected the resistors in parallel this time. We drew the voltage source as a box with two terminals. Notice that when the top terminal is positive, the bottom one is negative. When the top terminal becomes negative, the bottom one becomes positive.

Figure 15-2B shows a graph of the voltage across the resistors and the current through them. The voltage polarity reverses 10 times each

"The basic unit of frequency is the hertz. This unit is named in honor of Heinrich Rudolf Hertz (1857-1894). This German physicist was the first person to demonstrate the generation and reception of radio waves."

second. When the voltage polarity reverses, the current also reverses.

Let's make the top of the supply positive and the bottom negative. This is a positive voltage on the graph of Figure 15-2B. The *conventional current* flows clockwise through the circuit, from positive to negative. We drew this as a positive current on Figure 15-2B.

One tenth of a second later the voltage polarity reverses. Now the top of the supply is negative and the bottom is positive. This is a negative voltage on the graph. The current also reverses, so it moves in a

counterclockwise direction, still from positive to negative.

You must learn some important definitions about alternating current circuits. You will hear these terms frequently as you continue your study of electronics.

The *waveform* of an ac signal refers to the shape of the voltage or current. Our voltage source in Figure 15-2 produces a waveform with a square (or rectangular) shape. We say it is a *square-wave signal*.

Many ac signals have a regular repeating shape. Look at Figure 15-2B. Start when the signal is positive, changes to negative and then becomes positive again. This represents one complete *cycle* of the wave.

The time it takes to make one cycle is the wave's *period*. We measure period in time, so we use a capital T to abbreviate period. The Figure 15-2B wave changes polarity every 0.1 second. That means it takes 0.2 seconds to make a complete cycle from positive to negative and back to positive. The period of the wave in this example is 0.2 seconds.

The *frequency* of a wave is the number of complete cycles the wave makes in one second. Frequency is the reciprocal of period. Do you remember how to find a number's reciprocal? You divide the number

Figure 15-2 — This circuit includes a voltage source that changes polarity 10 times each second. There are two resistors in parallel. A voltmeter and an ammeter measure circuit conditions. The graph shown at B represents the voltage across the resistors and the total circuit current.

(A)

UBE0175 (B)

into one. Your calculator probably has a key labeled 1/X to make it easy to find reciprocals.

We measure frequency in hertz, abbreviated Hz. This is in honor of Heinrich Hertz, a German scientist who experimented with radio waves. You can combine any of the metric prefixes with this basic unit. A kilohertz (kHz) is 1000 Hz, or 1000 complete cycles in one second. A frequency of 5 megahertz (MHz) is 5 million cycles per second.

$$f = \frac{1 \text{ cycle}}{T} \qquad \text{(Equation 15-1)}$$

where f is frequency in hertz and T is time in seconds.

Now let's use Equation 15-1 to calculate the frequency of the wave in Figure 15-2.

$$f = \frac{1 \text{ cycle}}{0.2 \text{ s}} = 5 \text{ cycles/s} = 5 \text{ Hz}$$

This square wave has a period of 0.2 second and a frequency of 5 Hz.

Smoothly Varying AC is a Sine Wave

When you studied dc signals you learned that the voltage levels sometimes change gradually rather than abruptly. Voltage and current polarities also can change gradually. Many waveforms are possible with alternating current signals. Instead of a square wave, you might find that a circuit has a triangle-shaped waveform. You might even find a signal that has a sawtooth-shaped waveform. **Figure 15-3** shows a few possible ac waveforms.

An ac waveform that you will frequently find in electronics is the *sine wave*. A sine-wave voltage varies gradually between its peak positive and peak negative values. There are no sudden changes or "corners" on a sine wave. **Figure 15-4** shows a sine-wave voltage or current graph. We marked one complete cycle on this graph, starting when the wave crossed the

zero line going positive. Notice that the cycle doesn't end the next time the waveform crosses the zero line. At that point the wave has completed its positive half cycle and is ready to begin the negative half cycle.

We marked another complete cycle starting when the voltage or current is at the peak positive value. It doesn't matter where you start to measure a cycle, as long as you measure to that same point the next time it occurs.

Alternating current signals travel through conductors in much the same way as dc signals do. Alternating signals also produce *electromagnetic radiation*. We often refer to electromagnetic radiation as *radio waves*. Visible light, ultraviolet radiation, X-rays, gamma rays and other types of radiation also are electromagnetic radiation.

From our earlier discussion of

frequency, you should realize that alternating currents and voltages can change direction at almost any rate imaginable. Some signals have low frequencies. The power company supplies electricity to your house as 60-Hz ac. Other signals have higher frequencies. Radio signals, for example, can alternate at more than several million hertz.

If you know the frequency of an ac signal, you can use that frequency to describe the signal. Your toaster uses 60-Hz power, for example. Your favorite AM Broadcast station may have a frequency of 1080 kHz. Perhaps you like to operate on the 144-MHz Amateur Radio band. All these frequencies describe particular signals.

Wavelength is another quality that we associate with every ac signal. As the name implies, wavelength refers to the distance the wave travels

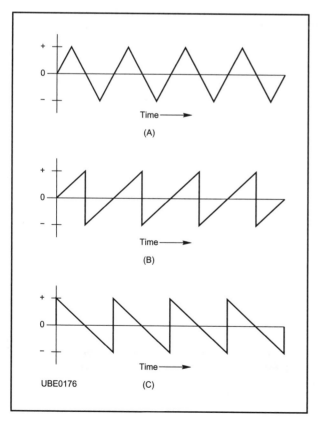

Figure 15-3 — These graphs show a few types of alternating-current waveforms. The signal at Part A is a triangle waveform. Part B shows a sawtooth or ramp waveform. The voltage increases gradually from its peak negative value. When it reaches its peak positive value the voltage (or current) suddenly drops to the peak negative value. Then the voltage or current begins to increase gradually again. The signal at C is a reverse sawtooth. In this example, the voltage increases suddenly to its peak positive value. Then it decreases gradually to its peak negative value.

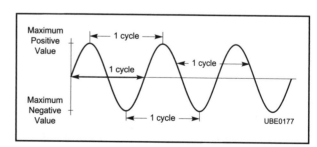

Figure 15-4 — This graph shows a sine-wave alternating current waveform. This is one of the most common ac signals. One cycle is marked off on the waveform starting at several places. Notice that it really doesn't matter where you start measuring a cycle. Wherever you start, you must measure to the same position on the waveform the next time it occurs.

through space in a single cycle. We use the lower-case Greek lambda (λ) to represent wavelength. All electromagnetic radiation travels through space at the speed of light, 300,000,000 meters per second. You can write that in scientific notation as 3.00×10^8 m/s.

The faster a signal alternates the less distance it can travel during one cycle. There is an Equation that relates a signal's frequency and wavelength to the speed of light.

$$c = f\lambda \qquad \text{(Equation 15-2)}$$

where:

c is the speed of light, 3.00×10^8 m/s

f is the frequency of the wave in hertz

λ is the wavelength of the wave in meters. (λ is the lower-case Greek letter *lambda*.)

You can draw an Equation Circle for this equation. The Equation Circle will help you solve the equation for frequency or wavelength. Use the Equation Circle of **Figure 15-5** to write Equations 15-3 and 15-4.

$$f = \frac{c}{\lambda} \qquad \text{(Equation 15-3)}$$

$$\lambda = \frac{c}{f} \qquad \text{(Equation 15-4)}$$

From these equations you should realize that as the frequency increases the wavelength becomes shorter. As the frequency decreases the wavelength gets longer.

Use Equation 15-4 to find the wavelength of a 7.125-MHz radio signal. (Remember to change the frequency in megahertz to frequency in hertz.)

$$\lambda = \frac{c}{f} \qquad \text{(Equation 15-4)}$$

$$\lambda = \frac{c}{f} = \frac{3.00 \times 10^8 \, \text{m/s}}{7.125 \times 10^6 \, \text{Hz}} = 42.1 \, \text{meters}$$

As another example, use Equation 15-3 to find the frequency of a radio signal that has a wavelength of 80.5 meters.

ARRL0498

Figure 15-5 — This Equation Circle represents the relationship between the speed, frequency and wavelength of electromagnetic radiation, or radio waves. Cover the quantity you want to calculate and the rest of the circle shows how to do that calculation.

$$f = \frac{c}{\lambda} \qquad \text{(Equation 15-3)}$$

$$f = \frac{c}{\lambda} = \frac{3.00 \times 10^8 \, \text{m/s}}{80.5 \, \text{meters}}$$

$$= 3.727 \times 10^6 \, \text{Hz} = 3.727 \, \text{MHz}$$

You should be familiar with several other alternating current and voltage measurements. The ac waveform graphs show the voltage and current change with time. For all the waveforms we looked at, the waveform is positive for half its cycle and negative for half its cycle. What good is this? Doesn't the negative part cancel the effects of the positive part? Do the electrons just move back and forth in the wire, never really going anywhere? You have probably asked these questions as we began our study of ac signals.

If you connect a dc voltmeter to an ac signal, the meter will read 0. Yes, half the time the needle tries to move positive, and half the time it tries to swing negative. So we can't use a dc voltmeter to measure ac voltage. (We can't use a dc ammeter to measure ac current for the same reason.)

Meters that measure ac voltage and current use a *diode* to change the ac signal to a dc signal. We say the diode *rectifies* the ac signal when it converts it to a dc signal. (You will learn more about diodes and how they rectify ac signals in Unit 4.) The manufacturer adjusts the meter scale to read the proper values.

Most ac meters read *effective* voltage or current. Start by putting some direct current through a resistor. Let's use 1 amp, for example. Measure the heat produced in the resistor. Then put an alternating

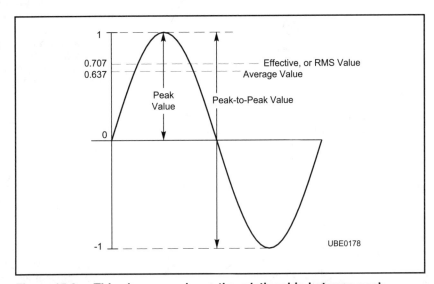

Figure 15-6 — This sine wave shows the relationship between peak, peak-to-peak, RMS and average current and voltage values. The RMS and average values shown here apply only to sine-wave signals.

current through the resistor. Adjust the current until it produces the same heating effect. Then you have an *effective* alternating current of 1 amp. (We also can make this measurement with voltage, to determine the effective ac voltage.)

Another name for effective voltage or current is *RMS voltage* or *current*. This name comes from the mathematical method of determining the value. The letters stand for *root mean square*. Mean is a mathematical term for average. The mathematics of the calculation are beyond the scope of this book. You will hear the term RMS voltage or RMS current used frequently in relation to ac signals.

Every ac waveform has a different RMS value compared to the peak voltage or current. You should be familiar with the values for a sine wave, because you will see them often. The RMS value of a sine-wave voltage or current is 0.707 times the peak value. If a sine-wave voltage reaches a positive peak of 100 volts

it has an RMS voltage of 70.7 volts. (This signal also will reach a negative peak of 100 volts.) This sine-wave signal has a peak-to-peak value of 200 volts. **Figure 15-6** shows the graph of a sine-wave signal with the peak, peak-to-peak and RMS values indicated.

RMS value = 0.707 × peak value
(Equation 15-5)

This equation applies to both voltage and current of a sine wave.

Most meters respond to the *average value* of the rectified ac signal. For a sine wave, this average value is equal to 0.637 times the peak value.

Average value = 0.637 × peak value
(Equation 15-6)

This equation also applies to both voltage and current of a sine wave.

You may be wondering whether an ac voltage, having a positive part of the cycle, and a negative part,

cancels itself over one complete cycle (or period). Think about a flashlight bulb (a kind of resistor that converts electrical power into power in the form of heat and light). If a flashlight bulb is connected to a dc source (a battery), voltage and current have one polarity (perhaps positive on top), and both voltage and current are positive, so the power delivered to the bulb is positive (P = I × E).

If we reverse the battery, both voltage and current reverse polarity. The bulb still lights up. Since two negative numbers, multiplied, give a positive result, the power is still positive (P = –I × –E = + I × E). Basically, the bulb doesn't care if the current flows in one direction or the other. Either way, it gets hot and gives off light on both the positive half-cycle and negative half-cycle of the sine wave. The bottom line is that an ac voltage produces electrical power for its entire cycle, during both the positive and negative half-cycles.

Sine Waves and a Rotating Wheel

The sine wave is an important ac signal waveform. It is the simplest waveform to study, because the voltage or current changes smoothly. You can combine sine waves that have different frequencies and amplitudes to produce more complex waveforms.

Figure 15-7 is a drawing of a sine wave. The horizontal, or X, axis represents time. The vertical, or Y, axis represents voltage. (It also could represent current.) The graph shows how the voltage changes with time. You can make two observations about this graph. First, the wave repeats at regular intervals. Second, there are no sudden changes or corners on the graph.

Let's conduct a simple experiment to help you understand the shape of a sine wave. Imagine a wheel, such as a bicycle wheel, a car wheel or even a Ferris wheel. Concentrate on a single spot on your wheel. Watch that spot as the wheel spins. **Figure 15-8** shows a bicycle wheel spinning clockwise. The motion of your spot repeats every time the wheel goes around. That motion is also very smooth. There

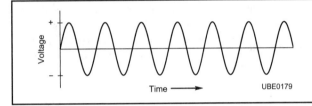

Figure 15-7 — This graph shows how a sine-wave voltage changes with time. (The graph also could represent the current.) The voltage varies between the peak positive and peak negative values. Those voltage variations repeat at a regular rate.

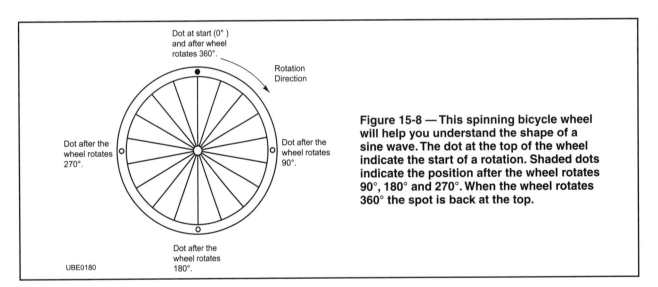

Figure 15-8 — This spinning bicycle wheel will help you understand the shape of a sine wave. The dot at the top of the wheel indicate the start of a rotation. Shaded dots indicate the position after the wheel rotates 90°, 180° and 270°. When the wheel rotates 360° the spot is back at the top.

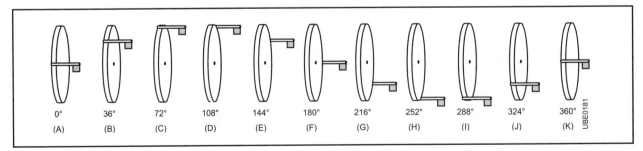

Figure 15-9 — This series of drawings represent snapshots of a rotating wheel. The flag will help you visualize the rotation. The drawings are 0.1 second apart. The wheel rotates 36° between each snapshot. Notice that the flag appears to move up and down, as it rotates away from you. It takes longer for the flag to go over the top or under the bottom than it does to move across the middle of the wheel.

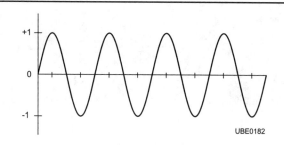

Figure 15-10 — This drawing represents the motion of the flag on the Figure 15-9 wheel, as the wheel moves from left to right in front of you.

UBE0182

are no sudden changes in the motion. The drawing shows the dot position at the start of a rotation. Shaded dots indicate the position after the wheel rotates 90°, 180° and 270°.

If you can, find a bicycle and turn it upside down so you can spin one wheel. Tie a string or ribbon around the tire so you can watch a single spot on the wheel. Spin the wheel, then stand back and watch it for a few seconds. (Stand so you are looking at the bicycle from the front or back, watching the wheel from the edge.)

It is difficult to show motion on the pages of this book. To help you imagine the wheel spinning, **Figure 15-9** is a series of "snapshots," freezing the wheel's motion. Figure 15-9 shows the wheel rolling away from you. We attached a flag to the wheel, so there is a marker for you to watch as the wheel spins. The flag, attached to the wheel's front edge, moves up and then down the back.

The wheel rotates 36° between each picture. We marked the rotation angles, measured from 0° at A, under

each wheel. We took these pictures 0.1 second apart. The wheel makes one complete rotation in 1 second.

Study the vertical motion of the flag. Can you see it moving up and down? This motion is similar to the voltage variations of a sine wave.

The wheel rotates at a constant speed. It doesn't speed up or slow down while we watch it. The same time goes by between each snapshot. The vertical movement between snapshots does change, though. Notice the vertical motion seems to slow down and stop as it changes direction at the top and bottom positions. The flag moves quickly past the center points.

Now imagine the wheel moving from the left to the right as it spins. Trace the flag movement onto the wall in the background. **Figure 15-10** shows the result. This drawing looks exactly like the sine-wave graphs we've been drawing!

Let the center line represent 0 volts. The flag goes between +1 and –1 volts, then. With this scale

Table 15-1

Values of the Sine Function for Angles Listed in Figure 15-9

Angle in Degrees	Sine Function
0°	0.000
36°	0.588
72°	0.951
108°	0.951
144°	0.588
180°	0.000
216°	–0.588
252°	–0.951
288°	–0.951
324°	–0.588
360°	0.000

you can easily calculate the position of the flag at any point of the wheel's rotation. Just find the sine of the wheel's rotation angle. Use your calculator to find the sine of each angle shown in Figure 15-9. Compare your answers with the results listed in **Table 15-1**.

Rotation Speed Relates to Wave Frequency

In the last section we studied the rotation of a wheel to help you understand the sine wave. We will continue that analogy in this section. Imagine two wheels with flags attached, like we used in the last section. See **Figure 15-11**. The first wheel makes one complete turn every second. The second wheel spins twice as fast, so it makes two turns every second. Now imagine that both wheels move left to right in front of you. Both wheels move across the room at the same speed. **Figure 15-12** shows two graphs that picture this motion.

Notice the graph at Part B moves up and down two times in the same distance the graph at Part A moves up and down once. This is because the second wheel spins twice as fast as the first.

What if we had another wheel

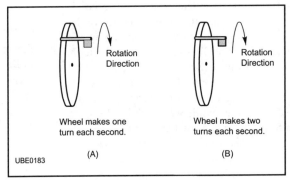

Figure 15-11 — Two wheels spinning at different rates produce sine waves with different frequencies. The wheel at A makes one complete turn each second. The wheel at B makes two complete turns each second.

spinning 10 times faster than the first wheel? Figure 15-12C shows a graph of this motion. Again, this graph goes up and down 10 times while Part A goes up and down once.

The wheel's rotation speed relates to the sine-wave *frequency*. *Frequency* of a wave relates to how many complete voltage or current variations the wave goes through each second. We measure frequency in *hertz*, abbreviated *Hz*. When the wheel spins faster it produces a higher-frequency sine wave. Suppose Figure 15-12A shows a sine wave with a frequency of 1 hertz. Then Figure 15-12B is a sine wave with a frequency of 2 hertz and Figure 15-12C has

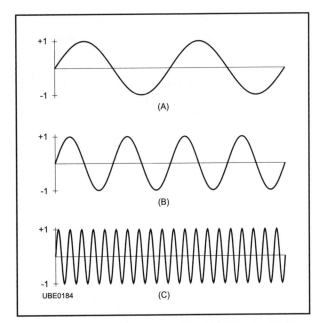

Figure 15-12 — When the two wheels of Figure 15-11 move across the room in front of you they trace out the motion shown in Parts A and B. The Part B sine wave has a frequency twice as large as the Part A wave. Part C shows the sine wave produced by a wheel spinning 10 times faster than the one from Part A.

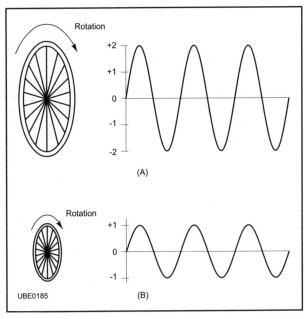

Figure 15-13 — Part A shows a wheel with a diameter of 1.0 meter. Part B shows a wheel that has a 0.5-meter diameter. When the wheels move across in front of you they produce the sine waves shown at C and D. The amplitude of the wave at C is twice as large as the amplitude of the wave at D.

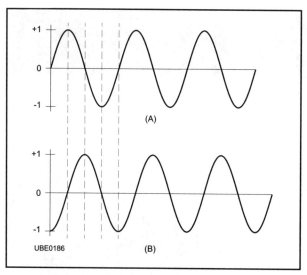

Figure 15-14 — These two sine waves have the same frequency. They don't both begin at the same time, however. These waves are 90° out of phase. The wave at A reaches its maximum positive value when the wave at B crosses the zero point. The wave at A has gone through one quarter of its cycle (90°) when the wave at B begins.

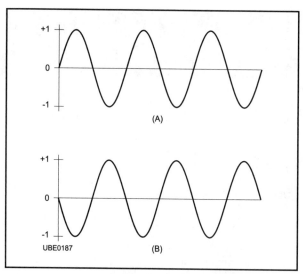

Figure 15-15 — These sine waves have the same frequency, but they are 180° out of phase. The first one crosses the zero point going toward its positive maximum when the second wave crosses zero going toward its negative maximum. Notice that when one wave reaches its positive maximum value the other wave reaches its negative maximum.

a frequency of 10 Hz.

All wheels don't have the same diameter. What if we use two wheels with different diameters? The graphs produced by these wheels won't have the same *amplitude*, or positive and negative peak values. **Figure 15-13** shows two wheels and the sine waves they trace. The Part A sine wave has twice the amplitude of the Part B wave. This could represent a wave that has twice the peak voltage or current as another wave. These two waves have the same frequency.

The Figure 15-13 sine waves start at the same time. When two or more waves reach the same point in their motion at the same time, we say the waves are *in phase. Phase* refers to the relative wave positions.

Waves aren't always in step, however. **Figure 15-14** shows two waves with the same frequency but which don't begin at the same time. These waves are *out of phase*.

We measure the position of a wave in degrees, related to the wheel rotation. It takes 360° to make one complete cycle, just as the wheel rotates 360° to make one complete turn.

We also measure phase as an angle. The two waves shown in Figure 15-14 are 90° out of phase. The second wave reaches the zero point as the first one comes to its 90° point. **Figure 15-15** shows two waves that are 180° out of phase.

The *phase angle* between two or more waves can be any angle. We commonly use angles between 0° and 180°, however. If you find a phase angle greater than 180° you can subtract 180° from it. Think about our wheel analogy again. Two points on the wheel can never be farther apart than half way around the wheel.

Math and Calculator Hints

MATH HINTS

For more background on math, refer to **Appendix A — Scientific and Engineering Notation.**

CALCULATOR HINTS

The following example shows how to use your TI-30X IIS calculator to solve equations like those in Chapter 15. Simpler numbers are used, so they will all be visible in the display of the calculator at the same time. For more information on using a calculator to work these examples, refer to **Appendix B — Understanding and Using Your TI-30X IIS Scientific Calculator.**

Example

$$f = \frac{c}{\lambda} \qquad \text{(Equation 15-3)}$$

$$f = \frac{c}{\lambda} = \frac{3.00 \times 10^8 \, m/s}{80.5 \, meters}$$

$$= 3.727 \times 10^6 \, Hz = 3.727 \, MHz$$

Calculator keystrokes

3 2ⁿᵈ EE 8 ÷ 8 0 . 5 =

The calculator's second display line shows the result: **3.7267 × 10⁰⁶**

[Note that $10^{06} = 10^6 = 1,000,000$ so $3.7267 \times 10^{06} = 3.7267 \times 1,000,000 = 3.267 \, MHz$]

Review Questions

15.1 **The shape of a voltage or current is known as:**
a)   sinusoidal
b)   rectangular
c)   hourglass
d)   a waveform

15.2 **A certain ac voltage has a frequency of 25 hertz. What is its period?**

15.3 **An ac current, when viewed on an oscilloscope, is seen to repeat itself every 5 microseconds. What is the frequency of this current?**

15.4 **What is the wavelength of a 4 MHz radio wave in free space?**

15.5 **An ac voltage has a RMS value of 20 volts. What does "RMS" stand for?**
a)   routine movement signal
b)   root mean square
c)   resistor measuring system
d)   real maple syrup

15.6 **The peak value of an ac voltage is 6 volts. What is the RMS value?**

Answers

15.1 d

15.2 Period = 1/frequency = 1/25 Hz = 0.04 seconds = 40 milliseconds

15.3 Frequency = 1/period = $1/(5 \times 10^{-6})$ = 0.2×10^6 = 0.2 MHz = 200 kHz
     = 200,000 Hz

15.4 $\lambda = c / f = [3 \times 10^8 \text{ m/sec}] / [4 \times 10^6 \text{ Hz}] = 0.75 \times 10^2$ meters
     = 75 meters

15.5 b

15.6 RMS value = 0.707 × peak value = 0.707 × 6 V = 4.24 volts RMS

Chapter 16

Capacitors with AC — Capacitive Reactance

Applied Voltage

Voltage Across Capacitor

Time

(A)

GLM0039

Capacitors oppose a change in applied voltage.

Current Through Capacitor

Time

(B)

Contents

Capacitors Oppose a Change in Applied Voltage

A constant direct voltage applied to a capacitor puts an electric charge on the capacitor. As the charge increases, there is less current into the capacitor. When the voltage across the capacitor plates equals the supply voltage, the current stops. **Figure 16-1A** shows a simple circuit to charge a capacitor. With the switch in position 1, there is current through R1 to charge the capacitor. Figure 16-1B is a graph of the circuit current and the capacitor voltage.

Now let's move the switch to position 2, as Figure 16-2A shows. This disconnects the voltage supply and puts R2 across the capacitor terminals. The capacitor returns the energy stored in it by forcing current through R2. As the capacitor returns its stored energy to the circuit it loses charge. The voltage across the capacitor decreases. Ohm's Law tells us the current through R2 decreases as the voltage decreases. Figure 16-2B is a graph of the current through R2 and the capacitor voltage after we change the switch position.

Can you guess what happens if we connect an alternating voltage to our capacitor? **Figure 16-3** shows a simple circuit with a sine-wave voltage supply. We'll make the voltage applied to the top capacitor plate positive for the first sine-wave half cycle. As the sine-wave voltage increases from zero there is a sudden rush of current as the capacitor begins to charge. That current tapers off as the charge increases.

The sine-wave voltage reaches a maximum, and begins to decrease

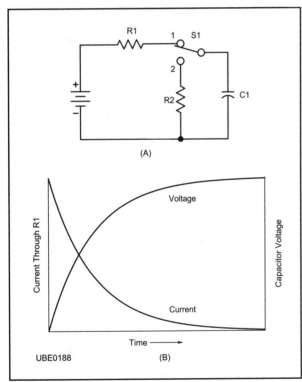

Figure 16-1 — We can charge a capacitor using the circuit shown at Part A, when the switch is in position 1. Part B is a graph of the circuit current and voltage across the capacitor plates as it charges. Notice there is no voltage on the capacitor to begin, and the current is large. As charge builds up on the capacitor plates, however, the voltage increases and the current decreases. When the voltage across the capacitor plates equals the battery voltage the current stops.

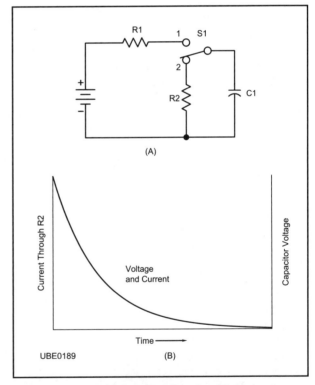

Figure 16-2 — Part A shows the circuit of Figure 16-1A with the switch moved to position 2. This removes the battery from the circuit and connects R2 across the capacitor terminals. The Part B graph shows the current through R2 and the voltage across the capacitor terminals. The capacitor releases its stored energy.

Figure 16-3 — We can apply an alternating voltage to a capacitor and observe the circuit current and capacitor voltage with this circuit. The text describes the results as the applied voltage goes through one sine-wave cycle.

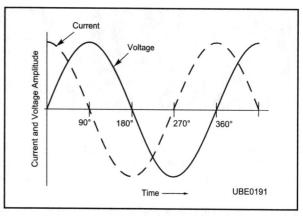

Figure 16-4 — The solid line shows the voltage applied to the capacitor plates of Figure 16-3. This is a sine-wave voltage that starts at zero. It applies a positive voltage to the top capacitor plate during the first half cycle. During the second half cycle the positive voltage goes to the bottom capacitor plate.

to zero again. When the voltage begins to decrease, the capacitor begins to return its stored energy to the circuit. It is interesting to realize that the current direction changes when the voltage begins to decrease. Electrons were moving onto the bottom capacitor plate of Figure 16-3 as the capacitor was charging. Now electrons move *off* the bottom plate, because the capacitor is returning energy to the circuit.

What happens during the next sine-wave half cycle? The voltage polarity reverses, so the voltage applied to the top capacitor plate is negative. Electrons continue to move *off* the bottom plate, and *onto* the top plate. Soon the capacitor returns all the original charge to the circuit, and it begins to charge in the opposite direction. As the capacitor charge increases the current decreases.

After the sine-wave voltage reaches its maximum negative value, the voltage begins to decrease to zero again. Now the capacitor returns its stored energy to the circuit again. Electrons flow *off* the top plate. The current changes direction again.

Figure 16-4 graphs the sine-wave voltage source and capacitor current. We used a solid line to represent the voltage and a dashed line to represent the current. There are no numbers on the vertical or horizontal scales because we are not trying to show specific values. The actual voltage,

current and time values depend on the resistor and capacitor values, the applied voltage and the sine-wave frequency.

As you study Figure 16-4, notice that capacitor current is a maximum at 0°. The applied voltage doesn't reach a maximum until 90° on the graph. This describes the *phase* relationship between the alternating current *through* a capacitor and the voltage *across* it. The alternating voltage reaches every point on its waveform 90° after the current. Sometimes we say the voltage across a capacitor *lags* the current through it. Another way of saying this is the current through a capacitor *leads* the voltage across it. In either case the *phase angle* between the voltage and current is 90°.

A handy way to remember this phase relationship is the phrase **"ELI the ICE man."** The current (I) through a capacitor (C), leads the voltage (E) by 90°. As we will find in the next chapter, the voltage (E) across an inductor (L) leads the current (I) by 90°. So try to picture Eli, the fellow who delivers ice,

as "ELI the ICE man," and you will always remember the phase relationship between voltage and current for inductors and capacitors.

It appears that capacitors don't like the applied voltage to change. They react to a voltage change in a way that opposes that change. When the voltage is increasing, they take energy from the voltage supply. You could view this as an attempt to prevent the voltage from increasing. When the voltage is decreasing, the capacitor returns stored energy to the circuit. Think of this action as working to prevent the voltage from decreasing.

Capacitors *react* to voltage changes, trying to prevent the change. We call this opposition to voltage change *reactance*. This opposition to voltage (and current) change in a capacitor is similar to the opposition to current of a resistor. In fact, we measure this opposition in *ohms*.

In the next section you will learn how to calculate *capacitive reactance*. You also will learn how the applied-signal *frequency* affects this opposition to voltage and current changes.

There Is More Opposition at Lower Frequencies

A discharged, or "empty," capacitor acts like a short circuit when you first connect voltage to it. There is a large current as the capacitor begins to charge. As the voltage builds up, the current through the capacitor will drop toward zero. Capacitors block direct current.

Capacitive reactance is the opposition capacitors have to current through them. Since capacitors won't pass a steady direct current, you could say they have a large reactance to dc.

Look at **Figure 16-5**. We applied a 10-hertz alternating voltage to a 1-microfarad capacitor. The voltage source applies 100 volts RMS to the circuit. The ac ammeter shows a 6.28 milliamp current through the circuit. How much reactance does the capacitor have?

Does this sound a bit like an Ohm's Law problem? It should. You know a circuit voltage and current, and want to know the opposition to that current. Use Ohm's Law to calculate the reactance in this problem instead of resistance.

Since this is a "thought experiment," we assume the components are *ideal*. That means there is no resistance in the capacitor. The wires don't have any resistance either. *Real* components always have some resistance. The math is more difficult if a circuit has both resistance and reactance. We won't try any problems like that here. You can learn how to handle the more difficult math after you learn the basic principles.

We use X to represent reactance. A subscript C reminds us we are working with a capacitor in this problem. Capacitive reactance is X_C.

$$E = I\,X_C \qquad \text{(Equation 16-1)}$$

Solve this equation for X_C, or use the equation circle given in **Figure 16-6**.

$$X_C = \frac{E}{I}$$

$$X_C = \frac{100\text{ V}}{6.28\text{ mA}} = 15,924\text{ ohms}$$

(Don't forget that 6.28 mA is 6.28 × 10^{-3} amperes.)

Let's change our circuit for the next part of our experiment. Replace the 1-µF capacitor with a 2-µF unit. This time the ammeter reads 12.56 mA. What is the new capacitor's reactance? Solve Equation 16-1 for X_C again.

$$X_C = \frac{E}{I}$$

$$X_C = \frac{100\text{ V}}{12.56\text{ mA}} = 7962\text{ ohms}$$

What did you learn from this experiment? When we double the capacitance value, the reactance becomes ½ the original value. What do you expect the reactance to be if we used a 3-µF capacitor? If you said 5308 ohms, you are correct. Capacitive reactance is inversely related to capacitance. Larger capacitance values produce smaller reactances.

Now let's make another change to our circuit. This time we will connect a 100 Hz voltage source. Change back to the original 1-µF capacitor. The voltage supply still produces 100 volts. This time the ammeter reads 62.8 mA. Calculate the reactance of the 1-µF capacitor with the new voltage source.

$$X_C = \frac{E}{I} = \frac{100\text{ V}}{62.8\text{ mA}} = 1592.4\text{ ohms}$$

The new signal frequency is 10 times the original frequency. Did you notice the current is 10 times larger than the first example? Were you surprised to find the reactance is 10 times smaller? This part of the experiment taught you that reactance is inversely related to frequency. Higher-frequency signals produce smaller reactances, for a given capacitor.

Do you think this is a reasonable

Figure 16-5 — We'll use this circuit for a thought experiment about capacitive reactance.

Figure 16-6 — Use this equation circle to solve Equation 16-1 for capacitive reactance, X_C.

conclusion? Let's think about what happens when we apply higher-frequency signals to a capacitor.

You know that capacitors have a high reactance to dc signals. When you connect a low-frequency ac signal, the capacitor charges to the full signal voltage. The capacitor takes as much charge as it can hold, for that voltage.

Now begin to increase the signal frequency. What if the signal voltage reaches its peak and begins to decrease before the capacitor takes a full charge? If the capacitor doesn't "fill up" with charge, it won't have as much opposition. As the frequency increases even more, the capacitor has less opposition. **Figure 16-7** is a graph of reactance and frequency. Reactance is highest at dc, and decreases quickly.

We found two factors that affect reactance in this section. When either capacitance or signal frequency increases, the reactance decreases. We can write an equation to calculate capacitive reactance, based on these two factors.

We normally express frequency as a number of waveform cycles per second, measured in hertz. We also can relate each cycle to the rotation of a wheel. Then we express frequency in radians per second. You can convert any frequency in hertz to radians per second. Just multiply frequency in hertz by 2π. This is the number of radians in one cycle. Equation 16-2 shows how to calculate capacitive reactance.

$$X_C = \frac{1}{2\pi f C} \qquad \text{(Equation 16-2)}$$

Figure 16-7 — This graph shows how capacitive reactance varies with signal frequency. At dc (frequency = 0 Hz), the reactance is very large. At high frequencies the reactance is very small.

where:

f is the frequency in hertz
C is the capacitance in farads

If you know a frequency in kilohertz or megahertz, you must write it in hertz for this equation. If you know the capacitance in microfarads or picofarads, you must convert those values to farads.

Calculate the reactance of a 1-μF capacitor with a 10 Hz signal applied. This is the example from Figure 16-5.

$$X_C = \frac{1}{2\pi f C} \qquad \text{(Equation 16-2)}$$

$$X_C = \frac{1}{2 \times 3.14 \times 10\,\text{Hz} \times 1 \times 10^{-6}\,\text{F}}$$

$$X_C = \frac{1}{6.28 \times 10 \times 10^{-6}} = \frac{1}{6.28 \times 10^{-5}}$$

$$X_C = 15{,}924\ \Omega$$

You shouldn't be surprised to discover this is the same answer we found using the voltage and current in Ohm's Law earlier. Let's try another problem. Find the reactance of a 2-μF capacitor with a 100 Hz supply. (This is not the same as the problem earlier in this section.)

$$X_C = \frac{1}{2\pi f C} \qquad \text{(Equation 16-2)}$$

$$X_C = \frac{1}{2 \times 3.14 \times 100\,\text{Hz} \times 2 \times 10^{-6}\,\text{F}}$$

$$X_C = \frac{1}{6.28 \times 200 \times 10^{-6}} = \frac{1}{1.256 \times 10^{-3}}$$

$$X_C = 796.2\ \text{ohms}$$

You can practice a few more capacitive reactance problems. Try calculating the reactance for the other circuits we studied at the beginning of this section. Your answers should agree with the ones we found there. You might even want to calculate the reactance of a few capacitance values for frequencies of 1 kilohertz and 1 megahertz. With practice (and your trusty scientific calculator) you'll soon be calculating capacitive reactance values with ease.

MATH HINTS

For more background on math, refer to **Appendix A — Scientific and Engineering Notation.**

CALCULATOR HINTS

The following examples show how to use your TI-30X IIS calculator to solve equations like those in Chapter 16. Simpler numbers are used, so they will all be visible in the display of the calculator at the same time. For more information on using a calculator to work these examples, refer to **Appendix B — Understanding and Using Your TI-30X IIS Scientific Calculator.**

Example 1

$$X_C = \frac{E}{I}$$

$$X_C = \frac{100 \text{ V}}{6.3 \text{ mA}} = 15{,}873 \text{ ohms}$$

Calculator keystrokes

1 0 0 ÷ 6 . 3 2ⁿᵈ EE - 3 =

The calculator's second display line shows the result: **15.873 × 10⁰³**

[Note that $10^{03} = 10^3 = 1{,}000$ so $15.873 \times 10^{03} = 15.873 \times 1{,}000 = 15.873 \text{ k}\Omega$]

Example 2

What is the capacitive reactance (X_C) of a 2 μF capacitor at a frequency of 9 Hertz?

$$X_C = \frac{1}{2 \pi f C} \qquad \text{(Equation 16-2)}$$

$$X_C = \frac{1}{2 \times 3.14 \times 9 \text{ Hz} \times 2 \times 10^{-6} \text{ F}}$$

$$X_C = \frac{1}{6.28 \times 18 \times 10^{-6}} = \frac{1}{113.1 \times 10^{-6}}$$

$$X_C = 8{,}842 \text{ ohms}$$

In order to show all the characters in the first line of the calculator display, we're going to do this calculation in two steps: first, calculate just the denominator **2 π f C**, and then take the result of that calculation and invert it (take the reciprocal).

Step 1 Calculator keystrokes

2 π 9 X 2 2ⁿᵈ EE - 6 =

The calculator's second display line shows the result: **113.1 × 10⁻⁰⁶**

Step 2 Calculator keystrokes

x⁻¹ =

The calculator's second display line shows the result: **8.8419 × 10⁰³**

Of course, we can do this calculation in one step, but all the characters entered won't show on the width of one screen. Here are two ways to do the calculation in a single step; try them both, and make sure you get the same answer as shown above.

Calculator keystrokes

(2 π 9 X 2 2ⁿᵈ EE - 6) x⁻¹ =

or

Calculator keystrokes

1 ÷ (2 π 9 X 2 2ⁿᵈ EE - 6) =

Review Questions ───────────────────────

16.1 Connecting a capacitor to a dc voltage source will:

a) place a charge on the capacitor

b) fully discharge the capacitor

c) cause a constant current to flow into the capacitor

d) turn the capacitor into an inductor

16.2 When an ac voltage is placed across a capacitor, the current will _____ the voltage by _____ degrees.

16.3 The opposition by a capacitor to changing the voltage across it is known as:

a) resistance

b) current limiting

c) reactance

d) having a bad attitude

16.4 A capacitor has an ac voltage of 8 volts across it, and the current through it is 25 mA. What is the reactance of this capacitor?

16.5 What is the reactance of a 5 μF capacitor at a frequency of 60 Hz?

16.6 Without doing the calculation, if the frequency changes to 120 Hz, what is the reactance of a 5 μF capacitor? See question 16.5.

Answers ───────────────────────

16.1 a

16.2 current will *lead* the voltage by *90 degrees*

16.3 reactance

16.4 $X_C = E / I = 8$ V / 25 mA = 320 ohms

16.5 $X_C = 1/(2 \pi f C) = 1/(2 \pi 60 \times 5 \times 10^{-6}) = 530.5 \ \Omega$

16.6 If the frequency changes to 120 Hz (two times 60 Hz), that means the reactance will decrease to one half of what it was at 60 Hz. So 1/2 of (530.5 Ω) = 265.3 Ω

Chapter 17

Inductors with AC — Inductive Reactance

Maximum Current from Ohm's Law

Inductors oppose any change in current.

GLM0040

(A)

(B)

Contents

Inductors Oppose Any Change in Current

Figure 17-1 shows a circuit with an inductor and a battery that supplies a steady direct voltage. There also is a variable resistor in series with the inductor. Since the inductor is just a piece of wire, it has very little resistance to this direct current. You can use Ohm's Law to calculate the circuit current. What is the current if we set the resistor for 5000 ohms?

$$E = I R \qquad \text{(Equation 17-1)}$$

You can easily solve this equation for the current.

$$I = \frac{E}{R} \qquad \text{(Equation 17-2)}$$

$$I = \frac{12 \text{ V}}{5000 \ \Omega}$$

$$I = 2.4 \times 10^{-3} \text{ amperes} = 2.4 \text{ mA}$$

There is a magnetic field around the inductor with this current through the circuit. As long as the current doesn't change, the magnetic field remains constant.

Suppose we increase the variable-resistor setting? With a resistance of 10,000 ohms, the circuit current decreases to 1.2 mA. (Can you prove that using Ohm's Law?) This smaller current also means the magnetic-field strength must decrease.

When we adjust the resistor, the current begins to decrease. The inductor *reacts* to this change by returning some of the energy stored in its magnetic field. This returned energy produces a voltage across the inductor that tries to keep the same current flowing through it. The current does decrease, however, as the magnetic-field strength decreases. The inductor prevents the change from occurring instantly. The new current maintains a smaller magnetic field.

What do you think will happen if we decrease the resistance? What will the current be if the new resistance value is 2500 ohms? Use Ohm's Law and Equation 17-2 to calculate this new current. You should calculate 4.8 mA.

The larger current creates a stronger magnetic field. Once again the inductor reacts to prevent this current change, however. There is a voltage across the inductor in a direction opposite to the battery voltage.

This *back EMF* as we often call it, works to prevent the current increase. Remember that *EMF* is short for *electromotive force*, which is another name for voltage. *Back EMF*, then, means a voltage produced across an inductor by a current change.

Figure 17-2 is a graph of the circuit current for this example. The current begins at 2.4 mA, and remains steady until we increase the resistance. Then the current decreases to 1.2 mA. Notice that this change does not occur instantly. The current decreases gradually, until it reaches the new value. When we decrease the resistance, the current increases to 4.8 mA. Once again, this change occurs gradually.

The resistance and the inductance determine how quickly the current reaches its new value. We won't show you how to do this calculation in this book. The *ARRL Handbook* contains more information about calculating

Figure 17-1 — We'll use this circuit to learn about the effects of changing current on an inductor. Adjusting the variable resistor changes the circuit current. A capital L represents an inductor on schematic diagrams and in equations.

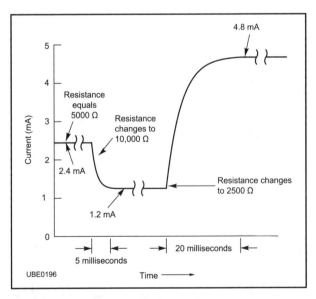

Figure 17-2 — This graph shows the current through the Figure 17-1 inductor. In this experiment, the variable resistance is 5000 Ω to start. At this setting, the current is 2.4 mA. Then we increase the resistance to 10,000 Ω and the current decreases to 1.2 mA. Finally, we decrease the resistance to 2500 Ω. The current increases to 4.8 mA.

the values used to plot the Figure 17-2 graph. For now, you should remember that the current through an inductor changes gradually.

When an inductor *reacts* to current changes, it works against that current change. Changes in the amount of energy stored in the magnetic field cause this opposition.

You should notice some similarities between inductors and capacitors. Capacitors react to prevent changes in the amount of electrical energy they store. The applied voltage determines the amount of charge on a capacitor. A capacitor reacts to a decreased voltage by supplying current. It reacts to an increased voltage by trying to block more current.

You can think of an inductor as the opposite of a capacitor. Inductors store energy in a magnetic field instead of an electric field. Inductors produce a voltage that tries to prevent current changes.

We use the term *reactance* to describe the opposition of an inductor to changes in current. We use the same term to describe the opposition of a capacitor to changes in current. We distinguish the two with the terms *inductive reactance* and *capacitive reactance*. A capital X represents reactance in equations. Subscripts C and L indicate capacitive reactance (X_C) and inductive reactance (X_L).

Can you guess what happens if we connect an alternating current to our inductor? **Figure 17-3** shows a simple RL circuit with a sine-wave voltage supply. **Figure 17-4** shows the inductor current and voltage during one complete cycle of the sine wave, from 0° to 360°. A solid line represents the voltage and a dashed line represents the current.

There are no numbers on the vertical scale because we are not trying to show specific values. The actual voltage and current values depend on the resistor and inductor values, the applied voltage and the sine-wave frequency.

During the first sine-wave half cycle of current, look carefully at the inductor current and voltage at 0°. Notice that the inductor current is

Figure 17-3 — An alternating (ac) voltage is applied to a resistor and inductor in series. The text describes what happens as the inductor current and voltage go through one complete cycle of a sine wave.

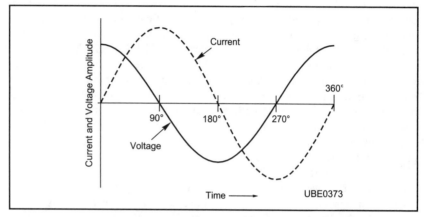

Figure 17-4 — The dashed line shows the current through the inductor, while the solid line shows the voltage across the inductor in Figure 17-3. The current is a sine-wave that starts at 0°.

zero. However, even though it is zero, it is changing quickly (the *rate of change*, or slope, is a maximum). As a result the inductor voltage, trying to oppose this rapid rate of change, is a maximum. The polarity of the voltage, or *back EMF*, is positive, which tends to oppose the change in current.

As the current increases from zero, heading towards a positive peak at 90°, its rate of change is becoming smaller, and the inductor voltage is heading towards zero.

At 90°, the current is at its maximum positive value, *but it isn't changing*. Recall that inductors oppose a change in current by creating a voltage (the *back EMF*); since the current isn't changing, the voltage is zero at the same instant the inductor current is a positive maximum.

As the current begins to decrease (between 90° and 270°), the inductor voltage once again opposes this change by creating a voltage of negative polarity. At 180°, the current is

at a negative peak, but is no longer changing, so the inductor voltage is zero at this instant.

Looking at Figure 17-4, we can see a *phase shift* between the inductor voltage and current. The inductor voltage is at a maximum at 0°, while the current doesn't reach a maximum until 90° on the graph. This describes the *phase* relationship between the alternating current *through* an inductor and the voltage *across* it. The voltage leads the current by 90°. Or, we can say the current *lags* the voltage by 90°.

A handy way to remember this phase relationship is the phrase **"ELI the ICE man."** The voltage (E) across an inductor leads the current (I) by 90°. The current (I) through a capacitor (C), leads the voltage (E) by 90°. So try to picture *Eli*, the fellow who delivers *ice*, as "ELI the ICE man," and you will always remember the phase relationship between voltage and current for inductors and capacitors.

There is More Opposition at Higher Frequencies

An inductor consists of a piece of wire wound to form a cylinder. Wire has a low resistance. When you connect a dc voltage source to the inductor, there is a large current. Many circuits have a resistor in series with the inductor to limit the current.

The current through an inductor won't change instantly. It quickly builds up to the value set by the series resistance, however. Inductors act like a short circuit to direct current.

Inductive reactance is the opposition inductors have to current changes. Since inductors act like a short circuit at dc, we say they have zero reactance at dc.

Consider the effects of applying a low-frequency sine-wave voltage to an inductor. **Figure 17-5** shows a simple circuit with a 100 hertz alternating voltage applied to a 10 millihenry inductor. The ammeter shows a 0.239 ampere current through the circuit with 1.5 volts RMS from the voltage source. How much reactance does the inductor have?

Does this sound a bit like another Ohm's Law problem? You know a circuit voltage and current, and want to find the opposition to that current. Use Ohm's Law to calculate the *reactance* in this problem instead of *resistance*.

Since this is a "thought experiment," we assume the inductor is *ideal*. That means the inductor's wire

has no resistance. The other wires in the circuit don't have any resistance either. *Real* components always have some resistance. The math is more difficult if a circuit has both resistance and reactance. We won't try any problems like that here. You can learn how to handle the more difficult math after you learn the basic principles.

We use X to represent reactance. A subscript L reminds us we are working with an inductor in this problem. Inductive reactance is X_L.

$$E = I\,X_L \qquad \text{(Equation 17-3)}$$

Solve this equation for X_L, or use the equation circle given in **Figure 17-6**.

$$X_L = \frac{E}{I}$$

$$X_L = \frac{1.5\ \text{V}}{0.239\ \text{A}}$$

$X_L = 6.28$ ohms

Let's change our circuit for the next part of our experiment. Replace the 10-mH inductor with a 50-mH unit. This time the ammeter reads 47.8 mA. What is the new inductor's reactance? Solve Equation 17-3 for X_L again. (Remember that 47.8 mA is 47.8×10^{-3} amperes.)

$$X_L = \frac{E}{I}$$

$$X_L = \frac{1.5\ \text{V}}{47.8 \times 10^{-3}\ \text{A}}$$

$X_L = 31.4$ ohms

What did you learn from this experiment? We made the inductance value five times larger and the reactance increased to five times larger than the original value. What do you expect the reactance to be if we use a 100-mH inductor? If you said 62.8 ohms, you are correct. Inductive reactance is directly related to inductance. Larger inductance values produce larger reactances.

Now let's make another change to our circuit. This time we will connect a 1000-Hz voltage source. Change back to the original 10-mH inductor. The voltage supply still produces

UBE0198

Figure 17-6 — Use this equation circle to solve Equation 17-3 for inductive reactance, X_L.

Figure 17-5 — We'll use this circuit for a thought experiment about inductive reactance.

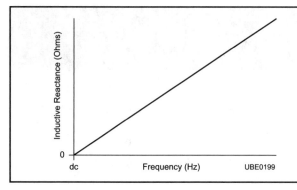

Figure 17-7 — This graph shows how inductive reactance varies with signal frequency. At dc, the reactance is zero. At high frequencies the reactance is very large.

1.5 volts. This time the ammeter reads 23.9 mA. Calculate the reactance of the 10-mH inductor with the new voltage source.

$$X_L = \frac{1.5 \text{ V}}{23.9 \text{ mA}} = 62.8 \text{ ohms}$$

The new signal frequency is 10 times the original frequency. Did you notice the current is only one-tenth as large compared with the first example? Were you surprised to find the reactance is 10 times larger? This part of the experiment taught you that reactance is directly related to frequency. Higher frequency signals produce larger inductive reactances, for a given inductor.

Do you think this is a reasonable conclusion? Let's think about what happens when we apply higher-frequency signals to an inductor.

You know that inductors act as short circuits to dc signals. When you connect a low-frequency ac signal, the inductor stores energy in a magnetic field. The inductor reacts to changing currents. If the current changes slowly, the inductor has almost no reaction trying to prevent that change. A low-frequency ac signal doesn't produce much reactance from an inductor.

Now begin to increase the signal frequency. It takes less time for the signal to go through one cycle at a higher frequency. You can conclude that the current and voltage change more rapidly. The inductor has a stronger reaction to this rapid current change. As the frequency increases, the inductor has more opposition to the current changes. Inductive reactance increases as the frequency increases. **Figure 17-7** is a graph of inductive reactance and frequency. Reactance is zero at dc, and increases as the frequency goes up.

We found two factors that affect reactance in this section. When either inductance or signal frequency increases, the reactance increases. We can write an equation to calculate inductive reactance, based on these two factors.

We normally express frequency as a number of waveform cycles per second, measured in hertz. We also can relate each cycle to the rotation of a wheel. Then we express frequency in radians per second. You can convert any frequency in hertz to radians per second. Just multiply frequency in hertz by 2π. This is the number of radians in one cycle. Equation 17-4 shows how to calculate inductive reactance.

$$X_L = 2\pi f L \qquad \text{(Equation 17-4)}$$

where:
  f is the frequency in hertz
  L is the inductance in henrys

If you know a frequency in kilohertz or megahertz, you must write it in hertz for this equation. If you know the inductance in millihenrys or microhenrys, you must convert those values to henrys. For example, 5 mH $= 5 \times 10^{-3}$ henrys.

Calculate the reactance of a 10-mH inductor with a 100-Hz signal applied. This is the example from Figure 17-5.

$$X_L = 2\pi f L \qquad \text{(Equation 17-4)}$$

$$X_L = 2 \times 3.14 \times 100 \text{ Hz} \times 10 \times 10^{-3} \text{ H}$$

$$\begin{aligned} X_L &= 6.28 \times 1000 \times 10^{-3} \\ &= 6.28 \times 1000 \times (1/1000) \\ &= 6.28 \times 1.000 \text{ ohms} \end{aligned}$$

$$X_L = 6.28 \text{ ohms}$$

You shouldn't be surprised to discover this is the same answer we found using the voltage and current in Ohm's Law earlier. Let's try another problem. Find the reactance of a 200 µH inductor with a 1000-Hz supply. (This is not the same as the problem earlier in this section.)

$$X_L = 2\pi f L \qquad \text{(Equation 17-4)}$$

$$X_L = 2 \times 3.14 \times 1000 \text{ Hz} \times 200 \times 10^{-6} \text{ H}$$

$$\begin{aligned} X_L &= 6.28 \times 200 \times 10^{-3} \text{ ohms} \\ &= 6.28 \times 2.00 \times 10^{-1} \text{ ohms} \end{aligned}$$

$$X_L = 1.256 \text{ ohms}$$

You can practice a few more inductive reactance problems. Try calculating the reactance for the other circuits we studied at the beginning of this section. Your answers should agree with the ones we found there. You might even want to calculate the reactance of a few inductance values for frequencies of 1 kilohertz and 1 megahertz. With practice (and your trusty scientific calculator) you'll soon be calculating inductive reactance values with ease.

Math and Calculator Hints

MATH HINTS

For more background on math, refer to **Appendix A — Scientific and Engineering Notation.**

CALCULATOR HINTS

The following example shows how to use your TI-30X IIS calculator to solve equations like those in Chapter 17. Simpler numbers are used, so they will all be visible in the display of the calculator at the same time. For more information on using a calculator to work these examples, refer to

Appendix B — Understanding and Using Your TI-30X IIS Scientific Calculator.

Example

What is the inductive reactance (X_L) of a 8 mH inductor at a frequency of 50 Hertz?

$$X_L = 2 \pi f L \qquad \text{(Equation 17-3)}$$

$$X_L = 2 \times 3.14 \times 50 \text{ Hz} \times 8 \times 10^{-3} \text{ H}$$

$$X_L = 6.28 \times 400 \times 10^{-3}$$
$$= 6.28 \times 400 \times (1/1000)$$

$$X_L = 6.28 \times 0.4 \text{ ohms}$$

$$X_L = 2.51 \text{ ohms}$$

Calculator keystrokes

2 π 5 0 X 8 2nd EE - 3 =

The calculator's second display line shows the result: **2.513×10^{00}**

Review Questions

17.1 *EMF* **is an acronym that means:**

a)   energy motion fraction

b)   electron mobility field

c)   electromotive force

d)   extremely merry fellow

17.2 An inductor has an ac voltage across it of 20 V at a frequency of 500 Hz, and the current through it is 80 mA. What is the reactance of this inductor?

17.3 Without doing the calculation, if the frequency of the ac voltage changes to 4000 Hz, what is the reactance of the inductor? See question 17.2.

17.4 When an ac voltage is placed across an inductor, the current will _____ the voltage by _____ degrees.

17.5 What is the inductive reactance of a 100 mH inductor at a frequency of 3 kHz?

Answers

17.1 c

17.2 $X_L = E / I$, $X_L = 20$ volts $/ 0.08$ A, $X_L = 250 \ \Omega$

17.3 If the frequency changes to 4,000 Hz (eight times 500 Hz), that means the reactance will increase to eight times what it was at 500 Hz. So $8 \times (250 \ \Omega) = 2000 \ \Omega$.

17.4 When an ac voltage is placed across an inductor, the current will *lag* the voltage by *90* degrees.

17.5 $X_L = 2 \pi f L = 2 \pi (3 \times 10^3)(100 \times 10^{-3}) = 1885 \ \Omega$.

Chapter 18

Quality Factor for Inductors and Capacitors

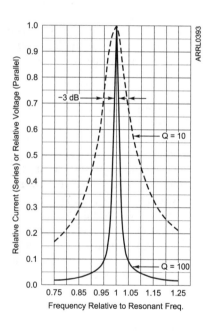

This graph shows the bandwidth of two resonant circuits. The circuit with lower Q has a wider bandwidth.

Contents

Circuit Reactance and Resistance Determine Q

Ideal components show only one type of circuit performance. It doesn't matter if the circuit has a steady direct voltage or an alternating signal source. Ideal wires connect parts of a circuit, but they have no resistance. When you connect an ideal resistor into a circuit it never behaves like a capacitor or an inductor. Ideal capacitors have capacitance but no resistance or inductance. Ideal inductors show only inductance. They have no resistance or capacitance.

Of course, real components don't meet these ideals. There is some resistance in the wires that connect circuit components. We often ignore this added resistance, however, when ignoring it makes almost no difference in understanding how a circuit works.

For example, **Figure 18-1A** shows a circuit that has three 1000-ohm resistors connected in series. Suppose the circuit wiring has a resistance of 0.1 ohm. Figure 18-1B shows the same circuit with an additional 0.1-ohm resistor added in series with the others. We labeled the new resistor R_W because it represents the wire

resistance. How much will this extra resistance change the circuit current you calculate with Ohm's Law? Not much! (As a practice exercise, you should add the resistances of Figure 18-1A and use Ohm's Law to calculate current. Then add the resistances of Figure 18-1B and calculate that current.)

Since capacitors include wire leads to connect them into a circuit, they have some resistance. The electrical energy stored in a capacitor may heat the dielectric, the insulating material between the capacitor plates. The electronic circuit can't use the electrical energy that gets converted to heat energy. The energy is lost to the electronic circuit, then. This is another way real capacitors vary from ideal components.

We refer to the lead resistance and dielectric loss as a resistance. You can't measure this resistance by connecting an ohmmeter across the capacitor, however. The lead resistance is too small to measure with most common ohmmeters. The insulating material will cause the ohmmeter to measure an infinite (too large to measure) resistance. The

ohmmeter indicates an open circuit when you connect it between the two capacitor leads.

The capacitor's wire leads have some inductance. Inductive reactance is small at low frequencies and increases as the signal frequency increases. This is why inductance becomes more important when we connect higher-frequency signals to the capacitor.

Figure 18-2 shows a circuit with a capacitor and an ac signal. We included a resistor and an inductor in the circuit. We drew these with dashed lines to show they represent the resistance and inductance of the real capacitor leads.

Most inductors consist of a length of wire wound into a coil. That wire has some resistance, so real inductors have resistance. Each turn of an inductor's coil is close to the turns on either side. When an alternating signal goes through the inductor, these adjacent turns act like small capacitors. **Figure 18-3** shows a circuit with an ac signal applied to an inductor. We drew a resistor and a capacitor in the circuit with dashed lines to represent the resistance and

Figure 18-1 — Part A shows three 1000-ohm resistors connected in series to a 15-V battery. Part B shows the same circuit, but with an additional resistor. R_W represents the resistance of the wires connecting the parts of this circuit. As an exercise, you should use Ohm's Law to calculate the current for both circuits.

Figure 18-2 — This diagram includes the small resistance and inductance that are part of a real capacitor. We drew the resistor and inductor with dashed lines to indicate they are part of the capacitor. They are not physical components in the circuit.

Figure 18-3 — Real inductors include a small amount of capacitance and resistance. The diagram shows a resistor and a capacitor drawn with dashed lines. This indicates they are part of the inductor. They are not physical components in the circuit.

Figure 18-4 — This 25-microfarad capacitor has 0.01 ohms of resistance. The ac signal generator applies a 40-hertz signal to the capacitor. Later the signal generator applies a 400-hertz signal. The text shows how to calculate the reactance and Q for these conditions.

$$X_C = \frac{1}{2\pi f C} \qquad \text{(Equation 18-3)}$$

$$X_C = \frac{1}{2 \times 3.14 \times 40\,\text{Hz} \times 25 \times 10^{-6}\,\text{F}}$$

$$X_C = \frac{1}{6.28 \times 10^{-3}}$$

$$X_C = 159\ \Omega$$

Now you can use Equation 18-1 to calculate Q.

$$Q = \frac{X_C}{R} = \frac{159\ \Omega}{0.01\ \Omega} = 15,900$$

Notice that the quality factor Q does not have a unit (like ohms or farads or hertz). Q is the ratio of two values (resistance and reactance), both measured in ohms, so the unit of ohms for both numerator and denominator cancels.

What if we connect this capacitor to a 400-Hz signal? Use Equation 18-3 to calculate the new reactance.

$$X_C = \frac{1}{2\pi f C}$$

$$X_C = \frac{1}{2 \times 3.14 \times 400\,\text{Hz} \times 25 \times 10^{-6}\,\text{F}}$$

$$X_C = \frac{1}{62.8 \times 10^{-3}} = \frac{1}{0.0628}$$

$$X_C = 15.9\ \Omega$$

Use this reactance to calculate the new Q value.

$$Q = \frac{X_C}{R} = \frac{15.9\ \Omega}{0.01\ \Omega} = 1590$$

capacitance of a real inductor.

We frequently ignore the small inductance of a capacitor and the small capacitance of an inductor. You must consider these limitations of real components for some circuits, however. They become important in radio-frequency (RF) circuits that operate in the very-high frequency (VHF) range, 30 MHz to 300 MHz, and higher frequencies. We will ignore these effects for the rest of this book, however.

We often must consider the wire resistance of these components. We usually want the resistance to be much smaller than the reactance of a capacitor or inductor. In general, better quality capacitors and inductors have a smaller resistance.

We can assign a number to a coil or capacitor to indicate that component's relative merits. This number represents a *quality factor*, and the symbol for *quality factor* is *Q*. An entire circuit also can have a Q value. A circuit Q value gives an idea of how close to the ideal that circuit performs.

We define Q as the ratio of reactance to resistance. This definition applies to both inductors and capacitors.

The Q of a real capacitor is equal to the capacitive reactance divided by the resistance. Equation 18-1 states

this definition mathematically.

$$Q = \frac{X_C}{R} \qquad \text{(Equation 18-1)}$$

The Q of a real inductor is equal to the inductive reactance divided by the resistance. Equation 18-2 is a mathematical statement of this definition.

$$Q = \frac{X_L}{R} \qquad \text{(Equation 18-2)}$$

The first thing you should notice about these equations is that smaller resistance values give larger Q values. Larger Q values indicate better-quality components.

You should remember that reactance varies with frequency. Capacitive reactance is largest at low frequency and decreases as the frequency increases. Inductive reactance is smallest at low frequency and increases as the frequency increases. How will this affect Q? Let's consider some examples.

Figure 18-4 shows a 25 µF capacitor that has 0.01 ohm of lead resistance (due to the wires and metal conductors inside the capacitor). Suppose we connect a 40-Hz signal to this capacitor. What is the capacitor's Q? First calculate the capacitive reactance.

The reactance of the capacitor at the higher frequency is one tenth as big, so the Q at that frequency is also one tenth as big. When you apply a higher-frequency signal to a capacitor the reactance and Q both become smaller.

The 5-millihenry inductor shown in **Figure 18-5** has 0.05 ohm of resistance. What is the Q of this inductor when we apply a 40-hertz signal? First calculate the inductive reactance.

$$X_L = 2 \pi f L \qquad \text{(Equation 18-4)}$$

$$X_L = 2 \times 3.14 \times 40 \text{ Hz} \times 5 \times 10^{-3} \text{ henrys}$$

$$X_L = 6.28 \times 200 \times 10^{-3} = 1.256 \text{ ohms}$$

Next, we will use Equation 18-2 to

Figure 18-5 — This 5-millihenry inductor has 0.05 ohms of resistance. The ac signal generator first applies a 40-hertz signal, and then a 400-Hz signal. The text explains how to calculate the reactance and Q for these applied signals.

calculate the inductor Q.

$$Q = \frac{X_L}{R}$$

$$Q = \frac{1.256 \ \Omega}{0.05 \ \Omega} = 25.1$$

What is this inductor's Q with a 400 Hz signal applied? Verify that the inductive reactance at this frequency is 12.56 ohms. Then use Equation 18-2 to calculate Q again.

$$Q = \frac{X_L}{R} = \frac{12.56 \ \Omega}{0.05 \ \Omega} = 251$$

What can you conclude about how the Q of an inductor depends on frequency? That's right, when you increase the frequency, the reactance and Q increase.

High Q Means Low Series Resistance in an Inductor or Capacitor

An ideal inductor or capacitor doesn't add extra resistance to a circuit. Real components always add some extra resistance, though. Good-quality real components will only add a small amount of resistance. Why not always use the highest-quality components available? Then we wouldn't have to worry about the inductor or capacitor quality factor, or Q.

There are many trade-offs to consider when selecting components. What is the circuit function? What purpose does the component serve in the circuit? What will be the frequency of signals applied to the component? Answers to these questions (and others) will help you select the proper components for the job. Other considerations are component cost, size and construction methods.

Your circuit may not require the best components available. Suppose you have a power supply that converts 120 V ac to 12 V dc. The output from this supply will have a 60- or 120-hertz ripple unless you add a filter capacitor. (**Figure 18-6** shows how this capacitor smoothes the ripples.) You needn't worry about the high-frequency characteristics of the capacitor in this case. You shouldn't be too concerned about a small energy loss in the capacitor either.

A capacitor that you plan to use in the radio-frequency portion of a VHF radio receiver must meet other requirements. This capacitor must have good high-frequency characteristics. Any signal loss in this circuit should be minimized.

Aluminum electrolytic capacitors are popular for power-supply filters. They pack a large amount of capacitance into a small package. While all capacitors have relatively high Q, aluminum electrolytic capacitors have a lower Q than some

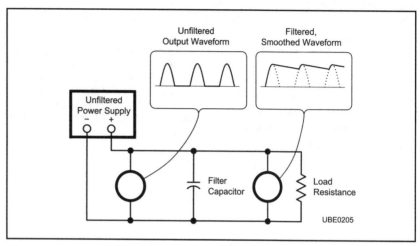

Figure 18-6 — A power supply converts the ac mains voltage to a dc voltage for use with an electronic circuit. The output signal has ripples or variations left over from the ac voltage. A filter capacitor smoothes these ripples to provide a steady dc output.

other types. This is because they have higher losses, especially at high frequencies.

Mica and ceramic capacitors are more popular for higher-frequency applications. It is not practical to make ceramic or mica capacitors with enough capacitance for use in power-supply filters. Such capacitors would be physically too large. These dielectric materials have much lower loss than electrolytics, however. Mica and ceramic dielectrics form high-Q capacitors.

How can we reduce an inductor's wire resistance? Larger diameter wire has less resistance than small diameter wire. Winding the coil on a larger diameter form and putting more space between the turns also reduces losses. Sometimes you don't have room in the circuit for a very large coil, however. If the application doesn't require a high-Q coil, you can use smaller wire and a small diameter coil form.

You may put an inductor in series with the power-supply lead to an RF amplifier. This inductor carries a

small direct current from the power supply. At dc, the inductor has a very small reactance. It also has the resistance of the wire that is inside the inductor. The inductor has a very large reactance at the amplifier's radio frequency, though. It blocks any RF current from flowing back to the power supply. Sometimes we call such a coil a *choke*, because it chokes off high-frequency signals while allowing lower-frequency signals to pass through. **Figure 18-7** shows a circuit with such a coil.

You don't need a high-Q coil to serve as a choke. You just use a power supply that can supply the current needed by the amplifier and any losses in the coil.

You do want a high-Q inductor for the output network of a high-power RF amplifier. You don't want to lose any of your hard-earned RF power in the coil. The output inductor must be able to carry several amperes of RF current for a 1500-watt amplifier. If the inductor wires have too much resistance, the losses will be large, and the RF power sent to the antenna will be unacceptably reduced.

Some high-power amplifiers use copper tubing as the conductor for this coil. The tubing's large diameter minimizes any conductor resistance, producing a high-Q inductor.

Any high-Q device or circuit has low resistance. High Q also means the component has low losses of other kinds. High-Q capacitors use low-loss dielectric materials.

A high-Q component will not lose much of the energy stored in it. Q relates the energy stored in a capacitor or inductor to the energy lost in the component. A high-Q component stores much more energy during each waveform cycle than it loses.

Figure 18-7 — An *RF choke* blocks the radio-frequency signal from following the power-supply leads back into the supply. The coil's high reactance at the radio's operating frequency "chokes off" the RF. At dc, however, the inductor has only the small wire resistance and no reactance. The direct current from the power supply travels through the inductor to supply the radio with the current it needs.

Math and Calculator Hints

MATH HINTS

For more background on math, refer to **Appendix A — Scientific and Engineering Notation.**

CALCULATOR HINTS

The following example shows how to use your TI-30X IIS calculator to solve equations like those in Chapter 18. Simpler numbers are used, so they will all be visible in the display of the calculator at the same time. For more information on using a calculator to work these examples, refer to **Appendix B — Understanding and Using Your TI-30X IIS Scientific Calculator.**

Example

What is the Q (quality factor) of an inductor with inductive reactance (X_L) of 12 ohms and series resistance of 0.05 ohms?

$$Q = \frac{X_L}{R} \qquad \text{(Equation 18-2)}$$

$$Q = \frac{12\ \Omega}{0.05\ \Omega} = 240$$

Calculator keystrokes

1 2 ÷ . 0 5 =

The calculator's second display line shows the result: **240 × 10⁰⁰**

Recall that the quality factor, calculated by dividing ohms by ohms, doesn't have a unit, so 240 × 10⁰⁰ = 240 × 1 = 240.

Review Questions

18.1 When discussing real inductors and capacitors, the term Q refers to:
a) quasi-realistic
b) qualified reactance
c) quick impedance
d) quality factor

18.2 A nearly ideal inductor or capacitor has a Q factor that is:
a) very small
b) 1.0
c) very large
d) 0

18.3 A type of capacitor that has a lower Q than most capacitors is the:
a) aluminum electrolytic
b) mica
c) ceramic
d) RF

18.4 What is the Q (quality factor) of an inductor with inductive reactance (X_L) of 90 ohms and series resistance of 1.5 ohms?

18.5 The unit associated with the quality factor is:
a) ohms
b) there is no unit for Q
c) farads
d) henrys

Answers

18.1 d

18.2 c

18.3 a

18.4 $Q = X_L/R = 90 \ \Omega/1.5 \ \Omega = 60$

18.5 b

Chapter 19

Transformers

120 V
Transformer

Primary

Secondary   UBE0371

A transformer takes one ac voltage and converts it to another. In this case, the transformer converts 120 volts from a wall outlet to 12 volts needed by an electronic device.

12 V

Contents

The Magnetic Field From One Coil Can Cause a Voltage in Another Coil

An electric current through an inductor produces a magnetic field around the inductor. There is no magnetic field without a current. When the current begins to flow, the magnetic field "grows" around the inductor. As the current increases, the magnetic field strength increases. While there is a steady direct current through the inductor, the magnetic field remains constant. If the current decreases, so does the magnetic field. When the current stops, the magnetic field collapses to zero.

Figure 19-1 shows a circuit that applies an alternating-current, sine-wave signal to an inductor. This current changes constantly. When the current changes, the magnetic-field strength in and around the inductor also changes.

When the ac signal increases from zero, the magnetic-field strength increases. The magnetic field decreases when the signal decreases to zero again. What happens when the ac signal's current direction changes? The magnetic field polarity also changes. **Figure 19-2** shows the magnetic field around a coil. Notice that when the current direction reverses, the North and South magnetic poles also reverse. You can visualize the magnetic-field strength as having a sine-wave pattern just like the applied signal current.

A changing electric current produces a changing magnetic field. Can a changing magnetic field also produce a changing electric voltage (and current)? Yes, it can! This is the principle of an electric generator.

How can we produce a changing magnetic field? One way is to move the magnet. **Figure 19-3** shows a horseshoe magnet moving into and out of a coil of wire. The wire connects to a very sensitive voltmeter. A current moving one direction through the coil moves the meter needle to the right. When the current moves in the opposite direction the needle moves to the left.

Any movement between a magnetic field and the turns of an inductor induces a voltage across the inductor. The coil can move through the field from a permanent magnet or a permanent magnet can move through the coil. An alternating-current signal through an inductor also produces a magnetic field that moves. The magnetic field grows, collapses and reverses direction with the current.

Figure 19-1 — An alternating-current signal source creates a changing magnetic field in and around an inductor.

Alternating-Current Signal Generator

L

UBE0207

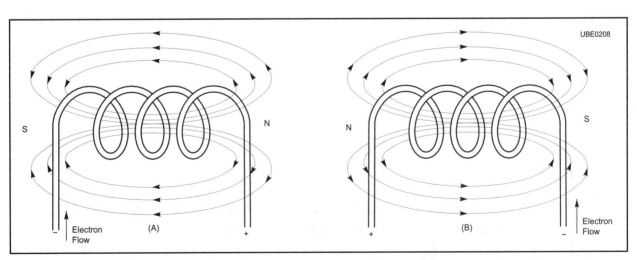

Figure 19-2 — When the current direction changes, the polarity of the magnetic field through an inductor also changes. In Part A, the electrons flow into the wire on the left. The North magnetic pole is to the right of the coil. In Part B the electrons flow into the wire on the right. This time the North magnetic pole is to the coil's left end.

Magnet moves
into coil

(A)

Magnet moves
out of coil

UBE0209   (B)

Figure 19-3 — Moving a wire coil through a magnetic field induces a voltage in the coil. This voltage produces a current through the wire. The voltage polarity and current direction change when the direction of magnet movement changes.

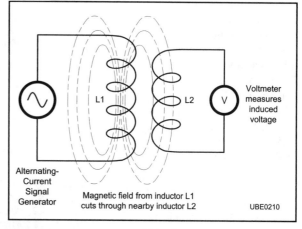

Alternating-
Current
Signal
Generator

Magnetic field from inductor L1
cuts through nearby inductor L2

Voltmeter
measures
induced
voltage

L1   L2   V

UBE0210

Figure 19-4 — The changing magnetic field from inductor L1 cuts through the turns of inductor L2. The magnetic field from L1 induces a voltage across L2, producing a current through it.

The changing magnetic field from one coil can induce a voltage across another coil. **Figure 19-4** shows two inductors that are physically close to each other. An ac signal through the left coil creates a changing magnetic field that moves through the coil on the right.

When the magnetic field from one coil cuts through another coil, we say the coils have *mutual inductance*. We also sometimes call inductors with mutual inductance *linked* or *coupled* inductors, also known as *transformers*.

Transformers Can Increase or Decrease Voltage Levels

When the changing magnetic field from one inductor cuts through the turns of another inductor, the coils have mutual inductance. The magnetic field induces a voltage across the second inductor.

Some circuits require that you minimize any mutual inductance. Induced voltages can disrupt circuit operation.

Other circuits depend on mutual inductance for proper operation. This section concentrates on the desired effects of mutual inductance.

Figure 19-5 shows two coils arranged so a changing current through one induces a voltage in the other. We call this combination a *transformer*. Transformers can have more than two coils.

One inductor has the input signal applied across it. This is the transformer *primary* winding. The transformer primary winding induces a voltage across one or more *secondary* windings. These secondary windings provide an output voltage to other parts of the circuit.

A transformer transfers energy from one part of a circuit to another part. There is no direct connection between the two parts of the circuit,

Figure 19-5 — A current through inductor L1 produces a magnetic field that cuts through the turns of inductor L2. The changing magnetic field across L2 produces a voltage. This combination of linked (or coupled) inductors forms a transformer.

however. The energy flows into the primary winding as electrical energy, is changed to magnetic energy, and then appears in the secondary winding as electrical energy.

We usually want to maximize the mutual inductance between the transformer primary and secondary inductors. This ensures good energy transfer between the windings. The two inductors must be physically

close to each other. Most of the primary winding's magnetic field must cut through the secondary coil. We usually wind the transformer inductors on a single form, or core. The core is often made from iron, powdered iron or ferrite materials.

Figure 19-6 shows a transformer primary winding connected to a battery. Batteries provide a source of direct current. A resistor connects

Figure 19-6 — The primary side of this transformer connects to a 20-volt battery. There is a 1-kΩ resistor across the secondary winding. The solid lines between the inductors indicate the windings of this transformer are on an iron core. There is no voltage across the secondary winding, and no current through the resistor. Transformers require a changing primary voltage to produce a secondary voltage.

Figure 19-7 — When we connect the Figure 19-6 transformer to an alternating signal source there is a voltage across the secondary. This induced voltage produces a current through the resistor.

across the secondary winding. The solid lines between the two coils indicate that the transformer has an iron core.

Can you describe the voltage across the secondary? How much current do you think will flow through the resistor? Remember that only a changing magnetic field will induce a voltage across the secondary.

Did you answer there is no voltage across the secondary and no current through the resistor? Good. By the way, connecting a transformer primary to a dc source (like a battery) is a very bad idea; the result can be smoke and damage to, or destruction of, the transformer.

We connected the transformer to an alternating-current signal in **Figure 19-7**. This time there is a voltage induced across the secondary, so a current will flow through the resistor.

The small "power cubes" that power many electronic devices contain transformers. These cubes plug directly into a wall outlet and have a wire that plugs into a radio, telephone, MP3 player or other device (**Figure 19-8**). The 120-V house current goes to the cube's primary winding. The secondary output voltage is usually some lower voltage, such as 9 or 12 volts.

Figure 19-8 — Small "cube transformers" power many electronic devices, such as this portable short-wave receiver.

UBE0214

We can make a transformer that will produce any desired output voltage. Some transformers produce an output voltage that is lower than the input voltage. Other transformers produce a higher output voltage than their input voltage.

Some transformers have more than one secondary winding. These transformers produce several output voltages from a single input voltage. You may even find transformers that produce one voltage higher than the input and another that is lower than the input.

Transformers come in many shapes and sizes. Larger transformers generally produce higher voltages or use heavier wire to carry more current. AC power transformers often have a core made from a stack of thin sheet-iron layers. A metal "can" or covering protects the wires. Transformers designed for use with radio-frequency signals often have powdered-iron or ferrite cores. *Toroidal*, or donut-shaped cores, are popular for RF transformers.

Turns Ratio Determines Voltage Transformation

The magnetic field strength around an inductor depends on several factors. The field is stronger when the voltage applied to the inductor is larger, and there is more current through the inductor. The field is also stronger when there are more turns of wire in the coil. Winding an inductor around a core of iron, powdered iron or ferrite material also makes the magnetic field stronger.

Figure 19-9 shows an ideal transformer with two identical windings. There are the same number of turns on the primary as there are on the secondary. An ideal transformer transfers to the secondary all the energy put into its primary winding. It does not lose any of the energy in wire resistance or losses in the transformer core.

In Figure 19-9 we connected the transformer to the 120-V house current. This primary voltage produces 120 volts on the secondary winding.

The voltage induced by a changing magnetic field is proportional to the number of turns on the inductor. The magnetic field induces a larger voltage across an inductor that has more turns. An inductor with fewer turns has a smaller induced voltage.

Figure 19-10 has a transformer with two secondary windings. The primary winding has 1000 turns. Secondary 1 has 500 turns and secondary 2 has 250 turns. Let's connect this transformer's primary winding to 120 volts and measure the voltage across each secondary. Did you notice that secondary 1 has only half as many turns as the primary? You should expect to measure 60 volts across this winding. How many volts do you think we will measure across secondary 2? It has half as many turns as secondary 1

and one fourth as many as the primary. Therefore, we will measure 30 volts across secondary 2.

The previous example demonstrates how easy it is to calculate a transformer's secondary output voltage. We only need to know the *primary-to-secondary turns ratio*. The number of turns on the primary divided by the number of turns on the secondary gives us the primary-to-secondary turns ratio. The turns ratio is the same as the input voltage divided by the output voltage. We can write this statement as an equation, and use the equation to calculate the output voltage when we know the input voltage.

$$\frac{N_P}{N_S} = \frac{E_P}{E_S} \qquad \text{(Equation 19-1)}$$

where:

N_P is the number of turns on the primary winding

N_S is the number of turns on the secondary winding

E_P is the primary voltage

E_S is the secondary voltage

Suppose we have a transformer with 300 turns on the primary winding and 100 turns on the secondary winding. What will the secondary voltage be when a 120-V ac supply connects to the primary? Substitute these numbers into Equation 19-1, and solve for E_S.

$$\frac{N_P}{N_S} = \frac{E_P}{E_S} \qquad \text{(Equation 19-1)}$$

$$\frac{300}{100} = \frac{120 \text{ V}}{E_S}$$

$$\frac{3}{1} = \frac{120 \text{ V}}{E_S}$$

(The easiest way to solve this equation for E_S is to multiply both sides of the

Figure 19-9 — This transformer has identical primary and secondary windings. With 120 V ac applied to the primary, 120 V ac appears across the secondary.

Figure 19-10 — Here is a transformer with two secondary windings. Secondary 1 has twice as many turns as secondary 2. The voltage induced across secondary 1 will be twice as large as the voltage across secondary 2.

equation by E_S. That cancels E_S on the right side, and puts the E_S on the left side. Then divide both sides by 3, and you have the answer.)

$$E_S \times \frac{3}{1} = \frac{E_S \times 120 \text{ V}}{E_S} = 120 \text{ V}$$

$$E_S \times \frac{3}{3} = \frac{120 \text{ V}}{3} = 40 \text{ V}$$

The secondary voltage from this transformer is 40 volts when the primary connects to 120 volts. Now suppose 12 volts ac connects to the primary. The secondary output would be 4 volts, in that case. Can you calculate this value? The output voltage is less than the input voltage, and the ratio of primary-to-secondary voltage is always 3:1. This is a *step-down transformer* because it reduces the input voltage, or steps it down.

Let's try another example. Suppose we find a transformer that has 500 turns on the primary winding and 4000 turns on the secondary winding. What is the turns ratio of this transformer? What is the secondary voltage if the primary connects to 120 V ac? We can calculate the turns ratio from the left side of Equation 19-1.

$$\frac{N_P}{N_S} = \frac{500}{4000} = \frac{1}{8} = 0.125$$

The turns ratio is less than 1, which tells us this is a *step-up transformer*. A step-up transformer increases, or steps up, the input voltage to a higher level. Equation 19-1 will help us calculate the secondary voltage.

$$\frac{N_P}{N_S} = \frac{E_P}{E_S} \qquad \text{(Equation 19-1)}$$

$$0.125 = \frac{120 \text{ V}}{E_S}$$

(Solve this equation for E_S, similar to the way we solved the equation in the earlier example.)

$$E_S = \frac{120 \text{ V}}{0.125} = 960 \text{ V}$$

Let's try one more example. Suppose you find a bargain transformer at your local Electronics Parts Palace. The store manager says

the box and papers that came with the transformer are missing. You aren't sure what the secondary voltage is, but you can't pass up a bargain, so you bring it home.

When you examine the transformer, you find a small P near one pair of wires and a small S near the other pair. You decide these markings indicate the intended primary and secondary windings. **Figure 19-11** shows how you can safely connect this transformer to the ac mains. Your test leads include 1 amp fuses in both leads, and you carefully insulate all the connections before you plug in the cord. The transformer connected to the ac mains has a 1:1 turns ratio (see Figure 19-11), and is called an *isolation transformer*. Its job is to provide 120 V ac on its secondary winding while providing electrical isolation from the ac mains.

When you measure the output voltage, you find 25 volts across the secondary winding. What is the turns ratio of your transformer?

Again, we use Equation 19-1. We don't know how many turns there are on either the primary or the secondary, so we can only calculate the ratio of primary to secondary turns.

$$\frac{N_P}{N_S} = \frac{E_P}{E_S} \qquad \text{(Equation 19-1)}$$

$$\frac{N_P}{N_S} = \frac{120 \text{ V}}{25 \text{ V}} = 4.8$$

There are 4.8 times as many turns on the primary as there are on the secondary. Congratulations! You may be able to use your bargain transformer

as part of a low-voltage power supply project.

There are step-down transformers in your neighborhood. If you have utility poles near your house, holding electrical power wires, telephone wires (and sometimes fiber optic cables), and cable TV fiber or *coaxial* cables, look carefully at the top of the poles. The wires furthest from the ground (and from people — for safety) are called the *primary* conductors, and the voltage between them may be 23,000 volts ac. They are extremely dangerous if they are knocked to the ground by a tree limb during a storm. Your house requires 120 V ac, and some utility poles will have a big gray can (about the size of a garbage can) up near the primary conductors. You guessed it — this is a step-down transformer, filled with copper wires (the primary and secondary windings), iron (the magnetic core of the transformer), and oil (to insulate and cool the conductors).

If your house has its utility services (electrical power, telephone and cable TV) underground, look carefully around your house and neighborhood. There likely will be a concrete slab somewhere near the street with a large metal enclosure. The enclosure houses a step-down transformer to transform the 23,000 V ac to the 120 V ac for your house.

Figure 19-11 — This test setup shows how you might test an unknown transformer to measure the output voltage. The fuses provide some protection against a short-circuit in the transformer. Be sure you insulate all connections to prevent accidental contact with the 120-V house current. You should not attempt a measurement like this until you are very familiar with proper test procedures and safety practices.

Isolation Transformer

120 V Primary

120 V Secondary

1 Amp Fuse

1 Amp Fuse

P   S

V

UBE0217

Transformers Change Current Levels, Too

You can change from just about any ac voltage to any other voltage using a transformer. Transformers transfer electrical energy from the primary winding to the secondary winding. If the secondary winding has more turns than the primary winding, you have a *step-up transformer*. The secondary voltage is greater than the primary voltage. If the secondary winding has fewer turns than the primary, you have a *step-down transformer*. In this case the secondary voltage is less than the primary voltage.

You may have thought, up to this point, that a transformer is some kind of a miracle device because it can increase voltage. But it's no more a miracle device than a see-saw (in a playground), or a claw hammer used to pull a nail from a piece of wood.

Let's look at a see-saw. A big person sits on the left, and a small person sits on the right. *If* the pivot point of the see-saw is located at exactly the right point between the two people, the small person can lift the big person. Is this a miracle, or is it using a *lever*, a mechanical machine, to increase the force of the small person? And there's no free lunch involved here. If the small person wants to lift the big person off the ground by 12 inches, then the small person must press down through a distance *more than* 12 inches. So the see-saw increases (steps up) force, but in doing so it decreases (steps down) the distance. See **Figure 19-12**.

The law of conservation of energy is a fundamental natural law that all transformers must obey. According to this law, the amount of energy in a system must remain constant. We can neither create nor destroy energy. We can change energy from one form to another.

This law tells us we can't get more energy out of the transformer

Figure 19-12 — Part A shows a lever, a simple mechanical machine, constructed with a board and a fulcrum (the pivot point for the board). There is an input force (force you apply) and an output force (force you produce). Part A shows a see-saw, with the fulcrum in the middle, with equal input force and output force. Part B, where the fulcrum is moved closer to the output force, shows that a smaller input force will result in a larger output force. The lever can be thought of as a mechanical "step-up" transformer for force.

secondary than we put into the primary. A real transformer will change some of the input energy into heat in the wires and core material. It takes some energy to overcome the wire resistance, which shows up as heat energy in the wire. It also takes some energy to magnetize the core material, and this appears as heat energy in the transformer core. The electrical energy converted to heat represents a *loss of electrical energy*, but not *lost energy*.

Power measures the rate of using energy. We calculate power by multiplying current times voltage. Let's use power to consider conservation of energy with a transformer.

We can calculate a transformer's input power by measuring the primary voltage and current. Equation 19-2 is a mathematical expression for transformer input power.

$$P_{in} = I_P \times E_P \qquad \text{(Equation 19-2)}$$

where:
P_{in} is the input or primary circuit power
I_P is the primary current
E_P is the primary voltage

Equation 19-3, which is similar to Equation 19-2, shows us how to calculate the transformer output power. The subscripts on these symbols represent output power and secondary current and voltage.

$$P_{out} = I_S \times E_S \qquad \text{(Equation 19-3)}$$

We will simplify the analysis by assuming we have a perfect, or *ideal*, transformer. There is no wire resistance, and it doesn't take any energy to magnetize the core material. Therefore, there is no electrical energy lost in the transformer. The law of conservation of energy tells us that the input power must be equal to the output power. Equation 19-2 must equal Equation 19-3.

$$P_{in} = P_{out} \qquad \text{(Equation 19-4)}$$

We also can write this equation using the voltage and current terms.

$$I_P \times E_P = I_S \times E_S \qquad \text{(Equation 19-5)}$$

Of course, *real* transformers will have some resistance in the primary and secondary windings, and it will take some energy to magnetize the core material. They will always convert some of the input power to heat, then. The output power will always be a little less than the input power for a real transformer.

Look at Equation 19-5 again. The products of voltage and current must remain equal. A step-up transformer increases the voltage, so the available current at the output must decrease. A step-down transformer decreases the voltage, which means the secondary current is larger than the primary current. Voltage and current are *inversely related*. An increase of one results in a decrease of the other.

Let's rewrite Equation 19-5, putting the voltage terms on one side of the equal sign and the current terms on the other side. Cross multiply the terms to rewrite the equation.

$$\frac{E_P}{E_S} = \frac{I_S}{I_P} \qquad \text{(Equation 19-6)}$$

You may remember that the ratio of primary voltage divided by secondary voltage equals the number of turns on the primary divided by the number of turns on the

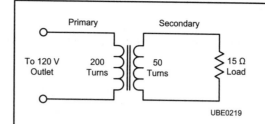

Figure 19-13 — This transformer changes the 120-V house current to 30 volts. As the text explains, the transformer draws 0.5 A from the 120-V outlet. The secondary circuit draws 2 amps.

secondary. Equation 19-7 shows this mathematically.

$$\frac{E_P}{E_S} = \frac{N_P}{N_S} \qquad \text{(Equation 19-7)}$$

Now we have a way to compare the transformer turns ratio with the current. Replace the primary-to-secondary voltage ratio in Equation 19-6 with the expression for the primary-to-secondary turns ratio from Equation 19-7.

$$\frac{N_P}{N_S} = \frac{I_S}{I_P} \qquad \text{(Equation 19-8)}$$

Notice the primary and secondary currents have the opposite order from the number of turns in the windings. This is an *inverse* relationship. The winding with more turns must carry a smaller current. This indicates that you should use larger-diameter wire for the winding with fewer turns. You can use smaller-diameter wire for the winding with more turns.

The wire size determines how much current the transformer can safely handle. Remember that smaller-diameter wire has more resistance. This is a design trade-off you must be aware of when you select a transformer for a particular application. A transformer made with smaller wire will be physically smaller (and less expensive). One made with larger wire can carry more current. So you must decide how much current the secondary will require, and allow a safety factor. Then select a transformer rated to handle the desired current.

Figure 19-13 shows a step-down transformer connected to a load that

draws 2 amperes. This transformer has 200 turns on the primary winding and 50 turns on the secondary winding. How much current will the primary draw from the wall outlet? Use Equation 19-8 to calculate the current.

$$\frac{N_P}{N_S} = \frac{I_S}{I_P} \qquad \text{(Equation 19-8)}$$

$$\frac{200}{50} = 4 = \frac{2\,A}{I_P}$$

Cross multiply to solve this equation for the primary current, I_P.

$$I_P = \frac{2\,A}{4} = 0.5\,A$$

Another transformer has a turns ratio of 5.5 to 1. That means the primary winding has 5.5 times as many turns as the secondary. How much current can you draw from the secondary, if the transformer primary can handle 4 amperes? Again, we will use Equation 19-8 to calculate this current.

$$\frac{N_P}{N_S} = \frac{I_S}{I_P} \qquad \text{(Equation 19-8)}$$

$$5.5 = \frac{I_S}{4\,A}$$

$$5.5 \times 4\,A = I_S = 22\,A$$

These examples show the important relationship between a transformer's primary and secondary voltages and currents. Transformers have many applications in electronic circuits. We usually think of transformers as devices that change between voltage levels. The current available from a transformer also changes.

Review Questions

19.1 When the magnetic field from one coil cuts through another coil, the coils have:
a) magnetic shielding
b) mutual inductance
c) linked loops
d) become good friends

19.2 To induce a voltage in a coil using a permanent magnet, which one of the following is true?
a) the magnet must be near the coil
b) the north pole of the magnet has to be used
c) the magnet must be inside the coil
d) the magnet or the coil must move relative to the other

19.3 Elwood connects a 1.5-volt "D" cell to the primary winding of a transformer, and is disappointed to find that there is no output voltage across the secondary winding. What would you say to Elwood to help him understand why there is no output?

19.4 Toroidal transformer cores are:
a) used only for step-up transformers
b) used only for step-down transformers
c) donut-shaped, and used for RF transformers
d) quite edible

19.5 A transformer has 1000 turns on the primary winding, and 250 turns on the secondary winding. This transformer is:
a) a step-down transformer
b) a step-up transformer
c) an isolation transformer
d) has a turns ratio of 1250:1

19.6 If the transformer in the question above had 100 volts applied to the primary winding, solve for the voltage across the secondary winding.

19.7 A step-up transformer:
a) has more output power than input power
b) will have more current in the secondary than in the primary
c) is located on the highest step of a stairway
d) will have less current in the secondary than in the primary

Answers

19.1 b

19.2 d

19.3 In order to have an induced voltage in any inductor, the magnetic field must be changing. The "D" cell provides a constant voltage, and current, to the primary winding. The constant (dc) current *does* create a magnetic field, but since it is not changing, there is no induced voltage in the secondary winding.

19.4 c

19.5 a

19.6 $\dfrac{1000}{250} = \dfrac{100 \text{ V}}{E_S}$

$\dfrac{4}{1} = \dfrac{100 \text{ V}}{E_S}$

$E_s = 25$ volts

19.7 d

Chapter 20

Impedance

Impedance is a term used to describe a combination of resistance and reactance in a circuit.

Contents

Ohm's Law Applies to AC Circuits, Too

Figure 20-1 shows a 12-volt battery connected to a 1200-ohm resistor. We can use Ohm's Law to calculate the current that flows in this circuit. Equation 20-1 gives Ohm's Law as a mathematical equation.

$$E = I R \qquad \text{(Equation 20-1)}$$

where:

    E is the voltage applied to the circuit

    I is the current through the circuit

    R is the circuit resistance, or opposition to current

We want to calculate the current, so we must solve this equation for I.

$$I = \frac{E}{R} \qquad \text{(Equation 20-2)}$$

$$I = \frac{12 \text{ V}}{1200 \text{ } \Omega} = 0.01 \text{ A}$$

You might want to write this current in milliamperes instead of amperes.

$$I = 10 \text{ mA}$$

Now, let's replace the Figure 20-1 battery with a sine-wave alternating-voltage source. **Figure 20-2** shows this new circuit. The sine-wave generator produces an *effective* output of 12 volts. The effective voltage of 12 V of the ac source is equal to the voltage of a dc source that would provide the same power to R1, the 1200 Ω resistor.

Remember that another name for the *effective value* of an ac waveform is *RMS*. RMS stands for the *root of* the *mean* of the *square*. The signal generator in this problem produces a 12 V RMS output. **Figure 20-3** is a graph of the waveform, with labels to identify the peak, peak-to-peak and RMS values. Notice the peak value is 1.414 times the RMS value, or 16.97 volts. The peak-to-peak value is twice the peak value, 33.94 volts.

Simply stated, the ac waveform voltage varies continuously, and while it reaches a peak of 16.97 V, it spends most of the time of a full cycle less than that. In fact, it has a value of 0 V twice each cycle. So the RMS or effective value of 12 V is the voltage of a constant dc source that would heat R1 the same as the sine ac voltage.

Which voltage should we use to calculate the circuit current? Well, we can use any of the values, as long as we specify the measurement used to make the calculation. Let's use Ohm's Law to calculate the RMS current, peak current and peak-to-peak current through this circuit. Equation 20-2 gives current.

$$I = \frac{E}{R} \qquad \text{(Equation 20-2)}$$

$$I_{RMS} = \frac{E_{RMS}}{R} = \frac{12 \text{ V RMS}}{1200 \text{ } \Omega}$$

$$I_{RMS} = 0.01 \text{ A RMS} = 10 \text{ mA RMS}$$

$$I_{peak} = \frac{E_{peak}}{R} = \frac{16.97 \text{ V peak}}{1200 \text{ } \Omega}$$

$$I_{peak} = 0.01414 \text{ A peak} = 14.14 \text{ mA peak}$$

$$I_{peak\text{-}to\text{-}peak} = \frac{E_{peak\text{-}to\text{-}peak}}{R} = \frac{33.94 \text{ V peak-to-peak}}{1200 \text{ } \Omega}$$

Figure 20-1 — We use Ohm's Law to calculate the current through this dc circuit.

UBE0220

Sine-wave Signal Generator — R1 — 1200 Ω

UBE0221

Figure 20-2 — We can calculate the alternating current through a resistor using Ohm's Law. Specify RMS, peak or peak-to-peak voltage to calculate the corresponding current value.

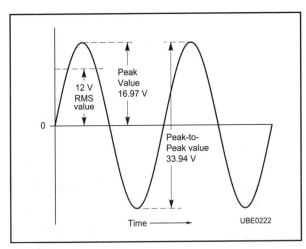

Figure 20-3 — Labels on this sine-wave graph point out the RMS, peak and peak-to-peak values.

Figure 20-4 — This ac signal generator supplies a 2-volt sine-wave output signal to the inductor. The text explains how to calculate the circuit current using Ohm's Law. Inductive reactance is a measure of the opposition to current through the inductor.

Figure 20-5 — This ac signal generator produces a 2-volt sine-wave signal, which we apply to a capacitor. Capacitive reactance is a measure of the opposition to current through a capacitor. The text explains how to calculate the circuit current using Ohm's Law.

$I_{\text{peak-to-peak}} = 0.02828$ A peak-to-peak

$I_{\text{peak-to-peak}} = 28.28$ mA peak-to-peak

Were you surprised to discover the peak current is 1.414 times the RMS current? You could probably have predicted the peak-to-peak current value without even using Ohm's Law, once you calculated the peak current.

Ohm's Law works with ac signals just as it does with dc voltages and currents. You must be careful to specify whether the value you calculate is an RMS or peak value, however. Most of the time we work with RMS values of ac signals. It isn't always necessary to write RMS, then. When we don't specify a measurement type, it is understood to be an RMS measurement.

Resistors aren't the only devices in an electronics circuit that oppose current. Inductors and capacitors also oppose alternating currents. This opposition depends on the frequency of the ac signal voltage. We call the opposition to current *reactance*. Equation 20-3 will remind you how to calculate *inductive reactance*, X_L.

$X_L = 2 \pi f L$ \hspace{1cm} (Equation 20-3)

where:
   π is a constant approximately equal to 3.14
   f is the signal frequency, in hertz
   L is the inductance, in henrys

If you aren't familiar with this equation, you should review the chapters on inductors and inductive reactance.

Figure 20-4 shows a circuit that has a sine-wave signal generator and

a 50 millihenry inductor. Let's set the output frequency to 5000 hertz. The generator produces a 2-volt output signal. What is the current through this circuit? We can use Ohm's Law to answer this question, but first we'll have to calculate the inductive reactance. Since inductive reactance is the opposition an inductor has to ac, this will take the place of resistance in Ohm's Law.

Use Equation 20-3 to calculate the inductive reactance.

$X_L = 2 \pi f L$ \hspace{1cm} (Equation 20-3)

$X_L = 2 \times 3.14 \times 5000$ Hz $\times$ 50×10^{-3} H

$X_L = 1570 \ \Omega$

Now use this reactance instead of resistance in Equation 20-2, Ohm's Law.

$$I = \frac{E}{X_L}$$

$$I = \frac{2 \text{ V}}{1570 \ \Omega} = 1.27 \times 10^{-3} \text{A}$$

$I = 1.27$ mA

What will happen if we reduce the generator frequency to 2500 hertz? The inductive reactance will have a new value, and that will cause the current to change. Let's calculate this new inductive reactance and the new current. (The voltage output from our generator stays at 2 volts.)

$X_L = 2 \pi f L$
   $= 2 \times 3.14 \times 2500$ Hz $\times 50 \times 10^{-3}$ H

$X_L = 785 \ \Omega$

$$I = \frac{E}{X_L} = \frac{2 \text{ V}}{785 \ \Omega} = 2.55 \times 10^{-3} \text{A}$$

$I = 2.55$ mA

Figure 20-5 shows a 0.02028 µF capacitor connected to our signal generator. We set the generator frequency to 5000 Hz again. The output voltage is 2 volts. What is the current through this circuit?

Capacitive reactance is a capacitor's opposition to alternating current. Equation 20-4 will remind you how to calculate capacitive reactance, X_C.

$$X_C = \frac{1}{2 \pi f C}$$ \hspace{1cm} (Equation 20-4)

where:
   π is a constant approximately equal to 3.14
   f is the signal frequency, in hertz
   C is the capacitance, in farads

Capacitive reactance takes the place of resistance in Ohm's Law to calculate the current in the Figure 20-5 circuit. Before we can use Equation 20-2 to calculate the current, we must calculate the capacitive reactance.

$$X_C = \frac{1}{2 \pi f C}$$

$$X_C = \frac{1}{2 \times 3.14 \times 5000 \text{ Hz} \times 0.02028 \times 10^{-6} \text{ F}}$$

$$X_C = \frac{1}{6.368 \times 10^{-4}} = 1570 \ \Omega$$

Now we can use Equation 20-2 to calculate the current in our circuit.

$$I = \frac{E}{X_C} \qquad \text{(Equation 20-2)}$$

$$I = \frac{2\,V}{1570\,\Omega} = 1.27 \times 10^{-3}\,A$$

$$I = 1.27\ mA$$

Suppose the generator frequency changes to 2500 Hz. As an additional practice exercise, prove that the current through the revised circuit becomes 0.637 mA. (Hint: You must calculate the new capacitive reactance first.)

Inductive reactance and capacitive reactance are not the same as resistance. We use them in place of resistance in Ohm's Law to calculate the current through an inductor or capacitor. We use the term *impedance* to mean either resistance or reactance, or some combination of both.

Imagine a circuit that includes a resistor and inductor or capacitor in series with a signal generator. Resistance and reactance are not the same, so you can't just add the values like you would with two resistors. When we talk about circuit impedance, then, we use a general term that may mean resistance, reactance or some combination of these quantities. You will learn more about circuit impedance, and calculations involving impedance, in the next few sections.

Voltage and Current Peaks May Not Occur at the Same Time

Ohm's Law relates voltage, current and resistance in circuits that include resistors and voltage sources. The voltage sources can supply direct or alternating current.

Ohm's Law also relates voltage, current and reactance in circuits that include only voltage sources and capacitors or inductors. Most circuits that include capacitors or inductors will have alternating voltage sources.

Do you remember what happens if you feed a dc signal through a capacitor? There is current for a short time, until the capacitor charges to the full applied voltage. Then the current stops. There is a large current at first, but it quickly decreases as the capacitor charges. We won't try to calculate this changing direct current. The math is a bit beyond the scope of this book. So we will only consider alternating current through capacitors.

Ideal inductors present no opposition to steady direct current. An inductor is a short circuit to a steady direct current. Only resistance of the wire used to make the inductor limits the current in this case. We will only calculate the current through inductors with an alternating voltage source applied in this book.

Suppose we apply an alternating voltage to a resistor, as the **Figure 20-6A** circuit shows. The sine-wave signal begins to increase from 0 volts. The current through the resistor increases when the voltage increases. When the applied signal reaches its maximum voltage, the current also reaches maximum value. Figure 20-6B shows the current and voltage waveforms for this circuit.

These signals have the same frequency and reach their positive peak values at the same time. We say the waves are *in phase* if they meet those conditions. *Phase* refers to time, such as the time between two events that repeat at regular intervals.

Each ac cycle takes exactly the

Figure 20-6 — This simple circuit illustrates the phase relationship between the alternating voltage applied to a resistor and the current through the resistor. Part B shows the voltage and current waveforms. Notice the waveforms are in phase.

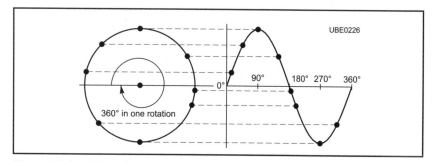

Figure 20-7 — We often relate each cycle of a waveform to a single rotation of a wheel. Each point along the waveform corresponds to a rotation angle on the wheel. There are 360° in one complete cycle. We use an angle measurement to indicate the phase between two waveforms.

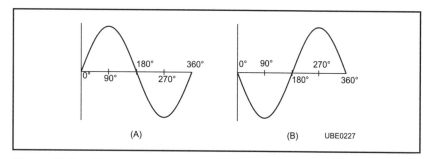

Figure 20-8 — These two waveforms appear to be exact opposites. When the waveform at A reaches its positive peak the waveform at B reaches its negative peak. We say the two waves are 180° out of phase.

same time as any other cycle of the same frequency. We relate one cycle to a single rotation of a wheel, or an angle of 360°. **Figure 20-7** shows how the various positions of a sine-wave signal relate to one rotation of

a wheel. By using an angle related to wheel rotation we can make phase measurements that don't depend on the actual wave frequency.

When current flows through a resistor, the resistor converts some of the electrical energy into heat energy. Capacitors and inductors store electrical energy when current flows through them. Ideal inductors and capacitors don't convert any electrical energy to heat energy, however. (Real inductors and capacitors do convert some energy to heat, but this should be a small amount. We'll ignore it for now.)

One result of this energy storage is that the voltage and current waveforms are *not in phase*. Sometimes we say these waves are *out of phase*.

Figure 20-8 illustrates two waveforms that are out of phase. The waveform at Part A reaches its positive peak at the same time as the Part B waveform reaches its negative peak. In this example, the waveforms are ½ cycle different, or 180° out of phase. Notice that we labeled the horizontal, or X axis in degrees instead of time.

You can measure a phase angle between any two waveforms of the same frequency. The waveforms can have any phase relationship between 0° and 360°. The waveforms are in phase only if the phase angle is 0° (or 360°).

The phase angle between the voltage and current in a circuit is 0° if the circuit only includes voltage sources and resistors. If the circuit includes capacitors or inductors, the phase angle will be larger than 0°. The phase angle depends on the amount of reactance and the amount of resistance in the circuit. Later in this chapter you will learn how to calculate the phase angle.

Voltage and Current in a Capacitor

Capacitive reactance is the opposition a capacitor has to alternating current flowing through it. At low frequencies the reactance is large, and it decreases as the frequency increases. When we apply an alternating voltage across a capacitor, the increasing voltage stores energy as an electric field. The capacitor returns that energy to the circuit when the voltage decreases.

Figure 20-9 shows a circuit with an ac signal generator and a capacitor. We can replace resistance with reactance in Ohm's Law to calculate current or voltage in a circuit like this one.

Let's review what happens when we apply an alternating voltage to a capacitor. We'll start with the voltage at zero, as it increases toward its maximum value. There is no charge stored on the capacitor when its voltage is zero, so a large current is needed to charge it as its voltage rapidly increases. As electrons build up on the negative capacitor plate, this charge tries to prevent more electrons from moving onto the plate. The current decreases as a result. By the time the voltage increases to its maximum value, the capacitor charges to this full voltage, and the current stops.

Next the applied voltage begins to decrease. The capacitor voltage is larger than the applied voltage, so electrons move off the negative capacitor plate. This changes the current direction. As the applied voltage decreases to zero, the capacitor current increases, draining all the charge off the capacitor plates. **Figure 20-10** is a graph showing these voltage and current relationships.

The second half of the applied-voltage cycle repeats the first half, but with opposite polarities. As the voltage increases toward the negative peak, there is a large current to charge the capacitor. This current drops to

Figure 20-9 — We will use this circuit to study the voltage and current relationship in a capacitor. When the circuit includes only voltage sources and capacitors, we can use capacitive reactance instead of resistance in Ohm's Law.

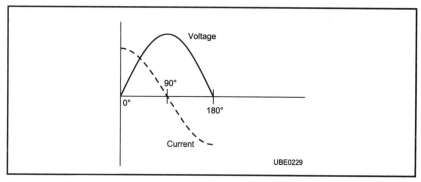

Figure 20-10 — This graph shows how the current through a capacitor varies during the positive half cycle of applied voltage. We drew the voltage waveform as a solid line and the current waveform as a dashed line. We did not include a voltage or current amplitude scale on the graph. The two waveforms have different amplitudes so it is easier for you to distinguish the two curves.

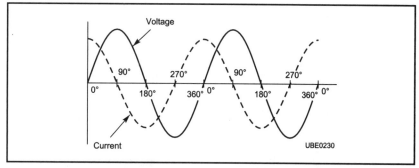

Figure 20-11 — This graph shows how the current varies during two complete cycles of the voltage waveform. The solid and dashed lines and different amplitudes will help you distinguish between the voltage and current waveforms.

zero when the voltage reaches its negative peak. When the voltage begins to decrease toward zero again, the current direction reverses. The current increases to its maximum value when the voltage reaches zero. **Figure 20-11** graphs two complete voltage and current cycles.

What is the phase relationship between the voltage across a capacitor and the current through it? Study Figure 20-11. Notice when the voltage waveform is at zero, beginning its positive half cycle, the current waveform is already at its positive maximum. When the voltage waveform reaches its positive peak the current waveform has already dropped to zero. By the time the current waveform reaches its negative peak the voltage waveform has only decreased to zero from its positive peak.

These waveforms are 90° out of phase. Measure the angle between the positive peaks or between the zero crossing points as the waveforms go from positive to negative. You will measure the same angle between the negative peaks of both waveforms. You also can measure the phase angle between the zero crossings as the waves go from negative to positive. Do you have to measure phase angle only at these points? No, you can measure phase angle from any point on a waveform, as long as you measure to the same point on the other waveform. The waveform peaks and zero crossings provide convenient reference points, however.

Did you notice that the current waveform reaches each point 90° before the voltage waveform? Figure 20-11 shows the current waveform first reaches its peak positive value at 0°. The voltage waveform doesn't reach its peak positive value until 90°. The current waveform reaches its peak negative value at 180°. The voltage waveform doesn't reach its peak negative point until 270°, which is 90° later than the current.

From these observations, you can understand why we say the current *leads* the voltage in a capacitor. We sometimes also say the voltage *lags* the current. Both statements mean the same thing. This is an important relationship.

Earlier we mentioned that the applied voltage stores electrical energy in an electric field. This field starts at zero when the voltage is zero. The field strength increases as the voltage increases, and it reaches a maximum when the voltage reaches its peak value. The electric field decreases as the energy returns to the circuit when the voltage decreases. So the electric field has a waveform that matches the applied voltage waveform. The electric field and the applied voltage are in phase.

Voltage and Current in an Inductor

Inductors oppose alternating current. We call this opposition inductive reactance. Inductive reactance is low at low frequencies and increases as the frequency increases. When alternating current flows through an inductor, the inductor stores some electrical energy as a magnetic field around the inductor.

The circuit of **Figure 20-12** includes an alternating current source and an inductor. We can replace resistance with inductive reactance in Ohm's Law to calculate current or voltage in a circuit like this.

Let's put an alternating current through an ideal inductor and review what happens. We'll start when the current is zero, just beginning to increase toward its positive peak value. The increasing current causes a magnetic field to build up around the inductor, storing energy. The current increases rapidly at this point, so the magnetic field strength also increases rapidly.

When the current through the coil reaches a positive peak and begins to decrease, the energy stored in the inductor reaches a maximum. As the current decreases, the magnetic field collapses, returning its energy to the circuit. When the current crosses zero the magnetic field returns all its energy, and the field strength also becomes zero.

Next the current direction reverses, and the current increases toward its peak negative value. The magnetic field direction also reverses, storing energy again. The magnetic field strength continues to increase until the current reaches its peak negative value. Then the current decreases again, and the inductor returns the energy stored in it as the magnetic field collapses.

Figure 20-13 is a graph of the current through an inductor and the magnetic field strength around the inductor. The magnetic field around

Figure 20-12 — This alternating signal generator feeds current through the inductor. This ideal circuit does not include any resistance. The inductor stores electrical energy as a magnetic field as the current through it increases. The inductor returns all this energy to the circuit as the current decreases. The process repeats each half cycle.

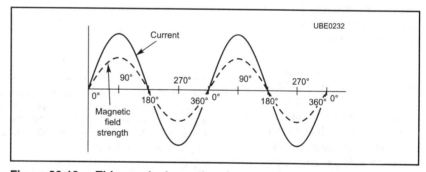

Figure 20-13 — This graph shows that the magnetic field strength around an inductor increases when the current increases. The magnetic field decreases when the current decreases. If the current reverses direction, the magnetic field direction also reverses. The magnetic field is in phase with the current through the inductor.

an inductor is in phase with the current through the inductor. Similar points on both waveforms occur at the same time.

Remember that a changing magnetic field induces a voltage across the inductor. The voltage depends on how fast the magnetic field changes. It is largest when the magnetic field changes fastest. A slowly changing magnetic field induces a small voltage. If the magnetic field doesn't change, it doesn't induce a voltage.

The current changes quickly when it starts at zero and begins to flow in either direction. The magnetic

field also is changing the most at this point. This is when the induced voltage has its maximum value. When the current (and magnetic field) reaches its maximum in either direction, there is a brief instant when it doesn't change. At this instant the induced voltage is zero.

The induced voltage always has a polarity that opposes the changing current. The induced voltage tries to maintain a steady, unchanging current. This means that when the current is in the positive direction, the induced voltage has a negative polarity!

Figure 20-14 graphs the current

through an inductor and the voltage induced across the inductor. Notice that as the current increases toward its peak *positive* value the induced voltage is decreasing from its peak *negative* value. The induced voltage becomes zero when the current reaches its peak value. As the current decreases from this peak value, the induced voltage becomes positive. (The positive induced voltage tries to prevent the current from decreasing.) As you can see from Figure 20-14, the induced voltage *lags* the current by 90°. (We also can say the current *leads* the induced voltage by 90°.)

You probably noticed that we haven't mentioned the *applied voltage* yet. You know the current source applies a voltage to the inductor to force current through it. The applied voltage is not in phase with the current through the inductor. The current produces the magnetic field around the inductor. The changing magnetic field induces the *back EMF*, as we sometimes call it.

The applied voltage tries to produce current through the inductor and the induced voltage tries to prevent it. This means the applied voltage and the induced voltage are trying to accomplish opposite goals. If the two voltages are opposite each other, that means they are 180° out of phase! **Figure 20-15** graphs current, applied voltage and induced voltage for an inductor.

Let's look at the phase relationship between the *applied voltage* and the current through an inductor. This is the relationship we're most often interested in when we discuss the phase relationship between voltage

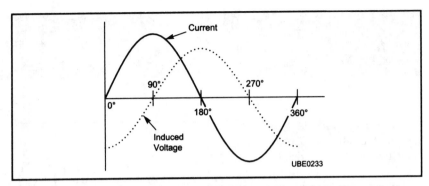

Figure 20-14 — A heavy solid line on this graph represents the current through an inductor. A dotted line represents the voltage induced across the inductor by the changing magnetic field. Notice the induced voltage lags the current by 90°. (The current leads the induced voltage by 90°.)

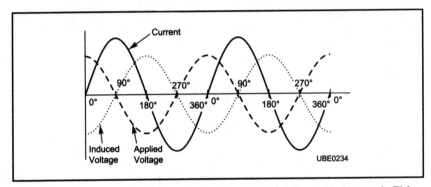

Figure 20-15 — Here we add a dashed line to the Figure 20-14 graph. This new line represents the applied voltage across an inductor. The applied voltage and the induced voltage are 180° out of phase. The applied voltage leads the current by 90°. We also can say the current lags the applied voltage by 90°.

and current for an inductor.

Figure 20-15 shows the applied voltage reaching its peak positive value at 0°. The current reaches its peak positive value at 90°. You also can see that the voltage reaches its peak negative value at 180° and the current reaches its peak negative value at 270°. This means the applied voltage is 90° ahead of the current. The applied voltage *leads* the current through an inductor by 90°. We also can say the current *lags* the applied voltage by 90°.

Circuit Reactance with Inductors and Capacitors

When we apply an alternating voltage to a capacitor there is a current that leads the voltage by 90°. An alternating voltage applied to an inductor produces a current that lags the voltage by 90°. An ac voltage applied to a resistor creates a current that is in phase with the applied voltage.

Figure 20-16 is a circuit that includes an alternating voltage source, a capacitor and an inductor. Let's see what we can determine about the voltage applied to each component and the current through it.

Is the Figure 20-16 circuit a *series circuit* or a *parallel circuit*? All the current that leaves the signal generator flows through each component to get back to the generator. There are no branches for the current to select an alternate path. Therefore, this is a series circuit.

The same current flows through each part of a series circuit. From this information, we conclude that the current through the capacitor is in phase with the current through the inductor. The voltages across each component are not in phase, however. In fact, the voltages are 180° out of phase! How do we know this? **Figure 20-17** will help you understand.

We begin drawing Figure 20-17 by forming a set of X-Y coordinates, as shown in Part A. We also mark the coordinates as a set of polar coordinates, with 0° to the right, and 90° to the top.

Next we mark the capacitor and inductor voltages on our graph. We'll calculate these voltages using Ohm's Law and the component reactance. For this example, we'll assume the ac ammeter reads 1 ampere. Figure 20-16 shows the reactances of the inductor and capacitor. Remember this represents the reactance at one frequency, the signal generator's output frequency. Both reactances

Figure 20-16 — We'll use this circuit to study the combined effects of capacitive reactance and inductive reactance on a circuit. The reactance values apply to one output frequency from the generator. Although we don't know what that frequency is, we don't need that value for our calculations. The ac ammeter measures a 1-ampere current through the circuit.

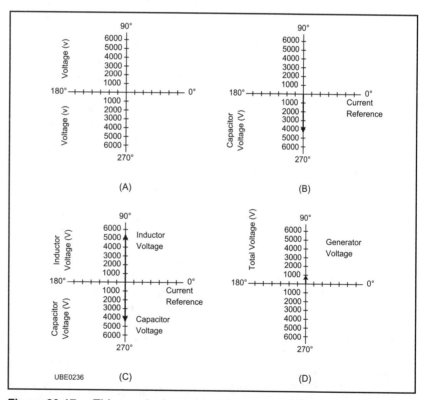

Figure 20-17 — This graph shows how we can represent series circuit voltages across inductors and capacitors. We measure angles starting from the right side of the X axis, and go counterclockwise. We drew the capacitor voltage along the 270° line because this voltage lags the circuit current by 90°. We use the 90° line for the inductor voltage, indicating this voltage leads the circuit current by 90°. We find the total generator voltage by subtracting the capacitor voltage from the inductor voltage. Part D shows this total combined voltage as 1000 volts.

will be different at other frequencies.

Let's calculate the capacitor voltage first. A 1-ampere current flows through a 4500-ohm reactance. Multiply these values to calculate the voltage.

$$E = I R \qquad \text{(Equation 20-5)}$$

$$E = I X_C = 1 \text{ A} \times 4500 \text{ }\Omega$$

$$E = 4500 \text{ volts}$$

The voltage across a capacitor lags the current by 90°. If we let 0° represent the current, we must draw the capacitor voltage at 270°. That puts the capacitor voltage 90° behind the current. Figure 20-17B shows the capacitor voltage added to our graph.

Next we'll calculate the inductor voltage. The same 1-ampere current flows through the inductor. Figure 20-16 shows the inductive reactance as 5500 ohms. Once again we multiply these values in Ohm's Law to calculate the voltage applied to the inductor.

$$E = I R \qquad \text{(Equation 20-5)}$$

$$E = I X_L = 1 \text{ A} \times 5500 \text{ }\Omega$$

$$E = 5500 \text{ volts}$$

The voltage applied to an inductor leads the current through the inductor by 90°. So we'll draw the inductor voltage at 90° on our graph. Figure 20-17C shows the inductor voltage added to our graph.

The inductor and capacitor voltages are 180° out of phase. When one reaches its positive peak value the other reaches its negative peak value. We can combine these two voltages to find the total applied voltage. This total voltage is the voltage the signal generator applies to the circuit. The inductor voltage goes in the positive Y direction on our graph. The capacitor voltage goes in the negative Y direction. To combine these values, we subtract! The total applied voltage is 5500 volts minus 4500 volts, or 1000 volts. How can the inductor and capacitor voltages be larger than the total applied voltage? That's one interesting property in a series circuit

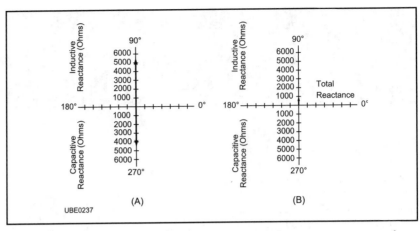

Figure 20-18 — We often represent series circuit reactances on a graph similar to the one from Figure 20-17. Inductive reactance is along the positive Y axis, at 90°. Capacitive reactance is along the negative Y axis, at 270°.

of reactance and the energy stored in the electric field of a capacitor, and the magnetic field of an inductor.

This could never happen in a series circuit with just resistors and no reactances. The sum of the voltages across the individual resistors must equal the applied voltage, because there's no energy storage in a resistor.

The capacitor stores energy in its electric field and then returns it to the circuit. The inductor stores the energy from the capacitor in its magnetic field and returns it to the circuit later. So the capacitor and inductor hand the energy back and forth between them. If there is no resistance (like our ideal circuit of Figure 20-16), this process will continue forever.

If you think about the mathematics for a moment, you should realize that we can find the applied voltage without calculating the inductor and capacitor voltages first. To do this, we simply combine the two reactances first, and then use this combined value in Ohm's Law.

$$E = I X \qquad \text{(Equation 20-6)}$$

where X is the combined circuit reactance

$$X = X_L - X_C$$

$$X = 5500 \text{ }\Omega - 4500 \text{ }\Omega = 1000 \text{ }\Omega$$

$$E = 1 \text{ A} \times 1000 \text{ }\Omega = 1000 \text{ V}$$

Why do we subtract capacitive reactance from inductive reactance? Why not subtract inductive reactance from capacitive reactance? Did we just select the larger value to start? No. Take another look at Figure 20-17D. We drew the capacitor voltage in the negative Y direction because this voltage lags the current by 90°.

Whenever we connect capacitors and inductors in *series*, we draw the capacitor voltage in the negative Y direction. We draw the inductor voltage in the positive Y direction.

We often use a similar graph to represent resistance and reactance on a graph. We draw resistance along the 0° line, or in the positive X direction. Inductive reactance is along the 90° line or the positive Y direction. Capacitive reactance is along the 270° line or the negative Y direction. See **Figure 20-18**.

The total reactance in this example is in the positive direction. This means there is more inductive reactance in the circuit than capacitive reactance. It also means the total voltage leads the circuit current by 90°. Remember, this can change if frequency changes. It's possible for there to be more capacitive reactance than inductive reactance at a different frequency, in which case the total voltage would *lag* the circuit current by 90°. Do you know if this could happen at a higher frequency, or a lower frequency? Think about how X_L and X_C vary with changes in frequency. If you thought there would be more capacitive reactance than inductive reactance at a *lower* frequency, you're right!

A circuit containing just an inductor and a capacitor, with no resistance, can't exist in reality. Even without a resistor in the circuit, a real inductor, made with windings of copper wire, has resistance within it. We've neglected the resistance of the inductor in the example above. However, in the next chapter, we'll look at a real circuit which takes into account having a resistor in series with the inductor and the capacitor.

Math and Calculator Hints

MATH HINTS

For more background on math, refer to **Appendix A — Scientific and Engineering Notation**.

CALCULATOR HINTS

The following example shows how to use your TI-30X IIS calculator to solve equations like those in Chapter 20. Simpler numbers are used, so they will all be visible in the display of the calculator at the same time. For more information on using a calculator to work these examples, refer to **Appendix B — Understanding and Using Your TI-30X IIS Scientific Calculator.**

Example

What current flows through a capacitor with a capacitive reactance of 1.570 kΩ when 2 volts are applied across it?

$$I = \frac{E}{X_c}$$

$$I = \frac{2\ V}{1{,}570\ \Omega} = 1.27 \times 10^{-3}\,A = 1.27\ mA$$

Calculator keystrokes

2 ÷ 1 5 7 0 =

The calculator's second display line shows the result: **1.2739 × 10⁻⁰³**

[The result of 1.2739 × 10⁻⁰³ is 1.2739 × 0.001 = 1.274 mA.]

Review Questions

20.1 If an oscilloscope were used to look at the 120 V ac power line, what would it show for the peak voltage?

20.2 At 500 Hz, a capacitor has a reactance of 300 Ω. If the frequency changes to 1000 Hz, its capacitive reactance will be:

a) 300 Ω

b) 150 Ω

c) 600 Ω

d) 500 Ω

20.3 At 500 Hz, an inductor has a reactance of 300 Ω. If the frequency changes to 1000 Hz, its inductive reactance will be:

a) 300 Ω

b) 150 Ω

c) 600 Ω

d) 500 Ω

20.4 A series circuit has the following components: an inductor with 40 Ω of inductive reactance, and a capacitor with 30 Ω of capacitive reactance. What is the total reactance of this series L-C circuit?

20.5 If the circuit above is connected to an ac voltage source so that 1 ampere of current flows, what is the voltage across the inductor, across the capacitor, and across the voltage source?

Answers

20.1 We know that the value of an ac voltage, unless stated otherwise, should be assumed to be the RMS (root mean square) value. $E_{peak} = E_{RMS} \times 1.414 = 120 \text{ V} \times 1.414 = 170 \text{ V}_{peak}$

20.2 b

20.3 c

20.4 Because the inductor voltage leads current by 90°, and capacitor voltage lags current by 90°, the voltages across the L and C are 180° out of phase. Because of this phase relationship, to get the total reactance we must subtract X_C from X_L.

$X_{TOTAL} = X_L - X_C = 40 \text{ Ω} - 30 \text{ Ω} = 10 \text{ Ω}.$

20.5 $E_L = I X_L = 1 \text{ A} \times 40 \text{ Ω} = 40 \text{ V}$

$E_C = I X_C = 1 \text{ A} \times 30 \text{ Ω} = 30 \text{ V}$

$E_{SOURCE} = E_{TOTAL} = I X_{TOTAL} = 1 \text{ A} \times (40 \text{ Ω} - 30 \text{ Ω})$
$= 1 \text{ A} \times (10 \text{ Ω}) = 10 \text{ V}$

Chapter 21

Resonant Circuits — Now We're Having Fun with AC Circuits

These capacitors and inductors in a high-power radio-frequency amplifier are adjusted to form a resonant circuit at a desired operating frequency.

Contents

What Happens if Inductive and Capacitive Reactances are Equal?

Inductive and capacitive reactances both store energy in an electrical circuit, but they have opposite effects on a circuit. The voltage across an inductor is 90° out of phase with the current through the inductor. The current through a capacitor is 90° out of phase with the voltage across it. The voltage leads the current in an inductor and lags the current in a capacitor.

In a *series* LC circuit, the inductor voltage and capacitor voltage are 180° out of phase. The current is the same through the series L and C, so the L voltage leads current by 90°, and the C voltage lags current by 90°. When the L and C voltages are equal in magnitude, they cancel each other, and you might be amazed by the voltages that can exist in a series LC circuit. The L and C voltages are often quite large, and in fact each can be *much* bigger than the voltage applied to the circuit. In fact, they can be Q times bigger (recall the quality factor Q).

For example, a series LC circuit with a Q of 20, with a generator of only 1 volt applied, will have 20 volts across the capacitor and 20 volts across the inductor. Don't worry about this, since the *total voltage* across the L and C adds up to only 1 volt because the two voltages are just about 180° out of phase.

Similar to the *voltages* in a series LC resonant circuit, in a *parallel* LC circuit, the inductor and capacitor *currents* are 180° out of phase. Because the voltage is the same across the parallel L and C, the L current lags this voltage by 90° and the C current leads the voltage by 90°. When the L and C currents are equal in magnitude, they nearly cancel each other and a very interesting situation exists.

The current through the L and the current through the C can each be quite large. In fact, the L and C currents can be much bigger than the current entering the circuit — by a factor of Q, the quality factor of the circuit. Don't worry about the currents in the L and C being so big while the *total current* flowing from the source into the parallel L and C circuit adds up to just about zero. This is because they are 180° out of phase and nearly cancel.

How does inductive reactance change when we decrease the signal frequency? Inductive reactance becomes smaller. What happens to the capacitive reactance when we decrease the signal frequency? Capacitive reactance becomes larger.

If we increase the signal frequency, opposite effects occur to inductive and capacitive reactance. Inductive reactance becomes larger and capacitive reactance becomes smaller when we increase the frequency.

Figure 21-1 includes a graph of inductive reactance for a coil. The straight line shows how inductive reactance increases as we change the signal frequency. Figure 21-1 also includes a graph of capacitive reactance. As we increase the signal frequency, the capacitive reactance decreases. We didn't include a frequency scale or a reactance scale because the exact values are unimportant. For any capacitor and inductor, their reactance lines will cross at only one point.

A special condition occurs when inductive and capacitive reactances are equal. This is true whether you have a series or a parallel circuit. We call this condition *resonance*.

Resonance occurs in many ways in our lives. Think of a tuning fork used by a musician or piano tuner, which always vibrates at the same frequency. Its *resonant frequency* is determined by the thickness and length of the arms of the tuning fork. When you whistle, your mouth forms a resonant chamber, and this determines the pitch (frequency) of the whistling sound. When you push

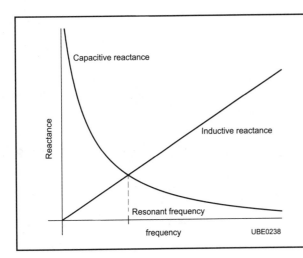

Figure 21-1 — The straight line on this graph represents the inductive reactance for a coil. The reactance increases as the frequency increases. The curved line represents the capacitive reactance for a capacitor. This reactance decreases as the frequency increases. There are no numbers along the X and Y axes because the exact values are unimportant here. We want to show the general shapes of the lines. For a specific inductor and a specific capacitor, there is only one point where the two lines cross. This point represents the resonant frequency of the combination.

Figure 21-2 —This circuit includes an inductor and a variable capacitor. You can change the oscillator operating frequency by adjusting the variable capacitor. Each capacitor setting produces a different resonant frequency in combination with the inductor. You can use this variable-frequency oscillator, or VFO, to set the operating frequency of a simple receiver or transmitter.

a child on a swing, you push once each swing cycle. If you do this at the resonant frequency, the swing (and the child) will reach quite large amplitudes. Your digital watch or clock has a quartz *crystal* in it, vibrating at 32,768 hertz, which determines how well the watch keeps time.

Every combination of inductance and capacitance has a single frequency at which the reactances are equal. This is the *resonant frequency* for that combination.

Resonance occurs when the reactances are equal. We can find an equation to calculate the resonant frequency of any inductor/capacitor pair. Do you remember how to calculate inductive and capacitive reactances? Equations 21-1 and 21-2 will refresh your memory.

$$X_L = 2 \pi f L \qquad \text{(Equation 21-1)}$$

$$X_C = \frac{1}{2 \pi f C} \qquad \text{(Equation 21-2)}$$

We know these values are equal at resonance, so we can set the equations equal to each other. Let's use f_r to represent resonant frequency, the frequency where $X_L = X_C$.

$$X_L = X_C$$

$$2 \pi f_r L = \frac{1}{2 \pi f_r C} \qquad \text{(Equation 21-3)}$$

Now we'll cross multiply and combine terms to simplify the equation.

$$1 = \frac{1}{(2 \pi f_r L)(2 \pi f_r C)}$$

$$1 = \frac{1}{(2 \pi)^2 (f_r)^2 (L C)}$$

$$(f_r)^2 = \frac{1}{(2 \pi)^2 (L C)} \qquad \text{(Equation 21-4)}$$

Finally, take the square root of both sides of the equation.

$$f_r = \frac{1}{2 \pi \sqrt{L C}} \qquad \text{(Equation 21-5)}$$

Let's use Equation 21-5 to calculate a resonant frequency. Suppose you have a 20-picofarad capacitor and a 6.28-microhenry inductor. What is the resonant frequency for these two components? Remember that we must write the inductance value in henrys and the capacitance value in farads for this equation.

$$f_r = \frac{1}{2 \pi \sqrt{L C}}$$

$$f_r =$$

$$\frac{1}{2 \times 3.14 \times \sqrt{6.28 \times 10^{-6} H \times 20 \times 10^{-12} F}}$$

$$f_r = \frac{1}{6.28 \times \sqrt{125.6 \times 10^{-18}}}$$

$$f_r = \frac{1}{6.28 \times (11.2 \times 10^{-9})} = \frac{1}{7.04 \times 10^{-8}}$$

$$f_r = 14.2 \times 10^6 \text{ Hz} = 14.2 \text{ MHz}$$

You can use Equation 21-5 to calculate the resonant frequency for any combination of inductor and capacitor values. You also can solve Equation 21-4 for values of inductance or capacitance. Given either an inductor or a capacitor, you can calculate the other component value to give a desired resonant frequency.

Resonant circuits are important in radio transmitters and receivers. A resonant circuit sets the operating frequency for an oscillator circuit. An oscillator sets the frequency of the signal sent out by a transmitter, and it sets the frequency of the signal received by a receiver. Resonant circuits also help select the desired signal and reject unwanted signals.

Figure 21-2 shows a somewhat complicated resonant circuit in a practical variable-frequency oscillator, or VFO. This circuit might set the operating frequency for a simple receiver or transmitter.

Conditions in a Series Resonant Circuit

Suppose you look around in your collection of used parts, and find a 200 pF capacitor. You also find a 2.44 µH inductor. Let's connect these two parts in series with a 20 Ω resistor and a sine-wave signal generator, and see what happens. **Figure 21-3** shows this circuit. First, we will find its resonant frequency. Equation 21-6 will help us to calculate this value.

$$f_r = \frac{1}{2\pi\sqrt{LC}} \quad \text{(Equation 21-6)}$$

$$f_r =$$

$$\frac{1}{2\times 3.14\times\sqrt{2.44\times 10^{-6}\text{H}\times 200\times 10^{-12}\text{F}}}$$

$$f_r = \frac{1}{6.28\times\sqrt{488\times 10^{-18}}}$$

$$f_r = \frac{1}{6.28\times(22.1\times 10^{-9})} = \frac{1}{1.39\times 10^{-7}}$$

$$f_r = 7.19\times 10^6 \text{ Hz} = 7.19 \text{ MHz}$$

Let's set the signal generator to 7.19 MHz and see what this circuit is doing. What is the current through the circuit if the generator output voltage is 10 V? Remember the inductor voltage and the capacitor voltage are opposite in phase, but equal in magnitude. At the resonant frequency the total circuit impedance is equal to the resistor value, 20 ohms, because the inductor reactance and capacitive reactance, being equal in magnitude, cancel each other. The entire generator voltage is across the resistor at the resonant frequency. Ohm's Law tells us the circuit current.

$$E = IR \quad \text{(Equation 21-7)}$$

$$I = \frac{E}{R} = \frac{10\text{ V}}{20\Omega}$$

$$I = 0.50 \text{ A} = 500 \text{ mA}$$

Let's think about the circuit current at frequencies above and below resonance. Do you think the current will change? Will it increase or decrease?

If we adjust the signal generator to produce a signal at 6.0 MHz, which is lower than the resonant frequency, what will happen to the current? You know the inductive reactance will decrease and the capacitive reactance will increase. At frequencies below the resonant frequency there is more capacitive reactance than inductive reactance. This means the total circuit impedance will increase, and current will be less than it was at the resonant frequency of 7.19 MHz.

As you go still lower in frequency the capacitive reactance becomes larger and the inductive reactance be-

Figure 21-3 — This schematic diagram shows a sine-wave generator connected to a series L-C-R circuit with a 200 pF capacitor, 200 µH inductor, and 20 Ω resistor. We'll use this circuit to see how changing frequency affects the current that flows below, at, and above the resonant frequency.

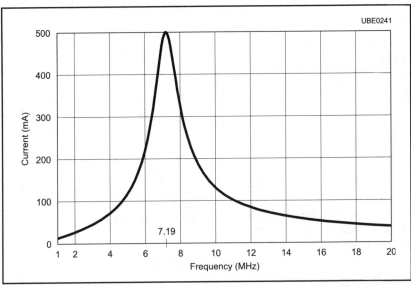

Figure 21-4 — This graph shows how current varies with frequency for the circuit of Figure 21-3, showing the resonant frequency at 7.19 MHz. The circuit with a Q = 11 has a peak current of 1.0 A, while the circuit with a Q = 5.5 has a peak current of 0.5 A (500 mA).

comes smaller. These effects produce a circuit impedance that increases as the frequency decreases. Therefore, the current gets smaller as the frequency decreases.

Now let's consider the effects of increasing the generator frequency above the resonant frequency. Let's adjust the generator for an 8.0 MHz output signal, which is higher than the resonant frequency. This time the inductive reactance increases to a value larger than it was at resonance. The capacitive reactance decreases to a smaller value. Combining these two values we get a net reactance that is inductive, so the total circuit impedance increases and the current is less than it was at the resonant frequency.

The important result of the above discussion is that the current in a series L-C-R circuit is a maximum at the resonant frequency, f_r, and decreases below, and above, f_r.

Figure 21-4 is a graph of the circuit current over a range of frequencies. Notice the shape of this graph. All series RLC circuits (those that include resistance, inductance and capacitance) have a similar current graph. The actual current value depends on the generator voltage and component values. Circuits with less resistance have higher current at resonance. If there is no resistor, only the resistances of the reactive components (L and C) limit the current.

Do you remember the quality factor, or circuit Q? We calculate Q by dividing the reactance by the resistance. Use *either* the inductive reactance or the capacitive reactance to calculate the Q of a resonant circuit. Calculate this reactance at the resonant frequency. Do not use the combined reactance, because that is zero at resonance!

Q helps determine how steep the graph's sides are. Any circuit resistance tends to widen the graph's base. Circuits with high inherent resistance have a wide current graph, while circuits with low inherent resistance have a narrow graph.

Figure 21-5 compares the current graphs for two circuits. One circuit has a Q of 5.5. The second circuit has a Q of 11. Let's assume both circuits

Figure 21-5 — **This graph shows how current varies with frequency for two circuits; both are resonant at 7.19 MHz. The circuit with a Q = 11 has a peak current of 1.0 A, while the circuit with a Q = 5.5 has a peak current of 0.5 A (500 mA). The** *bandwidth* **of the circuit with a Q = 11 is narrower than the bandwidth of the Q = 5.5 circuit.**

have the same reactance and applied voltage. The circuit with a Q of 11 has one-half the resistance of the circuit with a Q of 5.5.

We can prove this by solving for X_L (or X_C), since either one can be used, and then calculating Q. Using the formula for inductive reactance, we find XL at the resonant frequency as follows:

$$X_L = 2 \pi f L$$

$$X_L = 2 \pi \times (7.19 \text{ MHz}) \times (2.44 \text{ μH})$$

$$X_L = 6.28 \times (7.19 \times 10^6) \times (2.44 \times 10^{-6})$$

$$X_L = 6.28 \times (17.5 \times 10^0) = 110 \text{ Ω}$$

The low-Q circuit has a resistance of 20 Ω (see Figure 21-3), and a peak current of 0.5 A, or 500 mA, at resonance. Looking at Figure 21-5 we can infer that the high-Q circuit has a resistance of 10 ohms (half of 20 ohms), because its current at resonance is 1000 mA (twice as large as the low-Q circuit current).

Now we can calculate the quality factor, Q, for both circuits.

$$Q = \frac{X}{R} \qquad \text{(Equation 21-8)}$$

$$Q_1 = \frac{X}{R} = \frac{110 \text{ Ω}}{20 \text{ Ω}} = 5.5$$

$$Q_2 = \frac{X}{R} = \frac{110 \text{ Ω}}{10 \text{ Ω}} = 11$$

The high-Q circuit, with one-half the resistance (10 Ω), has twice the current. You can prove this using Ohm's Law. The shape of the high-Q current curve is much sharper, however. The current is low until the signal is close to the circuit resonant frequency. Then the current shoots up to a higher peak value at the resonant frequency. It quickly drops back to a low value as you increase the frequency above resonance.

Look closely at Figure 21-5. Find the current that is 0.707 of the peak current for each graph. This will be 1.0 A for the high-Q circuit and 0.50 A for the low-Q circuit. Now compare the frequency range for these values. It's hard to read the exact frequencies on this graph. You can see the high-Q circuit has a much smaller range than the low-Q circuit, however.

We call this frequency range the *bandwidth*. The signal has a value higher than some specified portion (in this case, 0.707) of the maximum value over this range of frequencies. Then we can measure the range of frequencies for which the signal has a level higher than the one specified.

Each of these measurements represents a bandwidth, although the frequency range will be different for each. We must always specify a signal level with a bandwidth. In our example, we measured the bandwidth determined by the frequencies, above and below resonance, where the current drops to 0.707 of the maximum current. You may be wondering where the value of 0.707 came from. Well, that's a great question, and here's the answer. If the current flowing through a resistor (R1 in Figure 21-3) drops to 0.707 of what it was at the resonant frequency, what happens to the *power* delivered to the resistor? Let's use the equations we already know for calculating power to answer this question.

First, call the current at the resonant frequency I_{RES}, and the power at resonance is P_{RES}. At resonance the power delivered to the resistor can by calculated using:

$$P_{RES} = I_{RES}^2 \times R$$

At the two frequencies (below and above resonance) where current has dropped to $0.707 \times I_{RES}$, let's call the current at these two frequencies I_{BW}, and call the power P_{BW}.

$$P_{BW} = I_{BW}^2 \times R$$

But we know that the current at these two frequencies, I_{BW}, is equal to $0.707 \times I_{RES}$. Writing that as an equation, we get

$$I_{BW} = 0.707 \times I_{RES}$$

If we substitute this expression for I_{BW} into the equation for P_{BW}, we get

$$P_{BW} = I_{BW}^2 \times R$$

$$P_{BW} = (0.707 \times I_{RES})^2 \times R$$

$$P_{BW} = (0.707)^2 \times (I_{RES})^2 \times R$$

$$P_{BW} = 0.49985 \times I_{RES}^2 \times R$$

Well, 0.49985 is really close to 0.5, so let's say that at the two frequencies (below and above resonance) where current has dropped to $0.707 \times I_{RES}$, the power P_{BW} has *dropped to one half* of the power at resonance, P_{RES}.

$$P_{BW} = 0.5 \times I_{RES}^2 \times R$$

$$P_{BW} = 0.5 \times P_{RES}$$

What we've just done is show that the bandwidth can be determined by looking at a graph of current (or voltage) versus frequency, and looking for the two frequencies (one below and one above) the resonant frequency at which the current (or voltage) has dropped to 0.707 of the value at resonance. Of course, this can be done on an actual circuit by measuring the voltage across the resistor while varying the frequency of the sine-wave generator.

The bandwidth discussed above is called the *half-power bandwidth*. You will often see this written as the *–3 dB bandwidth* or just the *3 dB bandwidth*. Reducing the power by one half represents a reduction of 3 dB. (If you want to learn more about what a decibel (dB) is, you should refer to that section in the Appendix.)

The voltage across the inductor and capacitor can be much higher than the generator voltage at resonance. You may think the voltage across the inductor or capacitor is zero at resonance. This is not true! The voltage across either part may be much higher than the generator voltage.

These large voltages develop because of energy stored in the capacitor's electric field and the inductor's magnetic field. The energy going into the electric field is coming out of the magnetic field. The energy going into the magnetic field is coming out of the electric field. The inductor and capacitor hand this energy back and forth.

It's actually very easy to calculate the voltage across the inductor and capacitor at resonance; simply multiply the sine-wave generator voltage (V_{GEN}) by the quality factor, Q. In the example above, for the low-Q circuit (Q = 5.5) with the generator output equal to 10 V, the voltage across both L and C is

$$V_L = V_C = Q \times V_{GEN}$$

$$V_L = V_C = 5.5 \times 10 \text{ V} = 55 \text{ V}$$

That may seem very strange, that a 10 V generator can produce 55 V across the L and the C. It should help to recall that the voltage across the inductor *leads* the current by 90°, and the capacitor voltage *lags* the current by 90°, so they are out of phase by 180°. In other words, the L and C voltages cancel each other, so if you measured the voltage across *both* L and C together, the voltage would be 0 V! This results from the capacitor and inductor handing stored energy back and forth during each cycle.

Conditions in a Parallel Resonant Circuit

Figure 21-6 shows a parallel circuit that includes a 200 pF capacitor and a 2.44 µH inductor. The signal generator produces 50 volts at any frequency. Normally, we would include a resistor in series with the generator. This would limit the circuit current. We'll omit the resistor for this discussion because it simplifies calculations. Most practical parallel-resonant circuits include some series resistance, though, including the resistance of the windings of the inductor.

Equation 21-9 helps us calculate the resonant frequency for this circuit. We used this same equation to calculate the resonant frequency of a series resonant circuit.

$$f_r = \frac{1}{2\pi\sqrt{L\,C}} \qquad \text{(Equation 21-9)}$$

$$f_r =$$

$$\frac{1}{2\times 3.14\times\sqrt{2.44\times 10^{-6}\text{H}\times 200\times 10^{-12}\text{F}}}$$

$$f_r = \frac{1}{6.28\times\sqrt{488\times 10^{-18}}}$$

$$f_r = \frac{1}{6.28\times(22.1\times 10^{-9})} = \frac{1}{1.39\times 10^{-7}}$$

$$f_r = 7.19\times 10^6\text{ Hz} = 7.19\text{ MHz}$$

Generator current has two paths to choose. There is some current through the inductor and some current through the capacitor. The two paths are *branch circuits*, and the current through each part is a *branch current*.

The inductor current lags the applied voltage by 90°. (Remember ELI the ICE man.) The capacitor current leads the applied voltage by 90°. This means the inductor current and capacitor current are 180° out of phase.

Figure 21-6 — The inductor and capacitor in this circuit connect to the generator in parallel. We will use this circuit to study the conditions in a parallel-resonant circuit.

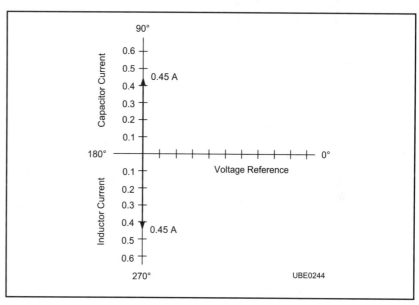

Figure 21-7 — Inductor current lags applied voltage by 90°, so we plot it along the −90° axis. The 0° axis represents the reference-voltage direction. Capacitor current leads applied voltage by 90°, so we plot it along the +90° axis.

Figure 21-7 is a graph showing the branch currents and the voltage reference. The inductor current is along the negative Y axis, or at −90 degrees. The capacitor current is along the positive Y axis, or at +90 degrees.

Points A and B on Figure 21-7 give us another way to think about the branch currents. At one instant the alternating current through the inductor seems to flow from A to B. At this same instant the current through the capacitor seems to flow from B to A.

During the next half cycle of the ac waveform, these directions reverse.

We find the total circuit current taken from the generator by adding the two branch currents. (This means the inductor-current value subtracts from the capacitor-current value.)

When you change the applied-signal frequency, the inductive and capacitive reactances change. Ohm's Law tells us the branch currents also change. **Figure 21-8** graphs the capacitor current, the inductor current and the total generator current. Remember, the capacitor current and the inductor current are in opposite directions at any instant. They are 180° out of phase.

When you examine Figure 21-8, you will see the total current becomes zero at the resonant frequency. This does not mean the current through the inductor or capacitor is zero, however. It only means the current into or out of the generator is zero at this point.

Well, the generator current is zero if we use an ideal inductor and capacitor. Real inductors and capacitors always have some resistance. The generator will supply the small current needed to replace the loss from this resistance in a practical circuit.

The generator current is very small at resonance. There can be large currents through the branches, however. The branch currents seem to circulate through the inductor and the capacitor.

The inductor and capacitor hand energy back and forth between them. The inductor's magnetic field stores energy, then returns it to the circuit. The capacitor stores the returned energy in its electric field, then hands it back to the inductor.

You may want to calculate the inductive and capacitive reactances for several frequencies. Then use Ohm's Law to calculate the current through those reactances. The generator in our circuit applies 50 volts to the circuit. Combine the capacitor current and the inductor current to find the total generator current. If you calculate enough values you could plot a graph like Figure 21-8. **Table 21-1** summarizes the values at several frequencies. Equations 21-10, 21-11 and 21-12 will help you with these calculations.

$$X_L = 2 \pi f L \qquad \text{(Equation 21-10)}$$

$$X_C = \frac{1}{2 \pi f C} \qquad \text{(Equation 21-11)}$$

$$I = \frac{E}{X} \qquad \text{(Equation 21-12)}$$

When you know the total circuit current and the applied voltage, Ohm's Law will help you calculate

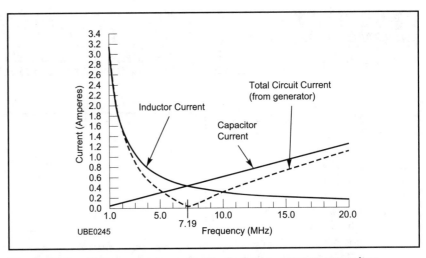

Figure 21-8 — This graph compares the inductor current, capacitor current and total generator current. Generator current is the difference between the capacitor and inductor current values. Notice that at the circuit resonant frequency the total current becomes zero.

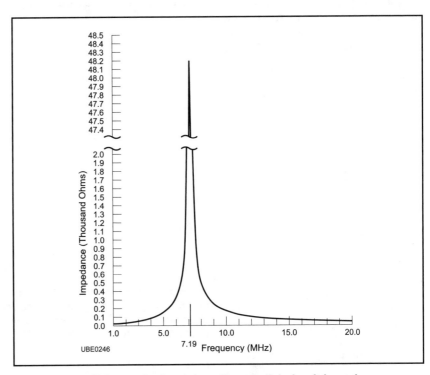

Figure 21-9 — This graph shows how the parallel-circuit impedance changes as the frequency changes. The impedance is low above and below the resonant frequency, but becomes very large at resonance.

the circuit impedance. Divide the voltage by the total current.

$$Z = \frac{E}{I_{TOTAL}}$$

Figure 21-9 is a graph of the circuit impedance over a wide frequency range. At frequencies below the reso-

nant frequency, the impedance is low. The capacitor has a high reactance so its current is small. The inductor has a low reactance at low frequencies, however, so most of the circuit current goes through it.

At frequencies above the resonant frequency, the impedance is also

Table 21-1
Calculated Circuit Values

Freq (MHz)	Capacitive Reactance X_C (ohms)	Inductive Reactance X_L (ohms)	Capacitor Current I_C (A)	Inductor Current I_L (A)	Generator Current I_T (A)	Circuit Impedance Z (ohms)
2.0	398	31	0.126	1.613	1.487	33.6
3.0	265	46	0.189	1.087	0.898	55.7
4.0	199	61	0.251	0.820	0.569	87.9
5.0	159	77	0.314	0.649	0.335	149.3
6,0	133	92	0.376	0.543	0.167	299.4
7.0	114	107	0.439	0.467	0.028	1785.7
7.19	110.7	110.2	0.452	0.454	0.002	25000.
8.0	100	123	0.500	0.407	0.093	537.6
9.0	88	138	0.568	0.362	0.206	242.7
10.0	80	153	0.625	0.327	0.298	167.8
11.0	72	169	0.694	0.296	0.398	125.6
12.0	66	184	0.758	0.272	0.486	102.9
13.0	61	199	0.820	0.251	0.569	87.9
14.0	57	214	0.877	0.234	0.643	77.8

low. Now the inductor has a high impedance, and a small current. The capacitor has a low impedance, though, so most of the circuit current goes through it.

At the resonant frequency, the reactances are opposite. The inductor current and the capacitor current are equal but opposite. The circuit current is zero with ideal components. When a large applied voltage produces no current, or a very small current, the impedance is large.

Circuit Q is important with parallel resonant circuits, just as with series resonant circuits. High-Q inductors and capacitors have little loss. Low-Q components have larger losses. High-Q circuits have a narrower bandwidth than low-Q circuits.

Math and Calculator Hints

MATH HINTS

For more background on math, refer to Appendix A — **Scientific and Engineering Notation**.

CALCULATOR HINTS

The following example shows how to use your TI-30X IIS calculator to solve equations like those in Chapter 21. Simpler numbers are used, so they will all be visible in the display of the calculator at the same time. For more information on using a calculator to work these examples, refer to **Appendix B — Understanding and Using Your TI-30X IIS Scientific Calculator**.

Example

What is the resonant frequency of a 6-millihenry inductor and a 5-microfarad capacitor?

$$f_r = \frac{1}{2\pi\sqrt{LC}}$$

$$= \frac{1}{2\times3.14\times\sqrt{6\times10^{-3}H\times 5\times10^{-6}F}}$$

$$f_r = \frac{1}{6.28\times\sqrt{30\times10^{-9}}}$$

$$= \frac{1}{6.28\times(173.2\times10^{-6})} = \frac{1}{1.088\times10^{-3}}$$

$$f_r = 918.9 \times 10^0 \text{ Hz} = 919 \text{ Hz}$$

Calculator Keystrokes

[There are more characters needed for this calculation than can fit in the screen of the display; try entering each character shown below, and you should see the answer in the second line of the display.]

1 ÷ (2 π 2nd √ (6 2nd EE - 3 X 5 2nd EE - 6)) =

The calculator's second display line shows the result: **918.88 × 10⁰⁰**

The result of 918.88 × 10⁰⁰ is 919 × 1 = 919 Hz.

Review Questions

21.1 When X_L (inductive reactance) equals X_C (capacitive reactance) in an LC circuit, this is called:

a) circuit optimization

b) synergy

c) obfuscation

d) resonance

21.2 At what frequency will $X_L = X_C$ for a 100 mH inductor and a 0.2 μF capacitor?

21.3 For a series resonant circuit connected to a voltage source, at the resonant frequency:

a) current is a maximum

b) current is a minimum

c) capacitor voltage is much greater than inductor voltage

d) inductor voltage is much greater than capacitor voltage

21.4 For a series resonant circuit connected to a voltage source, at frequencies above the resonant frequency:

a) current stops flowing

b) current is a maximum

c) inductive reactance is bigger than capacitive reactance

d) capacitive reactance is bigger than inductive reactance

21.5 A resonant circuit (series or parallel) has a resonant frequency of 3.6 MHz, and a bandwidth of 180 kHz. Solve for the quality factor of this circuit.

21.6 For a parallel resonant circuit connected to a voltage source, at the resonant frequency:

a) current is a maximum

b) current is a minimum

c) capacitor voltage is much greater than inductor voltage

d) inductor voltage is much greater than capacitor voltage

21.7 For a parallel resonant circuit connected to a voltage source, above the resonant frequency:

a) capacitor current is greater than inductor current

b) inductor voltage is greater than capacitor voltage

c) there is no current through either inductor or capacitor

d) inductor current is a maximum

Answers

21.1 d

21.2 When $X_L = X_C$, this is the resonant frequency, f_r.

$$f_r = \frac{1}{2\pi\sqrt{LC}} = \frac{1}{2\times3.14\times\sqrt{100\ \times\ 10^{-3}H\times\ 0.2\times10^{-6}F}} = 1125\,\text{Hz}$$

21.3 a

21.4 c

21.5 $Q = f_r/BW = (3.6\times10^6\ \text{Hz})/(180\times10^3\ \text{Hz}) = 20$

21.6 b

21.7 a

Active Device Concepts

Have you been studying this book through from the beginning? If so, you know many important electronics principles. You can calculate circuit conditions with a steady dc signal applied. You also can calculate many circuit conditions with an ac signal applied.

So far we have studied only *passive components* in our circuits. Passive components simply take an input signal and create an output signal. They require no additional voltage source. The output signals are normally smaller than the input signals. This means that the components lose some signal. (Actually, the components change some of the signal into heat or other energy forms.)

Passive components are important. Every electronic circuit includes passive components. There are electronics functions that passive components can't perform, however. Passive components can't amplify signals, or make them stronger. Passive components can't form an oscillator to generate an ac signal from a dc input. There are other types of signal processing that passive components can't do, either. These functions require another type of component — the *active component.*

Active components require an input voltage to make them work. Usually this is a dc signal that sets the operating point and gives the component the energy it needs to work properly. Active components use this

In this unit we will cover active devices such as diodes and transistors.

input voltage to amplify signals, create ac signals and perform other functions.

Active components are an important part of many electronics circuits. Without active components there would be no radio and TV transmitters or receivers as we know them. There would be no computers or electronic calculators.

Let's turn our attention to some active components. We'll learn about several types of components and how they work. We'll see how to use those components in electronic circuits. We also will learn about some of the functions these components perform in electronic circuits.

In This Unit You Will Learn
✓ what semiconductors are
✓ that diodes allow current in only one direction and how we use this principle in electronic circuits
✓ about bipolar and field-effect transistors and their use in circuits
✓ that integrated circuits (ICs) contain entire circuits on a tiny piece of semiconductor material

Chapter 22

Semiconductor Materials

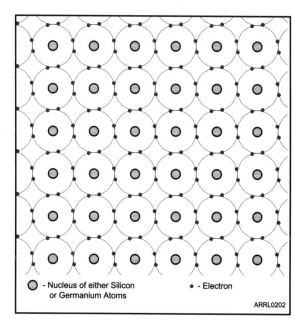

○ - Nucleus of either Silicon
  or Germanium Atoms
● - Electron

ARRL0202

Silicon and germanium atoms arrange themselves into a regular pattern. These materials have properties that are useful for making semiconductor devices used in electronic circuits.

Contents

Let's Start with Atoms

Many modern electronic circuits contain materials that we call *semiconductors*. Manufacturers make many different devices with semiconductor materials. It is important that you have a basic understanding of how these semiconductor materials work. That will help you learn about modern electronics.

We would have to study some physics and chemistry to gain a complete understanding of what is going on inside semiconductor materials. Don't worry, though. You can understand the basics of how the materials work even if you never studied these

sciences! In fact, we have already covered most of what you need to know in another section of this book. We described a simple model of an atom in the section about insulators and conductors.

Remember that tiny particles called *atoms* make up all matter. These atoms are so small that no one can see them without the help of a very powerful microscope. Atoms are the basic building blocks of all matter. Scientists call each different type of atom an *element*. They have found more than 100 elements and are always looking for more.

Atoms form larger building blocks, which we call *molecules*. Molecules are combinations of atoms from several elements or several atoms of a single element. Water molecules, for example, contain one oxygen atom and two hydrogen atoms. Oxygen and hydrogen are elements. The oxygen that we breathe, however, consists of oxygen molecules. Two oxygen atoms make up every oxygen molecule. **Figure 22-1** shows how atoms form molecules.

There are particles that are even smaller than atoms. *Protons, neutrons* and *electrons* combine to form atoms. Protons have a positive electric charge. Electrons have a negative charge. Neutrons have no charge; they are *neutral*. You probably remember seeing drawings that show a cluster of protons and neutrons in the center, surrounded by a "cloud" of electrons. Drawings like these represent the structure of atoms. (See **Figure 22-2**.) Scientists call the central cluster or ball of protons and neutrons the *nucleus* of the atom.

Every type of atom (or element) has a certain number of protons. A hydrogen atom has one proton, a helium atom has two and a copper atom has 29, for example. Atoms are electrically neutral, so they must contain just as many electrons as they do protons. This means that a hydrogen atom contains one electron, a helium atom has two and a copper atom has 29 electrons.

Sometimes it is helpful to relate a new concept to something familiar. Think of the nucleus as the sun.

Figure 22-1 — Atoms are the basic building blocks of all matter. Several atoms can combine to form molecules. Part A shows how hydrogen and oxygen atoms combine to form water molecules. Part B shows two oxygen atoms combined to form one oxygen molecule.

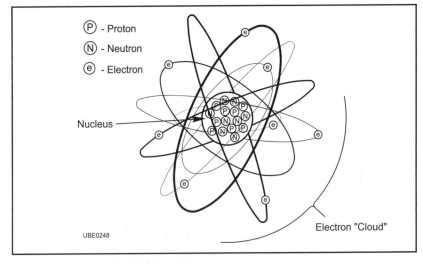

Figure 22-2 — A simple picture of an atom includes protons and neutrons in the nucleus. The electrons surround the nucleus like a cloud. This drawing represents an oxygen atom. It has eight protons and eight neutrons in the nucleus, and eight electrons surrounding the nucleus.

Then imagine the electrons as planets revolving around the sun. With this kind of picture, the electrons appear to be different distances from the nucleus. Scientists use a picture like this to describe atoms. The distances from the nucleus describe *orbitals* or layers into which the electrons fit. Each orbital can hold a certain number of electrons. (Some orbitals can hold only two electrons while others can hold six, 10 or 14.) Actually, the picture is a bit more complicated than the one shown in **Figure 22-3**. The electrons don't really fit into exact layers the way we have pictured them, either. This model is useful to help explain the inner workings of an atom, though.

The distance of the orbital from the nucleus is a measure of how much energy an electron in that orbital will have. Orbitals that are farther from the nucleus contain higher-energy electrons. This is the reason scientists often refer to such pictures as *energy-level diagrams*.

These orbitals are important. If the number of electrons in an atom just fills an orbital, that element will hold tightly to its electrons. Such atoms form good insulators. Suppose the number of electrons in an atom fills one orbital, with one or two additional electrons to go into the next orbital. The atoms will share those additional electrons or give them up to other atoms. Such atoms make

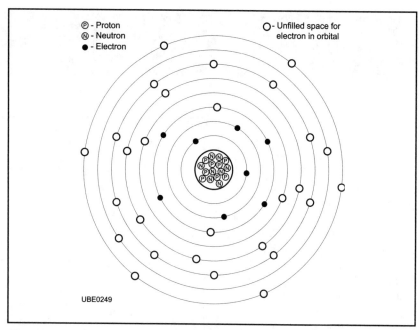

Figure 22-3 — Our picture of an oxygen atom can be drawn to show the electrons in shells, or layers, called orbitals. These orbitals can hold certain numbers of electrons each. Electrons have a specific amount of energy to be in a particular orbital. Orbitals farther from the nucleus have higher-energy electrons in them.

good conductors. The elements used to make semiconductor materials have four electrons in the last orbital. From this discussion you can see that they are neither good conductors nor good insulators. Can you guess why we call them semiconductors?

The electrons for an element follow a specific pattern to fit into this electron-orbital structure. This pattern helps determine how the atoms combine with other atoms. There are several ways for these combinations to occur, but you won't need to understand them. It *will* be helpful, though, for you to realize that the electron structure plays an important part.

Doping The Crystals

Silicon, germanium and gallium arsenide are the materials normally used to make semiconductors. (The element silicon is not the same as the household lubricants and rubber-like sealers called *silicone*.) A silicon atom has 14 protons and 14 electrons, while germanium has 32 of each. Silicon and germanium each have an electron structure with four electrons in the outer energy layers. The silicon and germanium atoms will share these four electrons with other atoms around them.

Some atoms share their electrons so the atoms arrange themselves into a regular pattern. We say these atoms form crystals. **Figure 22-4** shows how silicon and germanium atoms produce crystals. (Different kinds of atoms might arrange themselves into other patterns.) The crystals made by silicon or germanium atoms do not make good electrical conductors. They aren't good insulators either, however. That's why we call these materials semiconductors. Sometimes they act like conductors and sometimes they act like insulators.

Manufacturers add other atoms to these crystals through a carefully controlled process, called *doping*. The atoms added in this way produce a material that is no longer pure silicon or pure germanium. We call the added atoms *impurity atoms*.

As an example, the manufacturer might add some atoms of arsenic or antimony to the silicon or germanium while making the crystals. Arsenic and antimony atoms each have five electrons to share.

Figure 22-5 shows how an atom with five electrons in its outer layer fits into the crystal structure. In such a case, there is an extra electron in the crystal. We refer to this as a *free electron*, and we call the semiconductor material made in this way *N-type material*. (This name comes from the extra negative charge in the crystal structure.)

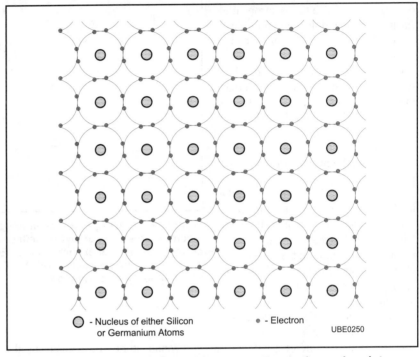

- Nucleus of either Silicon or Germanium Atoms   • - Electron   UBE0250

Figure 22-4 — Silicon and germanium atoms arrange themselves into a regular pattern, called crystals. Notice that each atom in this crystal structure is sharing four electrons with other nearby atoms.

The impurity atoms are electrically neutral, just as the silicon or germanium atoms are. The free electrons result from the crystal structure itself. These impurity atoms create (donate) free electrons in the crystal structure. That is why we call them *donor atoms*.

Now let's suppose the manufacturer adds some gallium or indium atoms instead of arsenic or antimony. Gallium and indium atoms only have three electrons that they can share with other nearby atoms. When there are gallium or indium atoms in the crystal there is an extra space where an electron could fit into the structure.

Figure 22-6 shows an example of a crystal structure with an extra space where an electron could fit. We call this space for an electron a *hole*. The semiconductor material produced in this way is *P-type* material. These im-

purity atoms produce holes that will accept extra electrons in the semiconductor material. That is why we call them *acceptors*.

Again, you should realize that the impurity atoms have the same number of electrons as protons. The material is still electrically neutral. The *crystal structure* is missing an electron in P-type material. Similarly, the *crystal structure* has an extra electron in N-type material.

Suppose we apply a voltage across a crystal of N-type semiconductor. The positive side of the voltage attracts electrons. The free electrons in the structure move through the crystal toward the positive side.

Next suppose we apply a voltage to a crystal of P-type material. The negative voltage attracts the holes, and they move through the material toward the negative side.

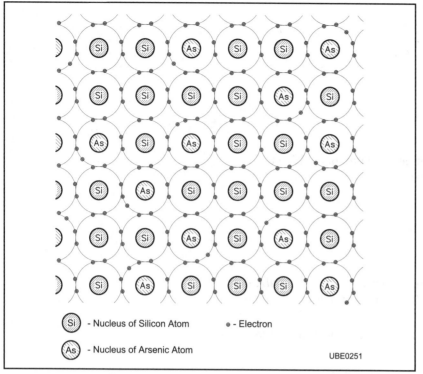

Free electrons and holes move in opposite directions through a crystal. This is why we call the electrons and holes *charge carriers*.

Manufacturers can control the electrical properties of semiconductor materials that they make. They do this by carefully controlling the amount and type of impurities that they add to the silicon or germanium crystals.

Manufacturers build N- and P-type semiconductor materials next to each other in various combinations. They produce a wide variety of electronic devices this way.

Semiconductors are solid crystals. They are strong and not easily damaged by vibration or rough handling. We refer to electronic parts made with semiconductor materials as *solid-state devices*.

Figure 22-5 — Manufacturers can add antimony or arsenic atoms to the silicon or germanium crystals. These *impurity atoms* add an extra electron to the crystal structure, producing N-type semiconductor material.

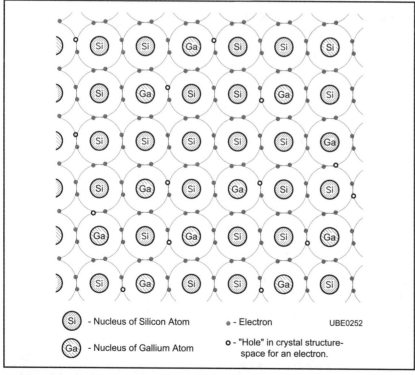

Figure 22-6 — Manufacturers can add gallium or indium atoms to the silicon or germanium crystals. These impurity atoms have only three electrons to share. This leaves a hole or space for another electron in the crystal structure. This produces P-type semiconductor material.

Review Questions

22.1 Which one of the following is *not* a passive device?

a)   resistor
b)   diode
c)   capacitor
d)   inductor

22.2 In order to make an amplifier, or an oscillator, in addition to R, L and C components, you must have:

a)   an active device
b)   a transformer
c)   a logic gate
d)   a variable capacitor

22.3 Surrounding the _____ of an atom are _____ containing _____ which determine the electrical properties of that atom.

22.4 Most semiconductor materials have this many electrons in the outermost orbital:

a)   1
b)   8
c)   2
d)   4

22.5 Can you name three common semiconductor materials?

22.6 If an impurity atom with three electrons in its outermost orbital is added to a semiconductor material, that atom is called:

a)   an acceptor atom
b)   a donor atom
c)   a neutralizing atom
d)   George

22.7 The charge carriers in semiconductor materials are called _____ and _____.

Answers

22.1 b
22.2 a
22.3 Surrounding the *nucleus* of an atom are *orbitals* containing *electrons* which determine the electrical properties of that atom.
22.4 d
22.5 Silicon, germanium, gallium arsenide
22.6 a
22.7 The charge carriers in semiconductor materials are called *electrons* and *holes*.

Chapter 23

Diodes — the Check Valves of Electronic Circuits

Anode

Cathode

Band

Bevel

Diodes come in several shapes and sizes.

UBE0382

Contents

Diodes Allow Current in Only One Direction

Remember that with a perfect resistor, it doesn't matter whether you pass dc or ac through it. The current through the resistor just depends on the applied voltage and the amount of resistance. **Figure 23-1A** shows the current through a resistor when we apply a steady direct voltage. Part B shows the current if we apply an increasing direct voltage. Part C shows the current through a resistor when we apply an alternating voltage.

With an ideal capacitor, however, you'll get different results. If you apply an alternating voltage to the capacitor, an alternating current will flow. When we apply a direct voltage, there will be a sudden rush of current while the capacitor plates charge. After the capacitor is fully charged, however, there will be no current. **Figure 23-2** shows capacitor operation with both dc and ac applied.

This chapter describes devices that allow current to flow in only one direction. It doesn't matter which type of voltage you apply to these devices. We refer to such devices as *diodes*. (The word diode comes from two Greek words. Di, used as a prefix, means two. Ode means a path or way. So diode refers to a device with two

paths or connections inside.) Several different materials and construction methods are used to make diodes. Diodes also serve a wide variety of purposes in modern electronic circuits. All diodes have one characteristic in common, however: they allow current to flow in only one direction.

A simple type of diode occurs when two different metals touch each other and make a poor electrical connection. Early radio receivers used a type of simple diode. A small galena crystal in a lead holder made part of the diode. (Lead is a soft gray metal, and galena is an ore that

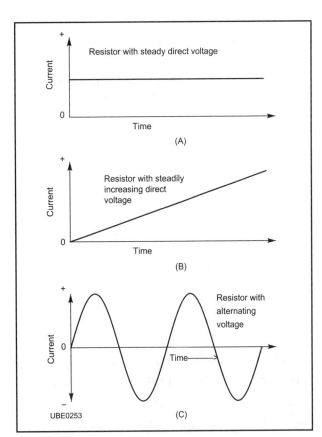

Figure 23-1 — Part A shows the current through a resistor when we apply a steady direct voltage to the circuit. The current through the resistor caused by a steadily increasing direct voltage is shown at B. Part C shows an alternating current through the resistor if we apply an alternating voltage.

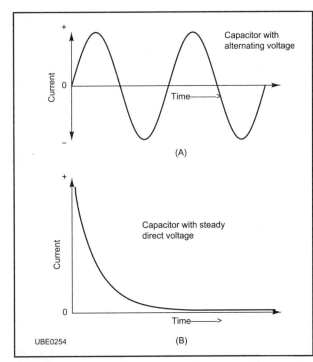

Figure 23-2 — When we apply an alternating voltage to a capacitor there is an alternating current through it, as shown at A. When we apply a direct voltage to the capacitor, as at B, there is no current, at least after the capacitor charges.

Figure 23-3 — Simple receivers used this type of diode to detect radio signals during the early days of radio.

Figure 23-4 — The symbol used to represent a diode on schematic diagrams looks like an arrow point stuck into a block of wood. The end with the bar, which the arrow point appears to have hit, is the cathode. The opposite end, at the back of the arrow point, is the anode.

Figure 23-5 — When you connect a diode into a circuit as shown, there will be a current through the diode (and the circuit).

Figure 23-6 — Here we connected the diode in the opposite direction to that shown in Figure 23-5. The positive battery terminal connects to the cathode and the negative terminal connects to the anode. In this case, there will be no current through the diode (or the circuit).

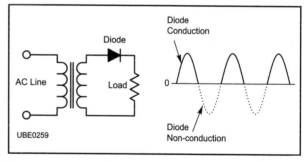

Figure 23-7 — This drawing summarizes how a diode works when we apply an alternating voltage to the terminals. When the top of the ac supply is positive, the diode anode is positive. There is a current. When the top of the ac supply is negative, the diode anode is negative. Then there is no current. B shows the applied voltage and the circuit current over several cycles of applied voltage.

contains lead.) A thin wire (called a *cat's whisker*) touched the surface of the galena. If you found just the right spot on the galena, radio signals would come alive in your earphones. See **Figure 23-3**. We still use diodes to detect the presence of radio signals in a receiver. A diode changes the signals into a form you can hear.

Figure 23-4 shows the symbol used to represent diodes on schematic diagrams. We call the end with the bar, at the arrow point, the cathode. The opposite end, at the back of the arrow point, is the anode.

How do diodes work? Let's look at a simple circuit. First, connect the anode to the positive side of a battery and the cathode to the negative side. See **Figure 23-5**. With the diode con-nected in this way, electrons will flow through the diode. We say the diode is *forward biased*.

Now let's reverse the battery con-nections to the diode. **Figure 23-6** shows the new circuit. This time the positive battery terminal connects to the cathode of the diode and the nega-tive terminal connects to the anode. No current will flow in the circuit under these conditions.

Your next question might be,

"What happens if we apply an alternating voltage?" The diode voltage polarity keeps changing. As you might expect, with a positive voltage on the anode, there is a current in the circuit. When the polarity reverses, there is a negative voltage on the anode. Now the current stops. When the next half cycle comes along, the anode connects to the positive voltage again. Then there is a current again. See **Figure 23-7**. This process continues as long as we apply the alternating voltage. Current flows through a diode in only one direction. The electrons move in a direction opposite to the way the arrow points in the diode symbol.

Diodes take an alternating voltage input and produce a direct voltage output. We call this process *rectification*. We sometimes refer to diodes as *rectifiers* because of this.

Solid-State Diodes from Semiconductor Materials

Most of the diodes in modern electronic circuits use semiconductor materials. Semiconductors normally have low operating voltage requirements and are rugged and reliable. In addition, they waste very little energy in the form of excess heat.

In the first chapter of this unit, you learned a little about manufacturing semiconductor materials. By now you are probably wondering how we can use these materials to make a diode. Well, the first step is to remember that a diode has two parts or sections. To make a solid-state diode, we need two pieces of semiconductor material. Since there are only two kinds of material (P and N type), we will need one piece of each type.

We make a diode by joining the two semiconductor material blocks, as shown in **Figure 23-8**. This forms a single piece of material. The N- and

P-type materials contact each other in the center, forming a *PN junction*. It is this junction between the two materials that interests us.

How do manufacturers form a PN junction? They usually start with a piece of either P- or N-type semiconductor material. Then they change a small area on the surface of this material into the other type of material. **Figure 23-9** shows an example. There are several processes that manufacturers use to form the PN junction, but you don't have to worry about those details.

Okay. You have some idea how manufacturers put a diode together. Now you are probably wondering how it works. Well, before we even connect our diode into a circuit, something interesting happens to it. Some *free electrons* in the N-type material travel across the PN junction. There they fill some holes in the P-type material! This causes two other effects. First, it forms a region around the PN junction that has no holes or free electrons. We call this area the

Figure 23-9 — Manufacturers usually form a PN junction by starting with a piece of P- or N-type semiconductor material. Then they change a small layer on one surface of that material into the opposite type of material.

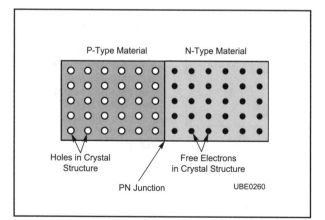

Figure 23-8 — A block of P-type semiconductor and a block of N-type semiconductor join to form a PN junction. We call a junction like this a solid-state diode.

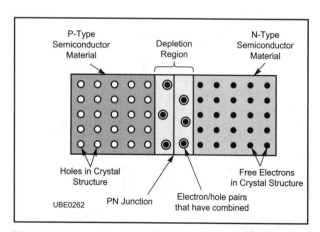

Figure 23-10 — Free electrons and holes near the PN junction will cross the junction and combine with each other. This forms a *depletion region* around the junction inside the diode.

depletion region. This is because the electrons and holes, or semiconductor *charge carriers*, are depleted. See **Figure 23-10**.

You might ask, "Why don't all the free electrons in the semiconductor move across the junction and fill holes in the P-type material?" It's a good question. As some electrons cross the junction, the impurity atoms that they came from become positively charged. (An atom is electrically neutral. If it loses an electron, it has a positive charge. If it gains an electron it has a negative charge.) As free electrons fill some holes in the P-type material, the acceptor atoms have a negative charge. This is because they have an extra electron now. Holes from the P side can move to the N-type material also. This movement leaves a negative charge on the P material and a positive charge on the N side.

Electron and hole movement across the PN junction both affect the semiconductor material the same way. The charge movement leaves a positive charge on the N-type material and a negative charge on the P-type material. As the depletion region grows larger, the negative charge on the junction's P side increases. This repels more electrons that might try to cross the junction. The positive charge on the junction's N side also increases, and that attracts electrons back to the N material.

The electric charges also prevent too many holes from crossing the junction into the N-type material. **Figure 23-11** shows the effects of these electric charges on the depletion region. The electric charges keep the depletion region from getting any larger. This electric charge is the second effect caused by electron and hole movement across the PN junction.

Now you have begun to understand the structure of a solid-state diode. So let's connect one into a circuit and see what happens. **Figure 23-12** shows a diode and an ammeter connected in series with a battery. The positive battery terminal connects to the P-type semiconductor material. The negative terminal connects to the N-type material. You already

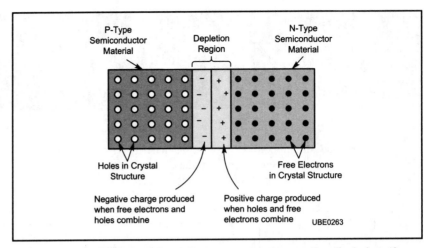

Figure 23-11 — Holes and free electrons move across the diode junction so electrons can fill the holes. This leaves a positive and negative electric charge on opposite sides of the material, however. This electric charge repels additional charge carriers and keeps the depletion region from becoming too wide.

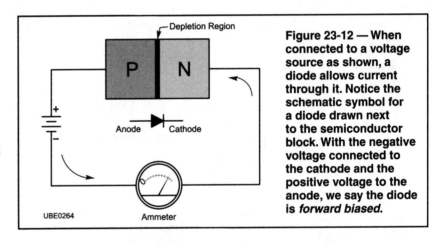

Figure 23-12 — When connected to a voltage source as shown, a diode allows current through it. Notice the schematic symbol for a diode drawn next to the semiconductor block. With the negative voltage connected to the cathode and the positive voltage to the anode, we say the diode is *forward biased.*

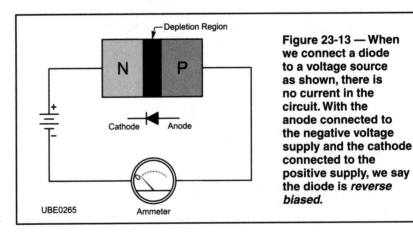

Figure 23-13 — When we connect a diode to a voltage source as shown, there is no current in the circuit. With the anode connected to the negative voltage supply and the cathode connected to the positive supply, we say the diode is *reverse biased.*

know that like electric charges repel and opposite charges attract. So the negative side of the battery repels the extra electrons in the N-type material. Similarly, the positive side repels the holes (which act as positive charges) in the P-type semiconductor.

The battery voltage must be high enough to push (and pull) the charge carriers across the depletion region.

(This takes about 0.3 volts if the semiconductor is germanium and about 0.7 volts if it is silicon.) Once the electrons and holes cross the depletion region, the voltage will attract them the rest of the way through the semiconductor. The positive voltage attracts electrons from the N-type material all the way across the junction, through the P-type material. Then the electrons travel through the circuit to the positive battery terminal.

In the same way, the negative battery terminal attracts the holes across the junction and through the N-type material. (Holes flow in the opposite direction from electrons in a circuit.) The meter in the circuit of Figure 23-12 indicates some current through the circuit. The diode acts like a small resistance in this example.

You may be wondering if all the free electrons can leave the semiconductor. Will the current stop then? Will that ruin the semiconductor? No, don't be afraid that all the electrons will get away! For every free electron that leaves the semiconductor on the P side, a new one comes onto the N side from the negative battery terminal. One purpose of the battery is to supply the electrons needed to maintain a current through the circuit.

The acceptor and donor impurity atoms in the crystal structure try to keep as many electrons as they started with. So when we remove the voltage, the semiconductor material will return to the same condition as before we applied the voltage. You can't remove all the free electrons or holes from a semiconductor by connecting it into a circuit.

Now let's reverse the battery connections to our diode, as **Figure 23-13** shows. This time the negative battery terminal connects to the P-type semiconductor. The positive terminal connects to the N-type material. Remember that like charges repel. The negative battery voltage repels free electrons in N-type semiconductor material and the positive side repels holes in P-type material. More electron/hole pairs combine in the depletion region, so it becomes wider. There is no current because electrons and holes do not make it all the way through the semiconductor. The depletion region becomes too wide for them to cross.

The diode junction is *forward biased* with positive voltage connected to P material and negative voltage connected to N material. A forward-biased diode allows current through it. With the voltage polarity reversed, we say the diode junction is *reverse biased*. A reverse-biased diode does not allow current through it.

Actually, the last sentence isn't completely true. There will often be a very small current going through a reverse-biased diode. The current is so small that we usually just ignore it, however. (There may be more than 10 milliamps of current flowing through a forward-biased diode. The reverse current in the same diode may be less than 1 microamp!) The *forward current* is generally at least 10,000 times greater than the *reverse*, or *leakage current*.

Diode Characteristics and Ratings

When you connect a diode in a circuit so it is *forward biased*, there will be current through the circuit. (The positive battery terminal connects to the diode's anode and the cathode connects to the negative battery terminal.) If we connect the diode so it is reverse biased, there is no current through the circuit. (In this case we connect the diode with its anode to the negative side of the voltage source. The cathode connects to the positive side.)

Let's look at what happens to the current through a forward-biased diode as we vary the voltage applied to it. We'll start with a diode connected in a circuit, as **Figure 23-14** shows. The power supply has a control to vary the output voltage. This provides a convenient way to adjust the voltage applied to the diode. With the power supply output set to 0 volts, we won't measure any current. Now we can gradually increase the voltage. A small current (less than one milliamp) will begin to flow. If we are using a germanium diode, the current will start to increase as the voltage approaches about 0.3 volts. With a silicon diode, the voltage must increase to about 0.7 volts before this current increase occurs. (These voltages represent a *threshold* or changing point, where the semiconductor material begins to conduct electricity.) As you increase the supply voltage beyond this point, the current increases very rapidly. **Figure 23-15** shows part of a typical diode *characteristic curve*.

Our diode is acting like a variable resistor. At voltages just above zero the resistance might be more than 100 ohms. As the voltage crosses the threshold value, the resistance decreases to only a few ohms. Take a look at the Figure 23-15 graph. The current gets very large for even a small voltage increase when you go above the threshold. If we neglect the small voltage (less than 1 volt) required to "turn on" the diode in the forward direction, we could say the diode passes

Figure 23-14 — Connect the anode of a diode to the positive terminal of a variable voltage power supply as shown. The meter will indicate a current through the circuit.

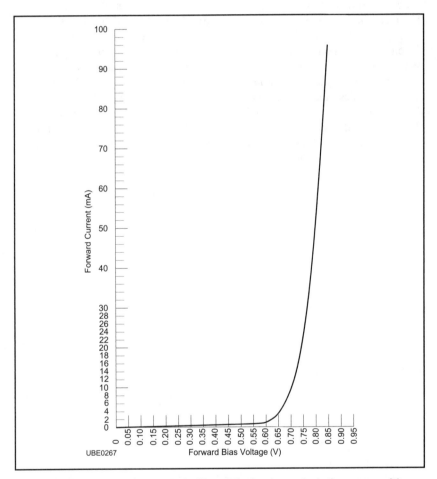

Figure 23-15 — This is a typical silicon-diode characteristic curve, with a forward bias voltage applied to the diode. When the voltage applied to a germanium diode reaches about 0.3 volts, the forward current begins to increase. If you allow more current through the diode than the average forward current rating specifies, the diode will usually destroy itself.

current without opposition.

This brings us to an important diode rating. There is a practical limit to how much current can flow through a diode. Since the diode has some internal resistance, it will produce heat when there is current through it. When there is more current through

Figure 23-16 — Solid-state diodes are available in a variety of sizes and shapes. In general, the larger the diode, the more current it can handle. Diodes made with a bolt for one lead can usually conduct at least several amperes safely.

Figure 23-17 — Connect the cathode of a diode to the positive terminal of a variable-voltage power supply, as shown. A very sensitive meter will indicate only a few microamperes of *reverse current* in the circuit.

Figure 23-18 — This graph shows the reverse-bias characteristic curve for a typical diode. The reverse bias voltage that causes the current through the diode to increase rapidly depends on the specific diode type. When this reverse conduction occurs, the diode will usually destroy itself.

the diode, it becomes hotter. If we allow the diode to become too hot, we will destroy it. Manufacturers describe a diode's ability to handle current with several different ratings. The one we are talking about here is the *average forward current*.

The average forward current rating is the largest current you should allow through the diode. (Under some conditions you might have a larger current pulse through the diode. This can only last a brief fraction of a second, however.) If the current through your diode exceeds the forward current rating, the diode is likely to destroy itself.

You must know a diode's average forward current rating before you select it for a particular circuit application. Some diodes will only handle a maximum average forward current of 100 milliamps. Some diodes can't even handle this much current. Other diodes can easily handle 10 amps or more. In general, diodes designed to handle larger currents are physically bigger. With a larger piece of semiconductor material and more surface area, the diode can get rid of more heat.

Manufacturers make some diodes with a bolt as one lead. With this

lead, you can attach the diode to a large piece of metal, or *heat sink*. The heat sink helps conduct heat away from the diode, so you can allow larger amounts of current to pass through it. **Figure 23-16** shows some typical semiconductor diodes. The photo includes a high-current device designed to mount on a heat sink.

Now let's change the direction of our diode in the test circuit. **Figure 23-17** shows the new circuit. This time the diode is reverse biased. We will have to use a meter that is very sensitive, so we can measure the small current. Again, we will start

to increase the voltage applied to the diode. The diode current may be only a few microamperes now. As the voltage across the diode increases, there will be almost no increase in current through it.

Eventually, as we increase the voltage, we will find a point where the diode suddenly allows current to pass through it. The *reverse current* will become very large unless there is enough resistance in the circuit to limit that current. You must limit the circuit current or the diode will quickly destroy itself with the heat it produces. **Figure 23-18** shows

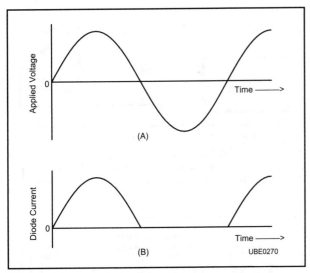

Figure 23-19 — The graph at A shows an alternating voltage waveform, which we connect to a diode. Part B shows the current through the diode that results from this alternating voltage. The diode conducts only when its anode voltage is positive.

Figure 23-20 — Part A shows how to measure the voltage across a resistor in a diode circuit. There is a voltage across the resistor only when there is current through the circuit. Part B shows the alternating voltage applied to the circuit. Part C shows the voltage measured across R as a result of this alternating voltage.

the characteristic curve for a reverse biased diode.

This brings up another important diode rating: *peak inverse voltage (PIV)*. This is the highest reverse-bias voltage that we can safely apply to the diode. The PIV is a voltage that's a bit less than one that would cause the diode to conduct a large reverse current. A diode with the reverse-current characteristic shown in Figure 23-18 has a PIV of about 85 volts. When you select a diode for a circuit, be sure to pick one with a PIV rating much higher than any reverse bias voltage that your circuit may apply to it. Otherwise, there may be a large reverse current through the diode, destroying it.

In summary, if we forward bias a diode, it acts like a small resistance or a short circuit. If we reverse bias the diode, it acts like a very large resistance or an open circuit. So far we have been talking about the diode operation with direct voltages applied. Now we'll take a brief look at what happens when we apply an alternating voltage.

Figure 23-19A shows an alternating-voltage waveform. Let's begin

at the point where the voltage is zero and beginning to increase in a positive direction. (This is the case at the left side of the graph.) With no voltage applied to the diode, it does not conduct. As the alternating voltage begins increasing, it forward biases the diode. The diode begins to conduct electricity, and as the voltage increases, so will the current. Figure 23-19B is a graph of the diode current. When the voltage reaches its positive peak and begins to decrease, the current through the diode also will decrease. As the alternating voltage goes to zero again, the current through the diode will stop. Next the voltage will start to increase in a negative direction, reverse biasing the diode. This time, though, the diode does not conduct. There is no current through the circuit. When the voltage again starts to become positive, the diode will conduct again. The Figure 23-19 graphs

illustrate this whole process.

This discussion shows a very important use for diodes. By placing a diode in a circuit, we can apply an alternating voltage and the diode will turn that into a series of current pulses. These pulses all flow in one direction instead of reversing direction as with an alternating voltage. **Figure 23-20A** shows a resistor connected in series with a diode. Part B shows the waveform of an alternating voltage applied to the circuit. Part C shows the waveform of the voltage across the resistor. The resistor voltage results from the diode current pulses.

The diode in the Figure 23-20 circuit is forward biased only half the time. This is when it conducts current through the circuit. Each pulse of current through the diode is twice the *average forward current* through the diode, because the other half of the time the diode current is zero.

The Half-Wave Rectifier Circuit

Let's connect a single diode in series with a resistor and an alternating voltage supply. See **Figure 23-21**. The "output voltage," taken across the resistor, is a series of pulses. A single pulse occurs every time the diode is forward biased by the alternating voltage. There is one pulse for every cycle of the input waveform. Between each pulse is a time with no output voltage, because the diode is reverse biased. **Figure 23-22** shows the input and output waveforms.

This circuit provides an output during only half of the input waveform. We call this circuit a *half-wave rectifier*. (Remember, the term *rectifier* refers to a device or circuit that takes an alternating voltage input and produces a direct voltage output.) A big advantage of a half-wave rectifier is that it is simple to build. The circuit makes inefficient use of the input voltage, however, and that is a big disadvantage.

The **Figure 23-23** output waveform shows that the output voltage is always on the same side of the zero axis. (It can be either positive or negative with respect to ground.

Figure 23-21 — A half-wave rectifier is a simple circuit that changes an alternating voltage to a direct voltage. A single diode and a resistor are all you need.

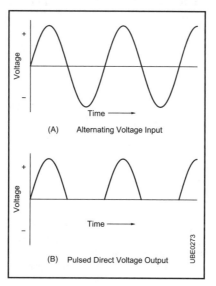

(A)   Alternating Voltage Input

(B)   Pulsed Direct Voltage Output

Figure 23-22 — Part A shows the alternating voltage input waveform to a half-wave rectifier. Part B shows the waveform of the pulsed direct voltage output.

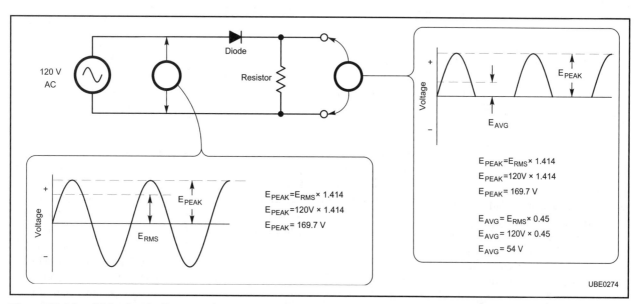

$E_{PEAK} = E_{RMS} \times 1.414$
$E_{PEAK} = 120V \times 1.414$
$E_{PEAK} = 169.7\ V$

$E_{PEAK} = E_{RMS} \times 1.414$
$E_{PEAK} = 120V \times 1.414$
$E_{PEAK} = 169.7\ V$

$E_{AVG} = E_{RMS} \times 0.45$
$E_{AVG} = 120V \times 0.45$
$E_{AVG} = 54\ V$

Figure 23-23 — This circuit diagram shows a half-wave rectifier connected to an alternating voltage generator with an RMS output of 120 volts. The input and output waveforms are also shown, with their peak and average values.

Input Waveform

Rectified Direct
Voltage Waveform
(without the capacitor
in the circuit)

Rectified, Filtered
Direct Voltage Waveform

Figure 23-24 — Here we added an output filter capacitor to our half-wave rectifier circuit. The drawing includes input, rectified and filtered-output waveforms, shown near where you would measure them in the circuit. Notice that the capacitor holds the voltage close to the peak while the diode is not conducting.

We can change the output-voltage polarity by reversing the diode direction.) The output voltage varies with time, and the current through the circuit changes with these variations. The current flows through the circuit in only one direction, however. Our circuit takes the alternating voltage input and changes it to a varying dc output.

The *rectified* output voltage is not a steady value. It varies from 0 to a maximum (peak) value for each pulse. The peak value of the direct output voltage is equal to the peak value of the alternating voltage supply. You can calculate the output peak voltage if you know the effective (RMS) value of the input voltage. Simply multiply the RMS value by the square root of two (1.414):

$$E_{PEAK} = E_{RMS} \times 1.414 \text{ (Equation 23-1)}$$

For example, let's suppose we have an ac generator with an RMS output of 120 volts. See **Figure 23-24**.

What will be the peak output voltage from a half-wave rectifier circuit connected to this generator? Equation 23-1 will help us answer this question.

$$E_{PEAK} = E_{RMS} \times 1.414$$
$$= 120 \text{ V} \times 1.414 = 169.7 \text{ V}$$

Output
Ripple Voltage

Voltage

Current

Average Direct
Voltage Output

Time

Filtered, Rectified
Waveform

Current Pulse to
Charge Capacitor

UBE0276

Figure 23-25 — Each time the diode is forward biased (to conduct electricity) there is a brief pulse of current. This pulse charges the filter capacitor to the peak voltage again. During the rest of the waveform cycle, the diode is reverse biased. Then the capacitor slowly discharges. The higher the capacitance of the filter capacitor, the slower the output voltage drops during the diode off times.

A half-wave rectifier connected to a 120-V (RMS) supply will produce a dc output with 169.7 V peak output.

We also want to know the average value of the direct voltage produced by a half-wave rectifier. Remember, there is a time when the output is zero between each positive pulse. Also, the output is at the peak value for only a brief instant during each cycle. On the average, then, the output voltage is much less than the peak value. In fact, you can calculate the average value by multiplying the RMS value of the input voltage by 0.45:

$$E_{AVG} = E_{RMS} \times 0.45 \quad \text{(Equation 23-2)}$$

For the example used above, we find the average direct output voltage by using Equation 23-2:

$$E_{AVG} = E_{RMS} \times 0.45 = 120 \text{ V} \times 0.45 = 54 \text{ V}$$

The diode must withstand a *peak inverse voltage (PIV)* that is equal to the peak voltage value given by Equation 23-1. You must consider PIV when you select a diode for a certain circuit. For the circuit of Figure 23-23, you would choose a diode with a PIV rating higher than 170 volts. Provide a wide safety margin. Select a diode that has a PIV rating of about twice the applied peak inverse voltage. (A diode with at least a PIV rating of 340 volts would be a safe choice in this case.)

Many electronic devices will not work properly with the pulsed direct voltage output from a half-wave rectifier. They require a steady value of direct voltage for proper operation. How can we make use of the output from a half-wave rectifier, then? We must *filter* the output voltage before using it. A filter will help fill in the gaps in the output voltage. It also will maintain the voltage at a fairly constant level. We can make a filter simply by connecting a large-value capacitor across the output terminals, as Figure 23-24 shows.

When we first close the switch, the capacitor will quickly charge to a voltage equal to E_{PEAK}. While the diode is not conducting, the voltage across the capacitor begins to decrease. The output voltage will drop more gradually, however, than it would without the capacitor. The next time the diode conducts, the capacitor will charge up to E_{PEAK} again. **Figure 23-25** shows the output voltage from the filtered half-wave rectifier.

The filter capacitor should have a large capacitance value, often 1000 microfarads or more. If the output current is small (less than a few milliamps) the output voltage will remain fairly constant. The capacitor voltage will drop while the diode is not conducting. If the circuit takes more output current, this voltage drop will be greater.

Using a filter capacitor in the circuit does make one important change in the required PIV rating of the diode. Since the capacitor charges to the peak voltage, the maximum reverse voltage applied to the diode is two times the peak value. (The circuit applies the peak output voltage from the capacitor to one side of the diode. At the same time, it applies the opposite-polarity peak voltage from the generator to the other side of the diode. So, the diode is in series with these two voltages.) With a capacitive filter, the peak inverse voltage (PIV) across the diode in a half-wave rectifier is given by:

$$PIV = E_{RMS} \times 2.828 \quad \text{(Equation 23-3)}$$

or:

$$PIV = 2 \times E_{PEAK} \quad \text{(Equation 23-4)}$$

Let's go back to our example of a 120-V generator and a peak output voltage of 169.7 volts. With a filter capacitor on the output, the peak inverse voltage applied to the diode is:

$$PIV = E_{RMS} \times 2.828 = 120 \text{ V} \times 2.828 = 339 \text{ V}$$

We should select a diode with a PIV rating of about 680 V.

The Full-Wave Rectifier Circuit

In the last section we talked about the half-wave rectifier circuit. How can we make more efficient use of the alternating input voltage than with that circuit? The *full-wave rectifier* produces a direct-voltage output pulse for each half of the input-voltage cycle. This circuit uses two diodes. We connect them so one diode conducts during the positive half cycle and the other conducts during the negative half cycle.

This increased efficiency is not without tradeoffs, however. The input-signal generator must have a terminal that is at a voltage half-way between the positive and negative voltage peaks. This terminal, called a center tap, is at ground potential. The generator alternately applies the positive and negative voltages to the two diodes. The common, or ground, connection provides a reference point between them. **Figure 23-26** shows such a circuit.

The most common source of alternating input voltage is a transformer connected to the ac mains supply. You choose a transformer with a secondary (output) voltage to give the desired peak direct voltage from the rectifier.

A full-wave rectifier circuit requires a center-tapped transformer to supply the input voltage. The full secondary voltage must be twice the

peak output voltage you want. In other words, the peak output voltage must appear on either side of the center tap. In contrast, the half-wave rectifier does not require a center-tapped transformer. In that case, the full secondary voltage only needs to be equal to the desired peak output voltage.

How does this full-wave rectifier work? Let's take another look at Figure 23-26. When the top of the supply is positive, diode D1 is forward biased, and conducts. The bottom half of the supply is negative with respect to ground, and D2 is reverse biased. When the polarity reverses, the bottom half of the supply is positive and the top half is negative. D2 conducts and D1 is reverse biased. Notice that the output from D2 connects to the load resistor with the same polarity as D1. So the output pulse from D2 is in the same direction as the pulse from D1. **Figure 23-27** shows there is an output pulse for each half of the input

waveform. Both pulses are in the same direction, so we have a pulsating dc output voltage.

Figure 23-27 shows the output waveform from the full-wave rectifier. It has two output pulses for every complete input waveform cycle. The ripple frequency of the output is twice the input frequency. The ripple frequency for a half-wave rectifier is the same as the input frequency. The greater the ripple frequency, the easier it is to filter the output to produce a smooth direct voltage. This means it is easier to filter the output from a full-wave rectifier than a half-wave rectifier. A smaller-value filter capacitor will give the same degree of smoothing to the output waveform as with the half-wave rectifier. **Figure 23-28A** shows a full-wave rectifier circuit with a filter capacitor on the output. Figure 23-28B shows how the charged capacitor smoothes the output ripple by holding the output voltage at a nearly constant level.

Figure 23-26 — This diagram shows a full-wave rectifier circuit. Notice that the alternating voltage input has a center, or ground, connection. The voltage on the other two terminals changes from positive to negative with respect to the center connection.

Figure 23-27 — Part A shows the input voltage waveform and Part B shows the output voltage waveform for the full-wave rectifier. Notice the two output pulses for every input cycle. The output voltage varies between zero and a maximum or peak value. It is always on the same side of the zero line, however. The output is a pulsating direct voltage.

(A)

(B)

UBE0279

**Figure 23-28 —
Part A shows a
full-wave rectifier
circuit with a
capacitor filter
on the output.
Part B shows
how the capacitor
serves to smooth
the ripple in the
output voltage.**

age output voltage with the half-wave rectifier was 0.45 times the RMS supply voltage. By using the entire input waveform to produce the direct voltage output, we have doubled the average output voltage! That's quite an improvement.

To select the proper diodes for the full-wave rectifier circuit, we must consider the peak inverse voltage across a diode. Look at **Figure 23-29**. When the top half of the transformer is positive, diode D1 conducts. The circuit applies the transformer peak positive voltage to the cathode of D2. At this instant, the bottom half of the transformer is at its peak negative value. So the circuit applies the transformer peak negative voltage to the anode of D2. D2 does not conduct. The peak inverse voltage across D2 is twice the transformer peak secondary voltage between the center tap and either side. When the transformer polarity reverses, the same conditions apply to D1.

The output voltage from the full-wave rectifier is a pulsating direct voltage. This voltage varies from zero to a peak value twice during every complete input-voltage cycle. You can calculate the peak value of these pulses. You must know the RMS value of the transformer secondary voltage between the center tap and either side.

$$E_{PEAK} = E_{RMS} \times 1.414 \quad \text{(Equation 23-5)}$$

We also want to know the average voltage of the output waveform. To calculate this voltage you must know the RMS value of the transformer secondary voltage between either side and the center tap.

$$E_{AVG} = E_{RMS} \times 0.9 \quad \text{(Equation 23-6)}$$

You may remember that the aver-

$$E_{PIV} = E_{RMS} \times 2 \times 1.414$$
$$= E_{RMS} \times 2.828 \quad \text{(Equation 23-7)}$$

When selecting diodes for the circuit, allow a safety factor of about two times the calculated E_{PIV}.

UBE0280

Figure 23-29 — This is an example of a full-wave rectifier circuit. It shows the input and output voltage waveforms at various points throughout the circuit. You can calculate peak and average output voltages from the RMS value of the input voltage. A large-value capacitor across the output takes the rectified pulses and turns them into a smooth output.

Let's work through an example to show how we use these equations to calculate practical information about a rectifier circuit. A center-tapped transformer supplies the input voltage to the rectifier circuit of Figure 23-29. The RMS output voltage of this transformer is 18 volts on either side of the center tap. First, let's calculate the peak output voltage from the circuit. Equation 23-5 will help with this calculation.

$$E_{PEAK} = E_{RMS} \times 1.414$$
(Equation 23-5)

$$E_{PEAK} = 18 \text{ V} \times 1.414 = 25.5 \text{ V}$$

Next, we will use Equation 23-6 to calculate the average output voltage.

$$E_{AVG} = E_{RMS} \times 0.9 \quad \text{(Equation 23-6)}$$

$$E_{AVG} = 18 \text{ V} \times 0.9 = 16.2 \text{ V}$$

Finally, we will use Equation 23-7 to calculate the peak inverse voltage across the diodes.

$$E_{PIV} = E_{RMS} \times 2 \times 1.414$$
$$= E_{RMS} \times 2.828 \quad \text{(Equation 23-7)}$$

$$E_{PIV} = 18 \text{ V} \times 2.828 = 50.9 \text{ V}$$

We should select a diode with a PIV rating of about 100 V to provide the suggested safety factor.

The Bridge Rectifier Circuit

The *bridge rectifier* offers the best features of the full-wave rectifier circuit without the major disadvantage. It gives two output pulses for each cycle of the input voltage, like the full-wave rectifier does. The bridge rectifier is a form of full-wave rectifier. The bridge rectifier does not require a center-tapped transformer, though. The peak alternating voltage across the entire transformer secondary appears at the rectifier output. **Figure 23-30** shows a bridge rectifier circuit with input and output voltage waveforms.

A bridge rectifier has one possible disadvantage: the circuit requires four diodes. Remember that a full-wave rectifier requires a transformer with a center-tapped secondary, though. Two extra diodes don't cost much compared to the cost of a center-tapped transformer with twice the full secondary voltage. So this is a fair trade-off. In fact, bridge rectifier circuits are so popular that manufacturers make units with the four diodes built into a single package.

Let's analyze how our bridge rectifier circuit works. The circuit may look complicated at first glance. However, it's easy to understand if we take it one step at a time.

First, we redraw the circuit from Figure 23-30 as shown in **Figure 23-31A**. Notice that the top transformer lead is positive and the bottom one is negative at this instant. This means that D1 is forward biased and D2 is reverse biased. We drew D2 in a dot pattern to show that it is not part of the circuit in this case. Since D1 is forward biased, the transformer voltage connects to the load, represented by R1. This voltage drops across R1, but is still more positive than the voltage on the bottom transformer lead. Therefore, D3 is forward biased and D4 is reverse biased. (We also drew D4 with a dot pattern to show that it is not part of the circuit in this case.) The electrons flow out the negative transformer lead, through D3, the

Figure 23-30 — This circuit is a bridge rectifier. The drawing includes alternating voltage waveforms at the transformer primary and secondary. It also shows the pulsed direct voltage output waveform from the rectifier.

Figure 23-31 — Part A shows the rectifier circuit when the top of the transformer is positive and the bottom is negative. Diodes D1 and D3 are forward biased and conduct. Diodes D2 and D4 are reverse biased and do not conduct. Part B shows the circuit conditions when the input polarity changes. Then the bottom of the transformer is positive and the top is negative. Both drawing parts show the reverse-biased diodes drawn with a dot pattern. This illustrates that those diodes act like an open circuit, effectively removing them from the circuit.

Figure 23-32 — Drawing the diodes as shown here may make it easier for you to understand how a bridge rectifier circuit works. The circuit operation described in the text still applies.

load resistor, D1, and finally back to the positive transformer lead.

What happens when the voltage polarity on the transformer reverses? Take a look at Figure 23-31B. Now the bottom transformer lead is positive and the top one is negative. D4 is forward biased and D3 is reverse biased. The transformer voltage connects to the load resistor, R1, through D4. There is a voltage drop across the resistor. The voltage at the junction of D1 and D2 is still more positive than the top transformer lead, however. D2 is forward biased this time, and D1 is reverse biased. The circuit is again complete, and there is a current. This time, electrons flow out the top trans-

former lead, through D2, the load resistor, D4, and finally to the bottom transformer lead.

Figures 23-30 and 23-31 show the bridge rectifier circuit drawn in a traditional way. The diodes form the sides of a diamond. You may find the circuit operation easier to understand if we redraw the circuit as shown in **Figure 23-32**. Again, D1 and D3 conduct on one half of the input waveform. D2 and D4 conduct on the opposite half cycle of the input waveform.

As you might expect, the output voltage from the bridge rectifier is a pulsating direct voltage. This voltage varies from zero to a peak value twice

during every complete input-voltage cycle. You can calculate the peak value of these pulses if you know the RMS value of the transformer secondary voltage.

$$E_{PEAK} = E_{RMS} \times 1.414$$

(Equation 23-8)

This equation applies any time you want to calculate the peak value of a sine-wave alternating voltage.

We also would like to know the average voltage of the output waveform. Calculate the average voltage using the RMS value of the transformer secondary voltage.

$$E_{AVG} = E_{RMS} \times 0.9 \quad \text{(Equation 23-9)}$$

This equation also gives the average output voltage from a full-wave rectifier circuit.

As with other rectifiers, we normally want to smooth the output pulses before applying the direct voltage to an electronic circuit. We can smooth these pulses by using a filter capacitor. **Figure 23-33** shows such a capacitor across the rectified output from a bridge rectifier. The capacitor provides a smoothed, steady direct voltage. There is only a small amount of ripple, or variation, in the output. In general, larger values of capacitance provide an output voltage with less ripple.

To select the proper diodes for the bridge rectifier circuit, we must consider the peak inverse voltage across a diode. Look at Figure 23-31 again. When the top of the transformer is positive, diodes D1 and D3 conduct. We are applying the transformer peak positive voltage across D2 and D4. When the transformer polarity reverses, diodes D2 and D4 conduct. We are applying the peak secondary voltage to D1 and D3. Each diode must withstand the peak secondary output voltage.

$$E_{PIV} = E_{RMS} \times 1.414 \quad \text{(Equation 23-10)}$$

When selecting diodes for a bridge rectifier circuit, allow a safety factor of about two times the calculated E_{PIV}.

An example will show how to use these equations to calculate practical information about a rectifier circuit.

Figure 23-33 — A bridge rectifier produces two output pulses for each complete input-waveform cycle. A large value capacitor connected across the output serves to smooth the pulses, leaving us with a smoothed, steady direct voltage.

Let's suppose the input voltage to our bridge rectifier circuit comes from a transformer with an RMS output of 18 volts. First, we'll calculate the peak output voltage from the circuit. Equation 23-8 will help with this calculation.

$$E_{PEAK} = E_{RMS} \times 1.414 \quad \text{(Equation 23-8)}$$

$$E_{PEAK} = 18 \text{ V} \times 1.414 = 25.5 \text{ V}$$

Next, we'll use Equation 23-9 to calculate the average output voltage.

$$E_{AVG} = E_{RMS} \times 0.9 \quad \text{(Equation 23-9)}$$

$$E_{AVG} = 18 \text{ V} \times 0.9 = 16.2 \text{ V}$$

Finally, use Equation 23-10 to calculate the peak inverse voltage across the diodes.

$$E_{PIV} = E_{RMS} \times 1.414 \quad \text{(Equation 23-10)}$$

$$E_{PIV} = 18 \text{ V} \times 1.414 = 25.5 \text{ V}$$

We should select a diode with a PIV rating of about 50 V to provide the suggested safety factor.

We Can Use Diodes as Switches

A forward-biased diode acts like a short circuit. (Remember that a forward-biased diode has a positive voltage connected to its anode and a negative voltage connected to its cathode.) Similarly, a reverse-biased diode acts like an open circuit. In that case, the diode cathode is positive and the anode is negative. This description begins to make a diode sound a bit like a switch. When the diode is forward biased, it is a closed switch. When it is reverse biased, it is an open switch. See **Figure 23-34**.

In fact, it is common to use diodes as switches to turn RF currents on and off in electronic circuits. You can turn such a switch off or on by controlling the diode bias voltage. **Figure 23-35** shows one simple example of such a *diode switch*. D2 serves as a switch to turn on a type 47 bulb with a 50-MHz RF source. When S1 is open, D2 is reverse biased. It is an open switch, and there is no current through the bulb. When S1 is in the closed position, the cathode of D2 is more negative than its anode. The diode is forward biased. It acts like a closed switch, and conducts current. Now there is a complete circuit for the RF supply. There is current through the bulb, C1 and D2 to ground. The bulb lights.

You are probably saying, "Hey, wait a minute! What good is a diode switch, if it takes a mechanical switch to turn it on and off?" That's a good question. For a simple circuit like the one shown in Figure 23-35, it really has no advantage. You could just as easily use a mechanical switch in place of D2 in this circuit. The switch would then control whether the bulb was lit or not. (See **Figure 23-36**.)

Let's suppose our circuit was a bit more complex. What if our electronic circuit was a radio receiver, and we wanted to select between several different filter circuits in the receiver. We might have four or five wires to connect or disconnect for each filter. We must switch each of these wires at the same time to change from one filter to the other. We could use a five-pole, double-throw switch (if we could find one). A few diodes also can do the switching. Now, one mechanical switch connects the bias voltage to all the diodes, and they will switch the circuit for us.

There is another important advantage of diode switches. You can place the diode right at the point in the circuit where you want to do the switching. Then you can apply the dc bias voltage through a mechanical switch located some distance away. The mechanical switch can be on a control panel or another convenient location. Otherwise, we would have to run long lengths of wire from the circuit to the

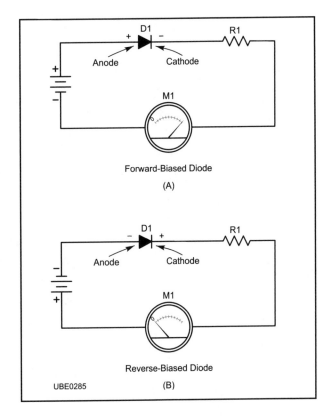

UBE0285

Figure 23-34 — A forward-biased diode acts like a closed switch, allowing current through the circuit, as Part A shows. A reverse-biased diode acts like an open switch, preventing current through the circuit, as Part B shows.

Figure 23-35 — Here is a simple diode switch. Closing S1 applies forward-bias voltage to D2. The diode conducts, allowing current through the bulb.

Figure 23-36 — There may not be much advantage to using a diode switch in the circuit of Figure 23-35. You could use a mechanical switch instead, and the circuit looks much simpler. There are several big advantages to using diode switches in circuits that are more complex, however.

Figure 23-37 — Part A shows a portion of an amplifier circuit, with a series diode switch. When S1 is in the position shown, D1 is forward biased. The signal flows through the diode to the amplifier. When the switch is in the opposite position, the diode is reverse biased. In this case the signal can't reach the amplifier. Resistors R1 and R2 serve to limit the diode current and isolate the signal current from the biasing circuit. Part B shows a section of an oscillator circuit. The shunt diode switch adds C2 to the circuit when it is forward biased (with +12 volts applied). The oscillator frequency decreases when the circuit capacitance increases. This diode switch provides two frequency ranges for the oscillator by changing the tuned circuit component values. This type of diode switching does not work well with dc or at frequencies below the VHF range.

switch location. Long leads may be okay for direct voltages. We want to keep the lead lengths as short as possible when we are switching audio or radio frequencies, however.

Perhaps the biggest advantage of a diode switch is the way it can operate automatically. Suppose part of the circuit measures a certain condition, and operates the switch based upon that condition. For example, you might have a circuit that would detect the presence of radio frequency (RF) energy from a transmitter. This circuit could operate a diode switch to connect the antenna lead to the transmitter. When the circuit finds no RF, the switch connects the antenna to the receiver.

We can connect diode switches in either of two ways. One is to wire the diode in *series* with a signal lead. The other is to wire the diode from the signal lead to ground (in *shunt*). **Figure 23-37** shows partial circuits using these two diode-switching techniques.

When selecting a diode to use as a switch, you should select a diode with a *peak inverse voltage (PIV) rating* suitable for your circuit. You should also pay attention to the *maximum forward current ratings* of the diode. This will depend on how much current you expect your circuit to draw. The most important rating for a switching diode is its *speed*, or *switching time*. Manufacturers make some diodes specifically for use as

rectifier diodes and others for use as *electronic switches*. You should select a diode designed for your intended application.

When a diode goes from forward to reverse bias, it takes some time before the diode cuts off. During this time, there is reverse current through the diode. In general, diodes designed for rectifier circuits have slower switching times than diodes designed as switches.

Review Questions ——————————————— Answers ———

23.1 Diodes allow:

a) current to flow through them in only one direction

b) current to flow through them in both directions at once

c) no current to flow through them

d) any old thing — they are very tolerant

23.2 A diode that is used to turn ac into dc is called a _____.

23.3 Between the P-type and N-type materials of a solid-state diode:

a) an inductor should be installed

b) is undoped semiconductor material

c) current flows freely in both directions

d) is the *depletion region*

23.4 Before current will flow in the forward direction through a silicon diode, a voltage of about 0.7 V must be applied across it. This voltage is known as the:

a) diode control voltage

b) threshold voltage

c) reverse voltage

d) power line voltage

23.5 Diodes carrying large forward currents may overheat unless they are attached to:

a) semiconductor thermal barriers

b) cooling fans

c) metal heat sinks

d) sheets of insulation

23.6 The highest voltage that can safely be applied to a diode when it is reverse biased is called the _____ _____ _____.

23.7 Diodes connected so that both halves of a sine wave input produce a dc output voltage are called a _____ _____.

23.8 Which two of the following are important diode ratings that must be considered when designing circuits?

a) maximum forward current

b) diode lead wire diameter

c) peak inverse voltage

d) coulomb capacity

23.1 a

23.2 A diode which is used to turn ac into dc is called a rectifier.

23.3 d

23.4 b

23.5 c

23.6 The highest voltage that can safely be applied to a diode when it is reverse biased is called the *peak inverse voltage (PIV)*.

23.7 Diodes connected so that both halves of a sine wave input produce a dc output voltage are called a *full-wave rectifier*.

23.8 a, c

Chapter 24

Bipolar Transistors (BJTs)

Bipolar transistors are found in many circuits.

Contents

Three-Layer Sandwich

Scientists experimented with semiconductor materials in the 1930s and 1940s. Three of them made a very important discovery in 1947 at the Bell Telephone Laboratory. William Shockley, John Bardeen and Walter Brattain discovered *transistor action.* They used this term to describe the action of "*trans*ferring current across a re*sistor.*" This discovery is the basis for modern solid-state electronics. The discovery was recognized as being so important that in 1956 the three men received the Nobel Prize in Physics.

Current passes through PN-junction diodes in only one direction. Connect the positive side of a battery or other voltage supply to the P-type material. The negative side connects to the N-type material. This puts a forward-bias voltage on the diode and there is a current through it. If we reverse these battery connections, the diode has a

reverse-bias voltage. In that case there is almost no current.

There is a very small *leakage current* through a reverse-biased diode. If we apply a large enough voltage, we can push a large *reverse current* through the diode. We call this reverse voltage the *breakdown voltage.* If we allowed this to happen (large reverse current with reverse breakdown voltage applied), it's likely we would create an *SED* (smoke-emitting diode) and it would be destroyed. **Figure 24-1** is a graph of the relationship between the voltage and current for a typical diode.

Shockley, Bardeen and Brattain made their discovery by forming a single piece of semiconductor with two diodes back-to-back. **Figure 24-2** shows three layers of semiconductor material. There is a thin layer of N-type material between two layers

of P-type material. The cathodes of the two diodes are connected in this example.

We can connect either diode to a voltage source, and this "sandwich" behaves like a diode. **Figure 24-3** shows the diode junctions connected to a battery one at a time. The resistors limit the forward current so we don't destroy the diodes.

Now we'll try another experiment. Connect one diode to a forward-bias voltage and the other to a reverse-bias voltage. **Figure 24-4** shows these circuit connections. You should expect a current through the forward-biased diode circuit. There should not be any current through the reverse-biased diode circuit, however.

Something amazing happens when we conduct this experiment. With current in the forward-biased circuit there also is current in the reverse-biased

Figure 24-1 — This graph shows how the current through a diode changes as the applied voltage changes. When the voltage applied to the anode or P-type material is positive, the forward current rises rapidly. For a silicon diode the forward bias voltage must be more than about 0.6 volt to cause this forward current. The forward bias voltage only needs to be more than about 0.2 volt for a germanium diode. When the voltage applied to the cathode or N-type material is positive, there is only a small leakage current. When the reverse-bias voltage exceeds the diode's breakdown voltage, however, there is a large reverse current. This will destroy many diodes.

Figure 24-2 — This drawing shows a three-layered sandwich of semiconductor materials. This sandwich forms two PN-junction diodes, as indicated by the diode schematic symbols shown at B. The dashed box indicates these diodes are coupled on one piece of semiconductor. They are not individual diodes.

Figure 24-3 — Each PN junction behaves like a typical diode. Parts A and B show the left junction forward and reverse biased. Parts C and D show the right junction with forward and reverse bias applied. Notice that both junctions conduct electricity when they have a forward-bias voltage. Neither junction conducts when it has a reverse-bias voltage.

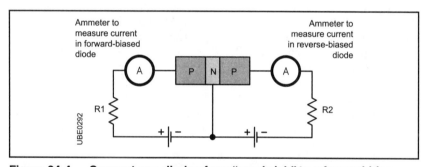

Figure 24-4 — Connect one diode of our "sandwich" to a forward-bias voltage and the other to a reverse-bias voltage. This circuit illustrates the *transistor effect*. Current in the forward-biased diode causes current in the reverse-biased diode.

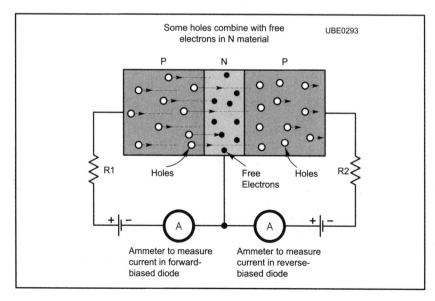

one. Increasing the current in the first part of the circuit increases the current in the second part. Decreasing the current in the first part decreases the current in the second part. This is what Shockley and his coworkers called the *transistor effect*. Current in the forward-biased diode is transferred across the resistance of the reverse-biased diode.

How can this action take place? **Figure 24-5** shows the semiconductor materials with *free electrons* in the N-type material and holes in the P-type material. Holes in the forward-biased P material move toward the negative voltage polarity on the N material. The voltage pulling on the holes makes them speed up as they move closer to the PN junction.

The motion of these holes causes them to move through the thin layer of N-type material without combining with free electrons there. The holes enter the second layer of P-type material. The negative voltage on that material pulls the holes all the way through the second layer of P-type material.

This device became known as a *transistor*, because it is a device that exhibits transistor action. We call the first layer of P material the *emitter*. The emitter puts current into the transistor, or emits current. The second layer of P material we call the *collector*, because it collects the holes that move through the N-type material. The section of N-type material in the middle is the *base*.

It is important to understand that you can't make a transistor by simply connecting two diodes. The diodes must be formed as a single unit, with a very thin base region. The two P layers must be in close contact with the thin N layer.

Figure 24-5 — This illustration shows the movement of holes and electrons in our three-layered sandwich. Holes move through the thin layer of N-type material. Then the negative voltage on the other side of the second layer of P-type material pulls the holes. The third terminal collects these holes. The holes create a current through the second diode.

PNP and NPN Transistors

In the last section you learned that a *transistor* is a three-layered sandwich of P- and N-type semiconductor material. All our examples in that section had two P-material layers and one N-material layer.

We pictured a transistor as a connection between the cathodes of two PN-junction diodes. This joint represents one transistor connection. The other two connections are to the diode anodes. **Figure 24-6** shows diodes connected this way. Part B shows the three-layered sandwich. Part C shows the schematic-diagram symbol we use to represent such a transistor on circuit diagrams.

The Figure 24-6 transistor has a layer of N-type material between two layers of P-type material. This is why we call it a *PNP transistor*. You will notice that the schematic diagram-symbol *emitter* lead has an arrow. This arrow points toward the transistor base. Remember that the arrow points toward the base for a PNP transistor. Just keep in mind that the

arrow **Points iN Proudly**.

You may be wondering if we can make a transistor from two layers of N-type material and one of P-type material. The answer is, "Yes, we can!" **Figure 24-7** shows a diode pair connected anode to anode. This forms a pair of PN junctions that have the P material in the center. We have an NPN sandwich, or *NPN transistor*. Part C shows the schematic-diagram symbol for an NPN transistor. There is an arrow on the emitter lead of this symbol. Notice that this arrow does *Not Point iN*.

The diode-symbol arrow points in the direction of *conventional current*. This is opposite to the direction of electron flow. The transistor-symbol arrows also point in the direction of conventional current. The arrows always appear on the emitter lead.

Figure 24-8A shows a PNP transistor connected in a test circuit. The emitter connects to the positive voltage supply. The collector connects to the negative side of a second voltage

supply. The emitter/base diode has a forward-bias voltage applied. The collector/base diode has a reverse-bias voltage.

Figure 24-8B is an NPN transistor test circuit. The NPN transistor emitter connects to the negative side of the voltage supply. The collector connects to the positive side of a second voltage supply. Again, the emitter/base diode has a forward-bias voltage. The collector/base diode has a reverse-bias voltage.

Transistor action occurs in a PNP transistor when the bias voltages pull holes from the emitter material through the base region. These holes move into the collector region, where the bias voltage continues to attract the holes through the material.

Transistor action in an NPN transistor is similar. This time the emitter has a negative voltage and the base has a positive voltage. The base region attracts free electrons from the emitter. These free electrons are moving fast enough to move right through

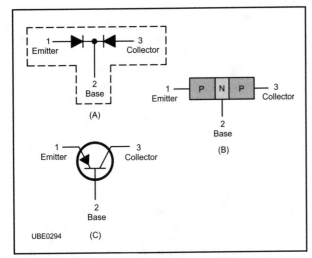

Figure 24-6 — This drawing shows a PNP transistor as a diode pair and a semiconductor sandwich. The dashed box indicates these diodes are coupled on one piece of semiconductor. They are not individual diodes. Part C shows the schematic diagram symbol for PNP transistors. The arrow in this symbol *Points iN Proudly*.

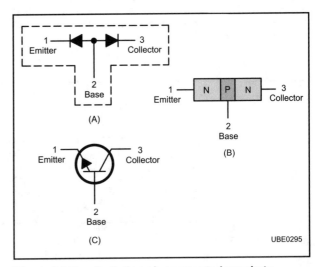

Figure 24-7 — A diode pair connected anode to anode form an NPN transistor. The dashed box indicates these diodes are coupled on one piece of semiconductor. They are not individual diodes. Part C shows the schematic diagram symbol for NPN transistors. The arrow on the emitter does *Not Point iN* on an NPN transistor.

Figure 24-8 — Part A shows a simple test circuit for a PNP transistor. V_{EE} and V_{CC} are common designators for the emitter and collector bias voltages. Resistors R1 and R2 limit the transistor current. Part B shows a similar connection for an NPN transistor.

the base. Once they enter the collector material, the positive bias voltage on that region continues to attract the electrons.

When we draw a transistor as a diode pair or as a semiconductor block, the construction looks symmetrical. You might wonder if you could use either end connection as the emitter. Transistors aren't usually manufactured to be symmetrical, though. Manufacturers create better transistors by making the emitter and collector sides different.

Controlling a Current with a Smaller Current

Figure 24-9 shows a PNP transistor circuit. The circuit includes ammeters and voltmeters to measure various circuit conditions. The transistor's emitter/base diode has a forward-bias voltage applied.

Ammeter M1 measures the current through the emitter/base junction. Ammeter M2 measures the current at the transistor base lead. Ammeter M3 measures current through the reverse-biased base/collector junction. Voltmeter M4 measures the voltage between the emitter and collector.

We will use the Figure 24-9 test circuit to measure circuit conditions for our transistor. By changing the bias voltages one at a time, we can learn a lot about *transistor action*. Let's conduct an experiment with this circuit and make some measurements. Assume we can vary the emitter and collector bias voltages as needed.

Begin with V_{CC} and V_{BB} both set to 0. Adjust V_{CC} until voltmeter M4 reads 5 volts. Then increase V_{BB} until ammeter M2 reads 0.2 mA. When we read ammeter M3, the current is 4.2 mA.

For the next part of our experiment, we increase V_{CC} until M4 reads 10 volts. Continue to increase this reading, 5 volts at a time, up to 40 volts. M3 displays the collector current.

It may surprise you to learn the collector current remains constant. With a collector voltage of 40, the collector current is still 4.2 mA. **Figure 24-10** is a graph of the collector current as the collector voltage changes. Ammeter M1 reads a constant 4.4 mA during these collector-voltage changes.

The experimental results given in this example are for an ideal transistor. The collector current actually does increase slightly for real transistors. The increase is normally small, however. Let's continue our experiment with this ideal transistor.

Set V_{CC} so meter M4 reads 5 volts again. Then increase V_{BB} and watch the base-current meter, M2. Set VBB so M2 reads 0.4 mA. What do you think M3 will read? Well, we doubled the base current, so if you guessed 8.4 mA, you are correct.

Now we are ready to increase the collector voltage again. Adjust V_{CC} for a reading of 10 volts on M4 and read the collector current on M3.

Continue increasing the collector voltage 5 volts at a time and reading the collector current. This time you shouldn't be surprised to learn that the current remains at 8.4 mA. Likewise, the emitter current remains a constant 8.8 mA.

Reset V_{CC} for 5 volts on the collector. Adjust V_{BB} until the base current is 0.6 mA. Note that the collector current reads 12.6 mA. Then increase the collector voltage in 5-volt steps and read the collector and emitter currents at each step. What is the reading from the emitter-current meter, M1? If you have followed the pattern, you can estimate that the emitter current is 13.2 mA.

Equation 24-1 shows the relationship between base current, emitter current and collector current.

$$I_E = I_B + I_C \qquad \text{(Equation 24-1)}$$

where:
  I_E is the emitter current
  I_B is the base current
  I_C is the collector current

We are measuring the transistor characteristics in this experiment. **Figure 24-11** is a graph of collec-

Figure 24-9 — This test circuit will help us measure transistor circuit conditions. V_{BB} and V_{CC} allow us to vary the transistor bias voltages. The meters help us measure the current at each lead and the voltage between the collector and emitter.

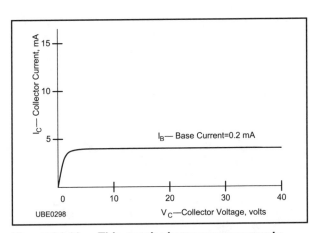

Figure 24-10 — This graph shows measurements taken from the Figure 24-9 circuit. The data shows that collector current remains constant while the collector voltage varies over a wide range.

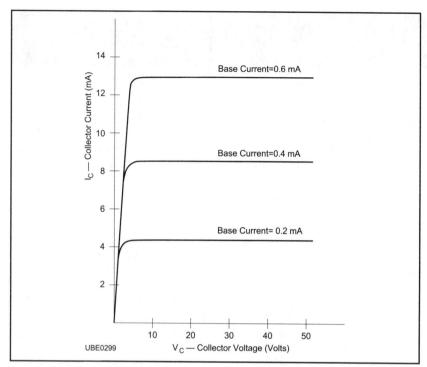

Figure 24-11 — This graph shows the characteristic curves for our sample transistor. Characteristic curves of other transistor types have similar shapes, although the specific voltages and currents are different.

tor current and collector voltage at each measured base-current value. Manufacturers make many different transistor types. The characteristic curves for each type have different specific numbers. The general shapes of the curves are similar, however.

Eventually, we find that increasing the base current further does not increase the collector current. For our sample transistor, this point might be at 1.2 mA of base current. When the collector current reaches a maximum value, we say the transistor is *saturated*. This means the collector circuit gathers all the charge carriers the emitter injects through the base. The charge carriers are holes for PNP and electrons for NPN transistors.

What else have we learned from our experiment? Small changes in base current produce larger changes in collector current. If we feed a signal into the transistor base, the collec-tor current will be an enlarged version of that signal. Suppose the base signal varies between 0.2 mA and 0.6 mA. The collector current varies between 4.2 and 12.6 mA.

A small base current controls a larger collector current. The output signal is an enlarged version of the input, so the circuit *amplifies* the input signal. Because of *transistor action*, our circuit is an *amplifier*.

You will hear two terms used to describe the *current gain* characteristics of transistors. These gain factors are important to circuit designers and engineers. You probably won't use these factors in circuit calculations until you study more advanced electronics. A transistor's *alpha* (α) and *beta* (β) help evaluate how effective a particular transistor type will be for an amplifier circuit.

Calculate current gain α by dividing collector current by emitter current. Current gain α is always a bit less than 1, normally in a range between 0.92 and 0.98.

$$\alpha = \frac{I_C}{I_E} \qquad \text{(Equation 24-2)}$$

where:
  I_C is the collector current
  I_E is the emitter current

Let's calculate α for the transistor in our example.

$$\alpha = \frac{I_C}{I_E} = \frac{4.2 \text{ mA}}{4.4 \text{ mA}}$$

$\alpha = 0.9545$

Try repeating this calculation us-ing the collector and emitter currents that go with any of the other base currents we measured. You will find the same answer.

Calculate current gain β by dividing collector current by base current. Current gain β normally varies between 10 and 200, and is not constant for a particular transistor type. If one transistor has a β of 100, another one of the same type may have a β of 85 or 130. Current gain β even varies with operating conditions (temperature and collector current) for a particular transistor. It is still an important parameter for designers and engineers.

$$\beta = \frac{I_C}{I_B} \qquad \text{(Equation 24-3)}$$

where
  I_B is the base current
  I_C is the collector current.

Use Equation 24-3 to calculate β for our sample transistor.

$$\beta = \frac{I_C}{I_B} = \frac{4.2 \text{ mA}}{0.2 \text{ mA}}$$

$\beta = 21$

You can repeat this calculation for other collector- and base-current values from Figure 24-11.

Biasing the Transistors

Voltages applied to transistor diode junctions set up the circuit operating conditions. In the last section we measured transistor characteristics and plotted the values on a graph. We found that base current controls collector current. What happens when we apply a changing signal, such as an ac sine wave, to the base?

Suppose the only voltage we apply to the transistor base is an ac signal. **Figure 24-12** is an NPN transistor circuit with no other base voltage. When the signal voltage is positive, it puts a forward-bias voltage on the base/emitter junction. This creates base current, which turns on the collector current.

What happens when the ac signal voltage is negative? The base/emitter junction has a reverse-bias voltage. There is no base current, so the collector current also stops.

The collector-current output is a pulse for every half cycle of the input voltage. This is similar to the

output from a half-wave rectifier circuit. That isn't the kind of output we usually want from a transistor circuit. The Figure 24-12 circuit is not producing an amplified version of the input signal.

A transistor circuit requires dc bias voltages to set the operating point on the transistor characteristic curves. Proper bias voltages set this *quiescent point* or *Q point*. Quiescent means "at rest," or without signal present.

Figure 24-13 shows a set of characteristic curves. Q marks the desired operating point, or Q point. The dc bias voltages set up these circuit conditions with no ac signal on the input.

Figure 24-13 also shows a *load line* on the graph. A load line provides a way for us to picture the circuit operation. Let's look at **Figure 24-14**, a schematic diagram of an amplifier. The equations and techniques for calculating the transistor bias values and circuit components are beyond the scope of this book.

You can use Ohm's Law to understand the basics, however.

If the transistor in Figure 24-14 was "off," its collector current would be 0 mA, and the collector voltage would be 30 V. This is point A on Figure 24-13.

If the transistor was "on" and saturated (conducting as much collector current as possible), the collector current would be approximately 30 V divided by 1k Ω, or 30 mA. This is point B on the load line. Can you see these two points on the load line of Figure 24-13?

Let's chose a base current, I_B, of 0.6 mA We can use Ohm's Law to select V_{BB} and R1 to provide 0.6 mA base current, but won't do that calculation now.

With a Q point established, alternating input signals vary the base/emitter junction bias voltage. If the input-signal voltage is within certain limits it won't reverse bias the base/emitter junction, however. For the

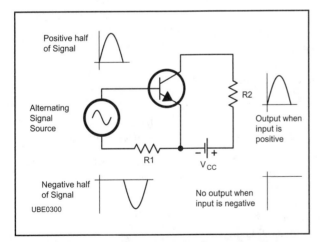

Figure 24-12 — This NPN transistor circuit has an alternating-current signal applied to its base. When this signal is positive, the base/emitter junction has a forward-bias voltage. This junction conducts, and there is collector current. When the signal voltage is negative, the base/emitter junction has a reverse-bias voltage. With no base current there is no collector current either.

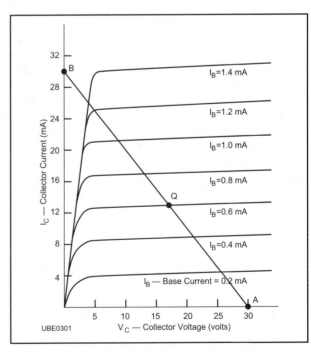

Figure 24-13 — This graph shows a typical transistor characteristic curve. Line AB is a load line with V_{CC} = 30 volts and R2 = 1 kΩ. Q marks the operating point, or Q point.

Figure 24-14 — This schematic diagram is a revised version of Figure 24-12. We added a base bias supply and coupling capacitors on the input and output. The coupling capacitors block the dc bias voltages from going to the ac signal source and the output circuit.

Figure 24-15 — This audio amplifier circuit uses a common 2N2222 NPN transistor. The resistors set the proper Q point bias voltages and make the circuit nearly independent of temperature and individual transistor variations. Capacitor C1 is the emitter *bypass capacitor*. Sometimes we refer to the input and output *coupling capacitors* C2 and C3 as *blocking capacitors*.

characteristic curves of Figure 24-13, the input signal current (which is base current, or I_B) can vary about ±0.4 mA. Since we have set the quiescent base current, I_B, at the Q point to 0.6 mA, the maximum and minimum base currents when the alternating input signal is present are calculated as follows.

Maximum I_B = 0.6 mA + 0.4 mA
= 1.0 mA

Minimum I_B = 0.6 mA – 0.4 mA
= 0.2 mA

Looking at Figure 24-13, and realizing that this circuit's operation is determined by the load line, when the base current is 1.0 mA, the collector current is about 21 mA, and the collector voltage is about 10 volts. Likewise, when the base current is 0.2 mA, the collector current is about 4 mA, and the collector voltage is about 26 volts.

An input current variation of ±0.4 mA produced an output current variation (the collector current) of 21 mA minus 4 mA, or 17 mA, which

is ±8.5 mA peak-to-peak.

This corresponds to a collector voltage variation of 26 V minus 10 V, or about 16 volts peak-to-peak. What did we just discover? That our transistor's *current gain* has produced a rather large output voltage swing caused by our input signal. So the *current gain* of the transistor has also created a *voltage gain* of the circuit, and we have made an amplifier that can make small input signals larger.

This example will help you understand why load lines and Q points are important. We must consider other factors to design a practical transistor circuit. Using two bias-voltage supplies is seldom practical. Variations in individual transistor characteristics and temperature stability also make a circuit like Figure 24-14 unreliable.

Figure 24-15 shows a circuit that uses a single voltage supply for both

the base and collector bias voltages. The additional resistors provide temperature stability and reduce the circuit dependence on individual transistor characteristics.

Capacitor C1 is the *emitter bypass capacitor*. It routes the signal current around the emitter resistor, R3. The bypass capacitor prevents R3, which helps to stabilize the Q point, from decreasing the gain of this amplifier circuit. If the signal current went through the emitter resistor, the gain would be dramatically decreased. The dc emitter current flows through R3, and the signal current flows through C1.

The input and output *coupling capacitors* C2 and C3 pass the alternating signal and block the dc bias voltages. We sometimes refer to these capacitors as *blocking capacitors* because they block the direct voltages.

The Common-Emitter Circuit

Bipolar transistors have three leads, the *base, emitter* and *collector*. For all the transistor amplifier circuits we studied so far, the input signal goes between the base and emitter. We take the output signal from the collector and emitter. The emitter lead is common to both the input and output circuits.

One transistor lead is always common to the input and output, because you need four connections and the transistor only has three. In the next two sections of this book you will learn about some other ways to connect transistors as amplifiers.

The circuit of **Figure 24-16** shows an NPN transistor connected as a *common-emitter amplifier*. This circuit should look familiar, because we studied it earlier. Notice there is one bias-voltage supply.

Resistors R1 and R2 form a voltage divider circuit, to supply the correct base/emitter junction bias voltage. The emitter resistor, R3, helps make the circuit stable and less dependent upon the individual transistor current gain β. Collector current through resistor R4 develops the output voltage. Capacitor C1 bypasses the ac signal

around the emitter resistor. Capacitors C2 and C3 couple the ac signal into and out of the amplifier. The amplified output signal is 180° out of phase with the input signal.

Figure 24-17 shows a PNP transistor connected as a common-emitter amplifier. Notice this circuit is nearly identical to the Figure 24-16 circuit. The bias-voltage supply has the opposite polarity, however.

We used a common-emitter circuit to measure the transistor characteristics in the previous sections. Manufacturers and circuit designers refer to these characteristics as *common-emitter characteristics*.

The input and output *impedances* of our transistor amplifier circuit are important. Let's begin by considering the input and output impedances of the transistor itself. Then we will learn how this relates to the circuit impedances.

The base/emitter junction is a diode with forward-bias voltage. A forward-biased diode conducts current. It has a low resistance, typically a few ohms or less. We can say, then, that a transistor has low input impedance.

The base/collector junction is a

diode with reverse-bias voltage. A reverse-biased diode does not conduct easily. It presents a very high resistance, typically a million ohms (a *megohm*) or more. Bipolar transistors have very high output impedance.

Don't confuse the transistor input and output impedances with our amplifier impedances. The amplifier impedances depend on the bias-resistor values, if we choose those values properly.

This book won't teach you to design transistor amplifiers. That is beyond the scope of the book. You can learn more about circuit design by continuing your studies. A few rules will help you understand the circuit operation, however. These rules also will help you evaluate and modify someone else's design.

The emitter resistor, R3, will usually be between 100 Ω and 1000 Ω. R2 should be about 5 to 10 times larger than R3. R1 and R2 form a voltage divider to set the base bias voltage. R1 should be about 10 times the value of R2. The output resistor, R4, should be about 5 to 10 times the emitter resistor value, R3. Let's summarize these rules with some equations.

Figure 24-16 — This diagram is a typical NPN common-emitter amplifier.

Figure 24-17 — A typical PNP common-emitter amplifier is very similar to the NPN version.

R3 is between 100 Ω and 1000 Ω

(Equation 24-4)

$R2 \approx 5 \times R3$ to $10 \times R3$

(Equation 24-5)

$R1 \approx 10 \times R2$ (Equation 24-6)

$R4 \approx 5 \times R3$ to $10 \times R3$

(Equation 24-7)

where ≈ is a symbol that means "approximately equal to."

We won't go through a complete mathematical analysis here. By making a few simplifying assumptions, such an analysis would show the input impedance of our amplifier circuit nearly equal to R2. You can look at a common-emitter amplifier circuit and quickly determine the circuit input impedance. Just look at the bias resistor between the base and the ground, or common, connection.

Are you uncertain about why R2 determines the input impedance? Think of it this way. The base/emitter junction has only a few ohms of resistance. The transistor's current gain β multiplies the emitter resistor value, however.

Suppose β is 50 for our transistor. With a 1000 Ω resistor at R3, this gives a value of 50 kΩ. In effect, R2 is in parallel with this value. You can calculate the resistance of this parallel combination. Since R3 is much larger than R2, the result will be only a little less than R2. This makes R2 a good approximation for the circuit input impedance.

You also can determine the circuit output impedance by looking at the circuit. The output impedance is approximately equal to the output resistor, R4.

To understand this output-impedance approximation, we'll consider the transistor output impedance. Remember the reverse-biased junction has a high impedance. This high impedance is in parallel with R4, which has a much smaller value. Again, the parallel combination is only a little smaller than the value of R4.

Gain refers to how much an amplifier will increase the strength of an input signal. Depending on the application, you may be interested in the *current gain*, the *voltage gain* or the *power gain* of an amplifier. Equations 24-8, 24-9 and 24-10 show these gains depend on the circuit resistors.

$$\text{Current gain} = G_I \; = \; \frac{R2}{R3}$$

(Equation 24-8)

$$\text{Voltage gain} = G_V \; = \; \frac{R4}{R3}$$

(Equation 24-9)

$$\text{Power gain} = G_P \; = \; G_V \times G_I = \frac{R2 \times R4}{R3^2}$$

(Equation 24-10)

Common-emitter amplifiers have high input and output impedances. The method used to stabilize the circuit conditions and make it independent of temperature and individual transistor variations reduces the current gain. Common-emitter amplifiers have good power gain, however. They are the most-used bipolar-transistor amplifier type.

The Common-Base Circuit

The emitter lead is common to both the input and output section for all the transistor circuits we studied so far. You may be wondering if either of the other leads can be common to both sections. Yes, any of the three leads can be common to the input and output sections.

Figure 24-18 shows a simple *common-base circuit*. We used a PNP transistor for this example, but we also could use an NPN transistor. Notice the emitter/base junction has a forward-bias voltage and the base/collector junction has a reverse-bias voltage. We would reverse the bias-battery polarities for an NPN transistor.

There is nothing surprising about biasing the common-base circuit. Separate batteries supply the emitter/base and base/collector-bias voltages. R1 and R2 limit the currents. C1 and C2 couple the alternating signal voltages into and out of the circuit.

We normally want to use a single bias supply instead of the two supplies shown in Figure 24-18. A voltage divider works well for this circuit, as it does for the common-emitter circuit. We also want our circuit to be stable with temperature variations. The circuit should be independent of individual transistor variations. **Figure 24-19** shows a PNP transistor with the proper biasing resistors.

Resistors R1 and R2 form a voltage divider to set the base/emitter bias voltage. The emitter resistor, R3, and the load resistor, R4, stabilize the circuit operation. The resistor combination sets the transistor Q point.

Figure 24-20 shows an NPN transistor connected as a common-base amplifier. The circuit is identical to the Figure 24-19 circuit, except the bias-voltage polarity reverses. Notice the input and output signals are in phase.

The input impedance of a common-base transistor circuit has a low value. This is because the base/emitter junction is a forward-biased diode. The impedance depends on the emitter current.

Shockley, who helped discover transistors, found the equation for input impedance:

$$Z_{in} = \frac{26}{I_E}$$ (Equation 24-11)

where I_E is the emitter current in milliamps.

As examples, the input impedance of a common-base circuit is 26 ohms when the emitter current is 1 mA, and is 13 ohms when the emitter current is 2 mA.

The transistor output impedance is a high value, because the base/collector junction has a reverse-bias voltage. A reverse-biased PN junction has a high impedance.

The load resistor, R4, sets the common-base cir-

Figure 24-19 — This PNP transistor serves in a common-base circuit. This circuit has a single bias supply. The amplifier is stable with temperature variations.

Figure 24-18 — This diagram shows a simple common-base transistor circuit. Separate emitter/ base and base/ collector-junction bias supplies help you understand circuit operation.

Figure 24-20 — This common-base transistor amplifier uses an NPN transistor. The circuit is similar to the Figure 24-19 circuit, with the bias-voltage polarity reversed.

cuit output impedance because this resistor is in parallel with the diode junction. The load resistor may vary between a few thousand ohms and 100 kΩ, depending on the desired circuit output impedance. In any case, the load resistor has a small value compared to the base/collector junction impedance. The circuit output impedance is approximately equal to R4's value.

You can calculate the amplifier current gain by dividing the output current by the input current. Output current is the same as collector current and input current is the same as emitter current. We can write Equation 24-12 for current gain.

$$G_i = \frac{I_O}{I_I} = \frac{I_C}{I_E} \qquad \text{(Equation 24-12)}$$

In an earlier section we defined a transistor's current gain α as collec-

tor current divided by emitter current. Equation 24-12 tells us that the common-base current gain equals the transistor α. Collector current is nearly equal to the emitter current. It is slightly less, though, because collector current and base current add up to the emitter current. Typical values for a range between about 0.90 to 0.99

$$G_i = \alpha \qquad \text{(Equation 24-13)}$$

Divide the output voltage by the input voltage to find the circuit voltage gain. Equation 24-14 shows another way to write the voltage gain.

$$G_V = \frac{\alpha \, R4}{Z_{in}} = \frac{\alpha \, I_E \, R4}{26}$$

$$\text{(Equation 24-14)}$$

where
  R4 is the load-resistor value
  I_E is the emitter-current value
    (in mA)

Equation 24-15 gives the power gain of a common-base circuit. This is the product of the current and voltage gains. Since current gain is slightly less than 1, power gain is a bit less than voltage gain.

$$\text{Power gain} = G_P = G_V \times G_I$$

$$\text{(Equation 24-15)}$$

A typical value for voltage gain is about 320. This value gives a typical power gain of about 310. The common-base circuit output power will be about 310 times greater than the input power.

A common-base amplifier has a low input impedance and a high output impedance. The circuit can be unstable, however, and may oscillate if the gain is set too high.

The Common-Collector Circuit

In this section we will study the third transistor-amplifier circuit type. These amplifiers have the collector lead common to both the input and output circuits. As you probably can guess, we call this a *common-collector circuit*.

Figure 24-21 shows a simple *common-collector transistor amplifier*. This example uses a PNP transistor, but we also could use an NPN transistor. The bias-battery polarities would have to reverse for a PNP circuit.

The Figure 24-21 circuit is not practical, because we normally want to use a single bias supply. The circuit helps us study the common-collector circuit operation, though.

Look at the bias circuit for this transistor. The base and emitter both have positive voltage relative to the collector. The voltage between the collector and emitter is more positive than the voltage between the base and collector. You might look at the circuit and decide the voltage between the transistor's collector and emitter is 12 volts. That is not the case, however. There is a voltage drop across R2. That voltage drop depends on the current through R2. (Remember Ohm's Law?) This voltage drop is important when the circuit designer

sets up the bias conditions.

There is also a voltage drop across R1 in the base/collector circuit. The voltage between the base and collector is somewhat less than 6 volts. The base current is small, so we often ignore this voltage drop. The emitter/base junction does have a forward-bias voltage, because the emitter is more positive than the base. Battery V_{BC} provides a reverse-bias voltage for the base/collector junction.

This bias circuit may look a little different from the other two amplifier types. The principles are the same, though. Separate batteries supply the emitter/base and base/collector-bias voltages. R1 and R2 limit the currents. C1 and C2 couple the alternating signal voltages into and out of the amplifier.

We normally want to use a single bias supply instead of the two supplies shown in Figure 24-21. A voltage divider works well for the common-collector circuit. We use a similar voltage divider for the common-emitter and common-base circuits. We also want our circuit to be stable with temperature variations. The circuit should be as independent of individual transistor variations as possible. **Figure 24-22** shows a PNP

transistor with the proper biasing resistors. Notice the input and output signals are in phase.

Resistors R1 and R2 form a voltage divider to set the base voltage. The emitter resistor, R3, also serves as the load resistor. The resistor combination sets the transistor Q point.

Figure 24-23 shows an NPN transistor connected as a common-collector amplifier. The circuit is similar to the Figure 24-22 circuit. The bias-voltage polarity reverses.

You may notice another difference between the Figure 24-22 and Figure 24-23 circuits. We take the output across R3, the load resistor, in Figure 24-23. We show it this way to introduce you to another name for the common-collector circuit.

A mathematical analysis shows the voltage across R3 varies directly with base-voltage variations. Suppose we feed an input signal into the amplifier. This signal causes a variation in base current, which in turn causes the emitter current to change. The emitter current is β times the base-current. This means the emitter current changes by a factor of β times the base-current change. The resulting emitter-current variation produces a changing voltage drop as

Figure 24-21 — This diagram shows a simple common-collector transistor circuit. Separate bias supplies help you understand circuit operation. Batteries V_{BC} and V_{EC} provide the proper forward and reverse bias voltages. See the text for an explanation.

Figure 24-22 — This PNP transistor serves in a common-collector circuit. The circuit has a single bias supply. The amplifier characteristics don't change with temperature variations.

it flows through R3.

Let's choose an input signal that varies the base voltage ±2.5 volts. This produces a variation of almost exactly ±2.5 volts across R3! We call the voltage across R3 the *emitter voltage*. The emitter voltage follows the base voltage in a common-collector circuit. For this reason, *emitter follower* is another name for the common collector circuit.

The input impedance of a common-collector transistor circuit has a high value. This is because the collector/base junction is a reverse-biased diode. A typical transistor used in a common-collector circuit has an input impedance of 50 kΩ. The circuit input impedance is approximately equal to the parallel combination of R1, R2 and 50 kΩ For the Figure 24-22 and 24-23 circuits, the input impedance is about 8333 Ω. This is nearly equal to the parallel combination of R1 and R2, 10 kΩ.

The transistor output impedance is a low value, because the base/emitter junction has a forward-bias voltage. A forward-biased PN junction has a low impedance.

A typical transistor has an output impedance of about 80 Ω when used

Figure 24-23 — This common-collector transistor amplifier uses an NPN transistor. The circuit is similar to the Figure 24-22 circuit, with the bias-voltage polarity reversed. The output signal is taken across R3, showing why we often call the common-collector circuit an *emitter-follower amplifier*.

in a common-collector amplifier. The circuit output impedance is approximately equal to the parallel combination of this value and the load resistor, R3. For our Figure 24-22 and 24-23 circuits the output impedance is about 74 Ω.

The voltage gain of an emitter-follower amplifier is approximately 1. This follows from our discussion about the circuit operation. The input and output voltages are nearly equal. Equation 24-16 shows we can find the voltage gain of an amplifier by dividing the output voltage by the input voltage.

$$G_V = \frac{V_o}{V_i} \text{ (Equation 24-16)}$$

We also can calculate current gain as the input current divided by the output current. For our common-collector circuit, current gain is the parallel combination of R1 and R2 divided by the load resistor, R3.

$$G_i = \frac{\dfrac{1}{\dfrac{1}{R1} + \dfrac{1}{R2}}}{R3}$$

(Equation 24-17)

For the Figure 24-23 circuit, current gain is 10.

Equation 24-18 gives an amplifier's power gain. This is the product of the current and voltage gains. Since voltage gain is 1, power gain is approximately equal to the current gain.

$$\text{Power gain} = G_P = G_V \times G_I$$
(Equation 24-18)

$$\text{Power gain} = G_P \approx G_I$$

The Figure 24-23 power gain is 10.

A common-collector amplifier has a high input impedance and a low output impedance. This makes a stable amplifier circuit that is ideal as a *buffer* between a low-impedance load and a high-impedance source. The common-collector amplifier acts like an *impedance transformer* in this case.

Transistor Specifications

All electronic components have maximum voltage and current ratings. Transistors are no different. Transistors have several voltage and current ratings with which you should be familiar. There also are several other specifications that you should know about. A circuit designer must be sure not to exceed these ratings. Applying too much voltage or drawing too much current will destroy a transistor.

There is a maximum voltage rating for each pair of transistor elements. You should never apply more than 30 volts between the collector and emitter of a 2N2222 NPN general-purpose transistor, for example. You should

not apply more than 60 volts across the collector/base junction of this transistor. The maximum safe voltage you can apply across the base/emitter junction of a 2N2222 transistor is 5 volts.

Other transistor types have different voltage ratings. We use the abbreviation V_{CEO} for the voltage between the emitter and collector. (The subscript letter O indicates the other terminal — the base in this case — is open, or has no voltage.) You will find transistors with a V_{CEO} rating as low as 15 volts or less, and others as high as 200 volts or more.

The abbreviation for the collector/

base junction voltage is V_{CBO}. Some transistors have V_{CBO} ratings of 30 V or less. Other transistors have V_{CBO} ratings of more than 200 V.

We use the abbreviation V_{EBO} to mean the emitter/base junction voltage. This rating varies from 3.0 volts or less to 10 volts for some transistors. **Table 24-1** lists these and other specifications for a few common general-purpose transistors.

The maximum collector current (I_{Cmax}) a transistor can handle is also important. Some transistors can handle a collector current of only 50 mA. Other transistors can safely carry 2 amperes or more of collector current.

Table 24-1

General Purpose Transistors

Device	Type	V_{CEOmax} Max. Collector-Emitter Voltage (Volts)	V_{CBOmax} Max. Collector-Base Voltage (Volts)	V_{EBOmax} Max. Emitter-Base Voltage (Volts)	I_{Cmax} Max. Collector Current (mA)	P_{Dmax} Max. Device Dissipation (Watts)	Current-Gain Bandwidth Product f_T (MHz)	Noise Fig. NF Max. (dB)
2N918	NPN	15	30	3.0	50	0.200	600	6.0
2N2102	NPN	65	120	7.0	1000	1.0	60	6.0
2N2218	NPN	30	60	5.0	800	0.8	250	
2N2218A	NPN	40	75	6.0	800	0.8	250	
2N2219	NPN	30	60	5.0	800	3.0	250	
2N2219A	NPN	40	75	6.0	800	3.0	300	4.0
2N2222	NPN	30	60	5.0	800	1.2	250	
2N2222A	NPN	40	75	6.0	800	1.2	300	4.0
2N2905	PNP	40	60	5.0	600	0.6	200	
2N2905A	PNP	60	60	5.0	600	0.6	200	
2N2907	PNP	40	60	5.0	600	0.400	200	
2N2907A	PNP	60	60	5.0	600	0.400	200	
2N3053	NPN	40	60	5.0	700	5.0	100	
2N3053A	NPN	60	80	5.0	700	5.0	100	
2N3904	NPN	40	60	6.0	200	0.625	300	5.0
2N3906	PNP	40	40	5.0	200	1.5	250	4.0
2N4037	PNP	40	60	7.0	1000	5.0		
2N4123	NPN	30	40	5.0	200	0.35	250	6.0
2N4124	NPN	25	30	5.0	200	0.350	300	5.0
2N4125	PNP	30	30	4.0	200	0.625	200	5.0
2N4126	PNP	25	25	4.0	200	0.625	250	4.0
2N4401	NPN	40	60	6.0	600	0.625	250	
2N4403	PNP	40	40	5.0	600	0.625	200	
2N5320	NPN	75	100	7.0	2000	10.0		
2N5415	PNP	200	200	4.0	1000	10.0	15	
MM4003	PNP	250	250	4.0	500	1.0		
MPSA55	PNP	60	60	4.0	500	0.625	50	
MPS6547	NPN	25	35	3.0	50	0.625	600	

Figure 24-24 — This photograph shows some common transistors and typical heat sinks. The heat sinks conduct excess heat away from the transistor to help cool the semiconductor junctions.

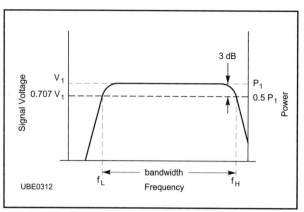

Figure 24-25 — This graph shows an ideal transistor amplifier frequency response. We can measure the output signal voltage or power to find this response. The bandwidth is the difference between the low-frequency cutoff point and the high-frequency cut-off point.

Another important transistor specification is maximum power dissipation, P_{max}. Power dissipation means the power converted to heat inside the transistor. We calculate power by multiplying a voltage times a current. For transistor power dissipation, we multiply the collector/emitter voltage times the collector current.

$$P_{max} = V_{CE} \times I_C \qquad \text{(Equation 24-19)}$$

Notice that we don't calculate maximum power dissipation by multiplying the *maximum* collector/emitter voltage, V_{CEO}, times the *maximum* collector current, I_{Cmax}. The maximum power a transistor can dissipate is usually much less than this product.

There is a trade-off here. If your circuit will apply a voltage close to the maximum rating, you must ensure the collector current is less than maximum. If you have a circuit that requires close to the rated collector current, then you must reduce the voltage.

Let's suppose a 2N2222A transistor has 20 volts applied between its collector and emitter. How much collector current can the circuit draw without exceeding the transistor's 1.2-watt power dissipation rating? We'll solve Equation 24-19 for collector current. (To solve the equation, divide both sides by V_{CE}.)

$$P_{max} = V_{CE} \times I_C \qquad \text{(Equation 24-19)}$$

$$\frac{P_{max}}{V_{CE}} = I_C \qquad \text{(Equation 24-20)}$$

$$I_C = \frac{P_{max}}{V_{CE}} = \frac{1.2\ W}{20\ V} = 0.06\ A$$

$$I_C = 60\ mA$$

Table 24-1 shows the maximum collector current of a 2N2222A is 800 mA. Our calculation shows that the current must be much smaller for the suggested circuit. You also can calculate the maximum collector/emitter voltage for an 800-mA current. This time solve Equation 24-19 for V_{CE}.

$$V_{CE} = \frac{P_{max}}{I_C}$$

$$V_{CE} = \frac{1.2\ W}{0.800\ A} = 1.5\ V$$

$$\text{(Equation 24-20)}$$

Semiconductor junctions are very sensitive to heat. Any power a circuit dissipates in the transistor heats the junction. If the transistor can't get rid of this heat fast enough, it destroys the junction. Transistors designed to handle higher power levels often require *heat sinks*. A heat sink is

a piece of metal designed to conduct the excess heat away from the transistor. Some heat sinks are thin metal strips that slip over the transistor body. Others are heavy blocks of metal that attach to the cabinet or chassis sides. **Figure 24-24** shows some common transistors and heat sinks.

You may want to build a radio-frequency amplifier as part of an Amateur Radio receiver or transmitter. You must consider the *frequency response* of the transistors you select for this circuit. Some transistors are useful to several hundred kilohertz while others operate well into the gigahertz range. You must select a transistor that will operate over the frequency range of your project. Price and other characteristics will influence your final selection.

Figure 24-25 shows a graph of an ideal frequency response. Resistors and capacitors in a practical circuit limit the low-frequency response. Transistor characteristics limit the high-frequency response. Ideally, the circuit should amplify all signals between the lower and upper limits the same amount. In practice, an amplifier isn't likely to have a response as flat across the top as the one we've shown in Figure 24-25.

We can measure the amplified signal voltage. As we vary the frequency, we find the upper and lower values at which the voltage drops to 0.707 times the top value. These frequencies define the circuit *bandwidth*. We also could measure the amplified signal power. The same upper and lower frequencies occur at the half-power points on the graph. When the power drops to half its original value, there is a 3-dB power decrease.

Table 24-1 lists the *current-gain*

bandwidth product. This term specifies a transistor's useful upper-frequency limit. At this point the circuit gain drops to 1. The output signal is no stronger than the input signal, so there is no gain.

One more transistor specification is worth mentioning here. That is the transistor's noise figure, NF. *Noise figure* is a measure of how much noise the transistor adds to the amplified signal. Manufacturers specify a transistor's noise figure in decibels.

They compare the transistor noise-signal power with the noise-signal power produced in a resistor as part of the test circuit.

As you continue your study of electronics you will learn about other transistor specifications. Many electronic circuits use transistors for purposes other than as amplifiers. The information you learned in this chapter will help you understand the other specifications and applications.

Review Questions

24.1 The three terminals of a BJT are the _____, the _____, and the _____.

24.2 The two types of BJTs are the _____ and the _____ transistor.

24.3 Explain what the term *transistor action* means.

24.4 When increasing the base current no longer causes a corresponding increase in the collector current, it is said that the transistor:
a) is tired
b) has depleted its region
c) needs to be replaced
d) is saturated

24.5 A transistor's current gain *alpha* (α) is always:
a) a bit less than 1.0
b) exactly 1.0
c) a bit more than 1.0
d) typically 80 to 100

24.6 Applying dc voltages to a transistor's diode junctions to set up the desired operating conditions is called _____ the transistor.

24.7 A transistor's current gain *beta* (β) is typically:
a) exactly 1.0
b) a bit less than 1.0
c) typically 80 to 100
d) a bit more than 1.0

24.8 Setting the bias voltages for a transistor circuit will make it operate at the "Q" point. Q stands for _____.

24.9 The three circuit configurations for BJT amplifiers are the _____ _____, _____ _____, and _____ _____.

Answers

24.1 The three terminals of a BJT are the *collector*, the *base*, and the *emitter*.

24.2 The two types of BJTs are the *PNP* and the *NPN* transistor.

24.3 A small current flowing from base to emitter, through the forward-biased base-emitter junction, controls a larger current flowing from collector to emitter, through a reverse-biased collector-base junction.

24.4 d

24.5 a

24.6 Applying dc voltages to a transistor's diode junctions to set up the desired operating conditions is called *biasing* the transistor.

24.7 c

24.8 Setting the bias voltages for a transistor circuit will make it operate at the "Q" point.
Q stands for *quiescent*.

24.9 The three circuit configurations for BJT amplifiers are the *common emitter*, *common base* and *common collector*.

Chapter 25

Field-Effect Transistors (FETs)

Field-effect transistors may look similar to bipolar devices, but they have different properties.

Contents

Controlling Current by Varying an Electric Field

Bipolar junction transistors rely on an input-signal *current* to control the output current. The input signal current variations produce a varying output current. That output current is an amplified version of the input signal.

An ideal amplifier would not draw any current from the source. Such an amplifier has a very large input impedance. A bipolar transistor amplifier circuit can have a fairly large input impedance. The practical need to draw some current always limits the actual value, though.

It is possible to make a semiconductor device that requires practically no current to operate. Such a device depends on the *electric field* of an applied voltage to control the output current. We call these devices *field-effect transistors* because they depend on an electric field for their operation. We often use the abbreviation *FET* for field effect transistor.

Figure 25-1 shows a block of N-type semiconductor material. Attached to each side of the N-type material are blocks of P-type material. This drawing looks similar to the three-layered sandwich of a bipolar junction transistor. The two blocks of P-type semiconductor material have a common connection between them. This connection may be inside the transistor or it may be an external wire.

The block of N-type material provides a direct path for an electric current from one end to the other. **Figure 25-2** shows a battery and resistor connected between the two ends. Free electrons in the semiconductor material move toward the positive battery terminal. These electrons *drain* out of the semiconductor at the positive end. We call this the *drain* connection of an FET. From the drain, electrons flow through the circuit to the other

UBE0313

Figure 25-1 — This diagram illustrates a *field effect transistor* (*FET*). It has a block of N-type semiconductor material with blocks of P-type material in each side.

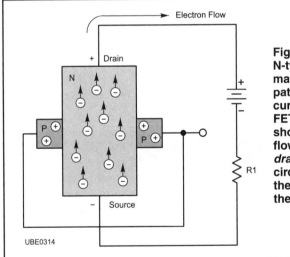

Figure 25-2 — The N-type semiconductor material forms a direct path for an electric current through an FET. This diagram shows the electrons flowing out of the *drain* lead, through the circuit, and back into the semiconductor at the *source* lead.

end of the block. Here they enter the N-type semiconductor. We call the end at which electrons enter the semiconductor the *source*.

In **Figure 25-3**, we connect the two P-material blocks to a negative battery terminal. The positive battery terminal connects to the source end of the N-material. The battery puts a reverse-bias voltage on the FET gate/ source junction.

With a reverse bias voltage on the junction, free electrons in the N-type material move toward the P-type material. Holes in the P-type material move into the N-type material. As these holes and free electrons combine, the *depletion region* increases. Figure 25-3A shows how the depletion region begins to close the chan-

(A)

(B)   UBE0315

Figure 25-4 — This circuit shows how an N-channel field-effect transistor operates. The gate-voltage battery ensures a reverse bias on the gate when the input signal is positive. The output current through R1 produces a voltage drop across the resistor. This voltage drop supplies an amplified output voltage.

nel for electrons to move from source to drain.

When the gate voltage is large enough, the depletion region pinches the channel completely off. Figure 25-3B shows this extreme condition.

Now let's see what happens when we connect a signal voltage to the FET gate. We also will connect the source and drain to a circuit, so we can use the transistor as an amplifier. **Figure 25-4** shows the complete circuit.

When the signal voltage is negative, the gate becomes more negative. This makes the N channel smaller, reducing current in the output circuit.

Next, the input signal voltage becomes positive, making the gate less

negative with respect to the source. (The gate-voltage battery ensures that the gate/source junction never has a forward-bias voltage.) The N channel becomes wider, increasing current through the output circuit.

As we learned at the beginning of this section, an FET has a large input impedance. There is almost no current across the gate/source junction because it has a reverse bias. FETs typically have an input impedance of a megohm or more.

A single block of semiconductor material controls a field-effect transistor's output impedance. This means FETs have a very low output-impedance value.

We only discussed FETs built around a block of N-type semiconductor material in this section. Perhaps you are wondering if FETs can be made with a block of P-type semiconductor material. The answer is, "Yes, there are FETs made with P-type materials." Then two blocks of N-type material form the gate. These are *P-channel FETs* instead of *N-channel FETs*. The operation is identical, except the voltage polarities reverse. A P-channel device has a positive gate voltage. The P-channel *drain* connects to the negative side of the output supply. Holes in the P type semiconductor material carry the current, instead of free electrons.

JFET Construction

In the last section you learned about *field-effect transistors*, or FETs. These transistors have a PN junction, which serves as a gate to control the current through the channel. The transistor's PN junction gives it the name *junction field-effect transistor*, or *JFET*. In this section you will learn more about JFET construction.

Manufacturers begin with a layer of P-type semiconductor material to build an N-channel JFET. Then they form the N-material channel on the P-type base. Next, the manufacturer forms a small area of P-type material on top of the N channel. The last step is to deposit metal contacts onto the semiconductor areas to form electrodes. These electrodes provide a way for you to connect the FET into a circuit. Before sealing the transistor into a protective plastic case or other package, the manufacturer attaches wire leads to the electrodes. **Figure 25-5A** shows this construction.

Figure 25-5B shows the similar P-channel JFET construction. A block of N-type material holds the P-material channel. The manufacturers add the second side of the gate as a thin N-material layer on top of the channel.

Field-effect transistors made this way have symmetrical channels. There is no difference between the source and drain channel sides. You could connect either side of the channel to the circuit source connection. You also could connect either side of the channel to the drain connection.

The channel isn't always symmetrical. Variations in the manufacturing process result in differences between the source and drain terminals. These differences provide specific transistor characteristics. When you build a circuit with junction field-effect transistors, you must carefully identify the source and drain terminals. Otherwise, you may damage the transistor.

Figure 25-6 shows the schematic-diagram symbols that represent N-channel and P-channel junction

Figure 25-5 — Part A shows the construction of an N-channel junction field-effect transistor. Manufacturers form an N-type material channel into a P-type semiconductor base. Then they add a small area of P-material to form the second side of the gate. They deposit a thin metal layer onto the semiconductor segments to serve as electrodes. P-channel JFET construction is similar, but with opposite semiconductor types, as Part B shows.

Figure 25-6 — The symbol at A represents an N-channel junction field-effect transistor on schematic diagrams. The symbol at B represents a P-channel JFET on schematic diagrams.

Figure 25-7 — FET packages are similar to those used for bipolar transistors. Some applications require a heat sink to conduct excess heat away from the transistor.

field-effect transistors. The N-channel JFET has a P-type gate section. Notice that the arrow symbol points away from the P-material gate *toward* the channel in an N-channel FET. The P-channel JFET has an N-type gate section. The arrow points *toward* the N-material gate and *away* from the channel in a P-channel FET. The arrows always point *away* from the P material and *toward* the N material in semiconductor devices.

FETs come in many package styles. Larger packages generally indicate devices that handle more power. Some FETs require you to use heat sinks to conduct excess heat away from the transistors. **Figure 25-7** is a drawing of some common FET package styles.

Manufacturers use silicon and germanium as the semiconductor materials for most JFETs. These are the same semiconductor materials we learned about earlier. They are also the materials used to make solid-state diodes and bipolar junction transistors.

Manufacturers use another semi-conductor material when they design FETs for use at UHF and microwave frequencies. Transistor noise becomes an important factor at these frequencies. Gallium arsenide is a semiconductor compound. It makes FETs that produce very little transistor noise at UHF. The chemical abbreviation for gallium arsenide is *GaAs*. This is why we call field-effect transistors made with gallium arsenide, *GaAsFETs*. GaAsFETs produce noise at lower frequencies, however, and are not particularly suited for use at HF.

MOSFET Construction

The field-effect transistors we studied so far all form their gates with PN junctions. There is another common field-effect transistor construction method. This method uses a thin layer of insulating metal oxide between the channel and gate blocks. We call these transistors *insulated gate field-effect transistors*, or *IGFETs*.

The insulating layer forms a capacitor. The channel forms one capacitor plate and the gate layer forms the other plate. This construction technique solves some problems that occur with JFET gate diodes. There is always some small leakage current through the reverse-biased PN junction. The insulated gate of an IGFET does not have this problem.

The most common insulating material is a thin layer of metal oxide on the semiconductor base. This construction technique leads to our name for this type of FET: *Metal-oxide semiconductor field-effect transistor*, or *MOSFET*. MOSFETs typically have an input impedance of several megohms, which is much higher than JFETs.

The insulating metal-oxide layer is very thin and has a low breakdown voltage. This makes MOSFETs sensitive to static electricity. A static charge can punch through the insulation, destroying the transistor. This is one disadvantage of MOS devices. You must be careful to discharge any static electricity from your body before you pick up a MOSFET. Handle them only by the case, not by the leads. Some MOSFETs have static-protective Zener diodes built into the device.

There are a variety of construction methods for making MOSFETs. First we'll discuss the construction and operation of a *depletion-mode* MOSFET.

We'll make an N-channel transistor by starting with a block of P-type semiconductor material. Next

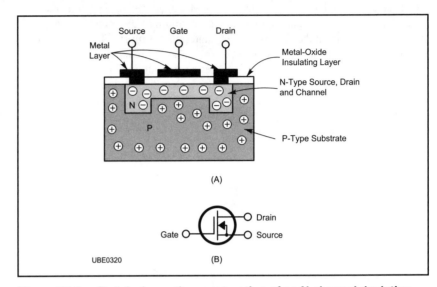

(A)

(B)

UBE0320

Figure 25-8 — Part A shows the construction of an N-channel depletion-mode metal-oxide-semiconductor field-effect transistor (MOSFET). Part B shows the schematic-diagram symbol for this transistor. The arrow points toward the channel for N-channel devices. Notice that the arrow is not on the gate lead, however.

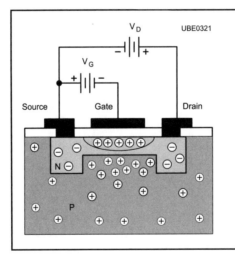

Figure 25-9 — A negative gate voltage attracts holes from the P-type substrate material. These holes combine with free electrons in the N-type channel material, reducing the effective channel width. Less current can flow through a narrower channel. A positive gate voltage repels holes, increasing the channel width so more current can flow.

we'll form the channel by depositing an N-material layer on top of the base, or *substrate*. A thin metal-oxide insulating layer goes over the top of these semiconductor materials. Now we must make some holes in the insulation for the source and drain connections. Deposit a metal layer through the holes and over the center to form a gate. Add wire leads and put the transistor in a protective package. Sounds simple, doesn't it? **Figure 25-8** shows this construction.

Figure 25-8B shows the schematic-diagram symbol for our N-channel depletion-mode metal-oxide-semiconductor field-effect transistor. The gate does not include a PN junction, so there is no arrow on the gate lead. There is an arrow pointing toward the channel, though, with a connection to the source. The arrow points toward the channel, indicating an N-channel device.

Figure 25-9 shows our MOSFET with a negative gate voltage. Notice that the negative gate voltage attracts some positive holes from the P-material substrate. These holes combine with some of the free electrons carrying current through the channel. This *depletes*, or reduces, the supply of charge carriers through the channel. This is why we call this a *depletion-mode MOSFET*.

You can imagine what happens when we apply a varying signal voltage to the gate. The varying voltage changes the current through the channel. A negative gate voltage reduces the channel width, resulting in less current flowing through the channel. A positive gate voltage repels holes, increasing the channel width so more current can flow.

Figure 25-10 shows the construction of an *enhancement mode MOSFET*. The most interesting aspect of the enhancement-mode construction is that there is no channel between the N-type source and drain. There is a connection between the P-type substrate and the source N-type material. For some transistors this is an internal connection; for others you must add the connection as part of the external circuit. The drain and substrate form a PN junction that produces a small leakage current when the drain is positive with respect to the source. The PN junction has a reverse-bias voltage under these conditions.

Let's apply a positive gate voltage, as **Figure 25-11** shows. The positive gate voltage attracts electrons in the P-type semiconductor material. We call these electrons *minority charge carriers* because there are more positive holes to carry charge in P-type material. The minority charge carriers collect at the P-material surface, but they cannot cross the insulating metal-oxide layer. This forms a negative channel in the P-type material between the N-type source and drain blocks. The number of minority charge carriers controls the amount of drain current. Thus, the positive

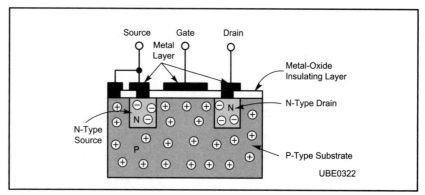

Figure 25-10 — This drawing shows the construction of an N-channel enhancement-mode metal-oxide-semiconductor field-effect transistor.

Figure 25-11 — This diagram shows the operation of an N-channel enhancement-mode MOSFET. A positive gate voltage attracts electrons in the P-type material. We call these electrons minority charge carriers because there are fewer free electrons than holes in P-type material. The electrons form an N-channel between the source and drain.

Figure 25-12 — This is the symbol used on schematic diagrams to represent an N-channel enhancement-mode MOSFET. Notice that the center line is broken into sections to represent the drain, channel and source.

gate voltage enhances the current-carrying ability of the transistor.

Figure 25-12 shows the schematic symbol for an enhancement-mode

MOSFET. Notice that the center line has divisions to represent the source, drain and substrate. This is a subtle difference from the symbol for a depletion-mode MOSFET, which has a solid center line.

There are other construction variations for metal-oxide semiconductor field-effect transistors. We won't try to cover all the possibilities here. One variation that you should be aware of, though, is the construction of dual-gate MOSFETs. Gate 1 is the *signal gate* and gate 2 is the *control gate*. This allows a control voltage to change the amplifier characteristics.

Manufacturers can make any of these MOSFET types with either N-channel or P-channel construction.

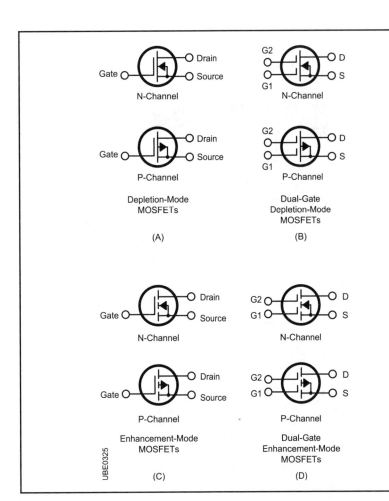

Figure 25-13 — These symbols represent various metal-oxide semiconductor field-effect transistors. The symbols represent N- and P-channel types in both depletion- and enhancement-mode devices. We also included symbols for dual-gate MOSFETs.

All the devices we studied in this section are N-channel types. To make P-channel devices, reverse the N and P material types and change the voltage polarities. **Figure 25-13** shows schematic symbols for N- and P-channel depletion- and enhancement-mode MOSFETs. Figure 25-13 also includes symbols for dual-gate devices.

Review Questions

25.1 The three terminals of a FET are the _____, the _____, and the _____.

25.2 The two types of FETs are the _____ FET and the _____ FET

25.3 A JFET channel through which current flows can be opened more, or closed more, by varying the _____ at the _____ of the JFET, which decreases, or increases (respectively) the width of the _____ _____.

25.4 The two kinds of MOSFETs are the _____-_____ MOSFET and the _____-_____ MOSFET.

25.5 Which of the following is not one of the three types of semiconductor material used to make field-effect transistors?

a) germanium

b) silicon

c) carbon

d) gallium arsenide

25.6 GaAsFETs are desirable for amplifiers at _____ frequencies because they have less _____.

25.7 IGFETs are very sensitive to, and are famous for being easily damaged by:

a) majority carriers in the channel

b) static electricity

c) not opening the drain often enough

d) amplifying jazz music

Answers

25.1 The three terminals of a FET are the *source*, the *gate*, and the *drain*.

25.2 The two types of FETs are the *N-channel FET* and the *P-channel FET*.

25.3 A JFET channel through which current flows can be opened more, or closed more, by varying the *voltage* at the *gate* of the JFET, which decreases, or increases (respectively) the width of the *depletion region*.

25.4 The two kinds of MOSFETs are the *depletion-mode* MOSFET and the *enhancement-mode* MOSFET.

25.5 c

25.6 GaAsFETs are desirable for amplifiers at *UHF* frequencies because they have less *noise*.

25.7 b

Chapter 26

Integrated Circuits – Putting It All in One Tiny Package

There's a lot going on inside these eight-legged integrated circuits.

Contents

Linear Devices

Silicon and germanium semiconductor materials form many electronics parts. These semiconductor materials form diodes, bipolar transistors, field-effect transistors and many other devices.

Manufacturers produce many transistor types. They control the amount and location of P- or N-type semiconductor materials added to the *substrate*, or base material. By carefully controlling the manufacturing process they can set the material's resistance. They use the same process to make resistors on a silicon or germanium base.

Do you remember the construction of a metal-oxide semiconductor field-effect transistor? A MOSFET's gate is a capacitor. (**Figure 26-1** shows this construction.)

Can manufacturers place several transistors and diodes on a single substrate piece? Of course. They also can add resistors and capacitors between the transistors, as part of the semiconductor. Does this begin to sound like a complete electronics circuit on a single piece of semiconductor material?

An *integrated circuit* is a single piece of semiconductor material that replaces many parts in an electronic

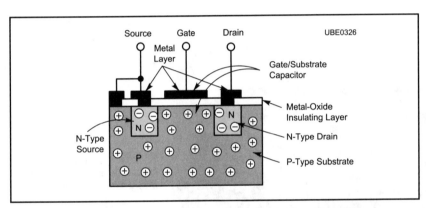

Figure 26-1 — A metal-oxide semiconductor field-effect transistor (MOSFET) includes a semiconductor capacitor.

Figure 26-2 — This photo shows several integrated circuit package styles.

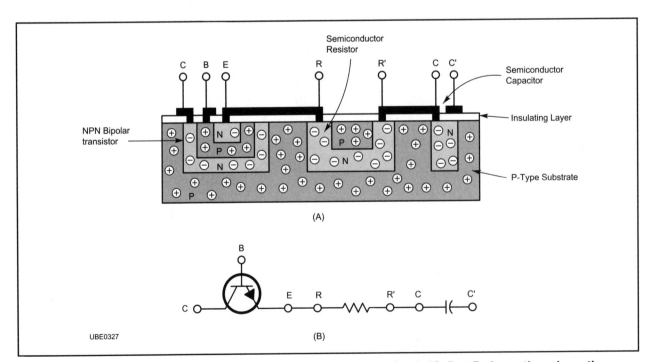

Figure 26-3 — Part A shows the semiconductor materials forming a simple IC. Part B shows the schematic diagram of the circuit from Part A.

circuit. You will often hear *integrated circuit* abbreviated *IC*. You also will hear these devices called chips, because they use a small piece, or "chip," of silicon.

Manufacturers build these circuits and package them in a variety of ways to make them easy to use. **Figure 26-2** shows some common integrated circuit packages. The package must provide some way to connect the IC to the outside world. The wire leads make up a significant portion of the size of an IC. Manufacturers are always looking for new ways to package the chips to produce a smaller package.

Some ICs may have only a few transistors and other components. Many chips include hundreds or thousands of transistors, diodes, resistors and capacitors on a single block. These components consist of semiconductor-material layers formed on the substrate. **Figure 26-3** shows this construction with a simple circuit that has a bipolar transistor, a resistor and a capacitor. Of course most ICs are much more complicated than this circuit.

Linear integrated circuits work with signals that change smoothly from one value to another. A sine wave is a good example of such a signal. You will learn about *digital integrated circuits* later in this chapter.

Linear ICs serve as amplifiers, oscillators and many sections of

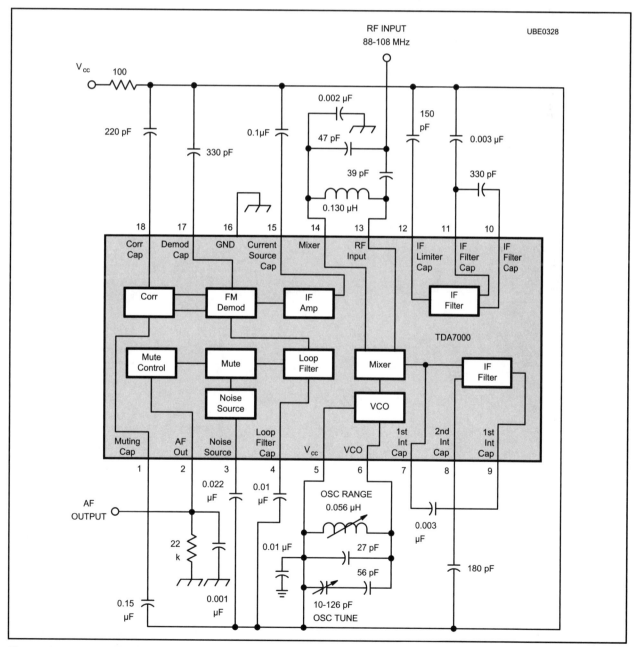

Figure 26-4 — The TDA7000 is an FM-radio subsystem IC. You only need to add a few external parts to make a complete receiver.

receivers, transmitters and other electronics circuits. There are even linear ICs that are complete receivers, requiring only a few external components such as a power supply and speaker or headphones.

Some linear ICs are general-purpose chips. These devices adapt well to many uses in various circuit types. *Operational amplifiers* are popular general-purpose devices. *Op amps* find their way into many circuits, including small-signal amplifiers and filter circuits. Op amps are used in hearing aids, cell phones, computer hard drives and MP3 players, to name a few applications. You will learn more about op amps in the next section.

Other linear ICs are special-purpose devices designed to perform one specific circuit function. You will find many of these special-purpose ICs in consumer electronics devices like stereos, radios and TV sets.

Figure 26-4 is a diagram of the TDA7000 IC. This chip is a complete FM radio, as the block diagram shows. You only need to add a few resistors, capacitors and inductors to complete the receiver. These components provide filtering and oscillator-frequency control. A power supply to provide the necessary input voltage rounds out the external components.

You will learn about many specific ICs as you continue to study electronics. Remember that ICs are electronic building blocks. Manufacturer's data sheets and application notes are good sources of specific information about an IC. This information tells you what input-voltage range is safe for the chip. It also tells what additional circuit components you must add to complete the circuit.

Operational Amplifiers

There are many types of linear integrated circuits. One common example is the *operational amplifier*. Operational amplifiers take their name from the days of analog computers. Analog computers represented numbers with analog voltages. Larger numbers had higher voltages. Such computers used direct-current amplifiers to perform mathematical *operations*, such as addition and subtraction, and even calculus operations like integration and differentiation.

Modern IC *op amps* are high-gain dc-coupled differential amplifiers. A differential amplifier has two input connections and amplifies the *difference* between those inputs. A dc-coupled amplifier amplifies both direct-current signals and alternating-current signals.

There are six ideal amplifier characteristics by which we judge operational amplifiers. An ideal op amp should have:

1) infinite voltage gain
2) infinite input impedance
3) zero output impedance
4) infinite bandwidth
5) zero noise
6) zero drift with time and temperature changes.

Modern IC op amps come close to realizing the first three conditions. They don't do quite as well with the last three, but manufacturers constantly try to improve performance in these areas.

Figure 26-5 shows a schematic diagram that represents the circuit inside a 741 op amp IC. Don't be concerned about understanding how this circuit operates. In fact, don't even think about it; most engineers don't fully understand all the circuitry in an op-amp, and that is not a problem. That's one good point about ICs. You don't have to know what goes on inside the "black box." The manufacturers' data sheets will tell

Figure 26-5 — This diagram represents a 741 op-amp circuit. There are inverting and noninverting inputs and one output. Positive and negative voltage supply inputs allow you to use the op amp as a differential amplifier. With the offset control connections, you can adjust the amplifier so there is no output when both inputs have the same signal.

you what voltages and signals to connect to each IC lead, and provide application notes that help a circuit designer use the op-amp in a wide variety of applications.

There are 20 transistors on this integrated-circuit chip. All these transistors are on one substrate, so their characteristics are carefully matched. You would not have much success trying to build a similar op amp from individual transistors and resistors.

You also should notice the two input connections. One has a + INPUT label, which is the *noninverting input*. The other input has a –INPUT label, which is the *inverting input*.

Figure 26-6 shows the schematic-diagram symbol for an op amp. Part A shows a sine-wave signal connected to the noninverting input. The amplified output signal is in phase with the input signal.

Part B shows a signal connected to the inverting input. This time the amplified output signal is 180° out of phase with the input. This shows the difference between these two inputs. With the inverting input, as a signal becomes more positive, the output becomes more negative.

There are two operating-voltage inputs to the IC. Many op amps require a split voltage supply. One supply gives a positive voltage to ground. A second supply gives a negative voltage to ground. This is necessary to operate the differential amplifier input circuit.

Suppose you supply one input signal to the + input and another identical signal to the – input. The difference between these signals is 0 volts. Therefore, the output signal will be 0 volts.

Sometimes the two input amplifiers aren't exactly balanced. This means there may be some

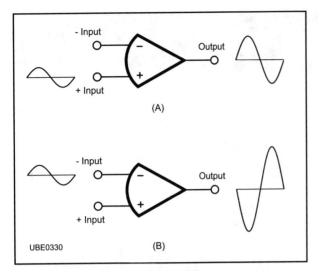

(A)

(B)

UBE0330

Figure 26-6 — Part A shows a sine-wave signal applied to the op amp noninverting input. The input and output signals are in phase. When the input signal reaches its positive maximum so does the output. The output signal reaches its negative maximum at the same time as the input signal. Part B shows the input signal applied to the inverting input. In this case the input and output signals are 180° out of phase. The output signal reaches a negative maximum when the input signal reaches its positive maximum.

UBE0331

Figure 26-7 — Here is the schematic diagram of an audio amplifier that you can use to increase the signal from a microphone. The input and output connectors are coaxial types, because you would use shielded, or coaxial, cable to make these connections.

output signal with identical input signals. That brings us to the last two op-amp connections. The OFFSET CONTROL leads provide an adjustment so you can set the output signal to zero when the input signals are identical.

You can make an audio amplifier using an op amp. **Figure 26-7** shows an amplifier you can use to increase the output from a microphone. This circuit feeds a signal to a radio transmitter or other device. The negative voltage-supply lead connects to ground. You don't have to use a negative supply with this circuit because the only input signal goes to the noninverting input. The inverting input connects

UBE0332

Figure 26-8 — This active band-pass filter is suitable for use as a CW filter with an Amateur Radio receiver. It has a center frequency of 750 Hz. You can use a 741 or TL081 op amp.

to the output through the gain-control resistor. This provides some negative feedback to the amplifier, stabilizing the operation.

Active filters are another popular operational amplifier application. **Figure 26-8** shows an audio band-pass filter that you can build. This circuit has a center frequency of 750 Hz, so you could use it as an external CW (continuous-wave) filter for an Amateur Radio receiver to make listening to Morse code transmissions easier.

There are many other op-amp applications. The ones described here will help you become familiar with this class of devices.

Digital Devices

Digital electronics is an important branch of modern electronics. Digital circuits use signals that have specific voltage levels. Signals that fall between the specific values for the circuit round up or down to the set values. **Figure 26-9** shows a digital representation of a sine wave. Notice the stair-step appearance to the values.

Many digital circuits use two voltage levels. We call these *binary circuits*. The *binary number system* uses only two digits, 0 and 1. We use the binary numbers, 0 and 1, to represent the two voltage levels or circuit conditions. They may represent ON and OFF circuit conditions. The binary states also may represent space and mark signals in a digital communications system such as Morse code or radioteletype.

The actual voltages depend on the circuit, but OFF is normally 0 volts. The ON condition may be around 5 volts, or it may be 12 volts or another value. Some circuits reverse these conditions. **Figure 26-10** shows a series of digital pulses from a binary circuit.

Digital computers use digital logic circuits. These circuits represent decimal numbers using a binary coding system. The computer works with these binary numbers to perform many complex tasks.

Digital logic circuits measure one or more inputs and produce a 1 or a 0 output. The first digital computers used vacuum tubes and mechanical relays to form logic circuits. These were large machines that required lots of power and produced lots of heat. Later, transistors replaced the vacuum tubes and relays.

Digital integrated circuits replace logic circuits built from

individual transistors. A digital IC is a complete logic network. It usually needs only one or more input signals and a power source. Most digital ICs produce one or more output signals.

Table 26-1

Inverter Truth Table (NOT Function)

Input (A)	Output (B)
0	1
1	0

Table 26-2

AND Gate Truth Table

Input (A)	Input (B)	Output (C)
0	0	0
0	1	0
1	0	0
1	1	1

Table 26-3

OR Gate Truth Table

Input (A)	Input (B)	Output (C)
0	0	0
0	1	1
1	0	1
1	1	1

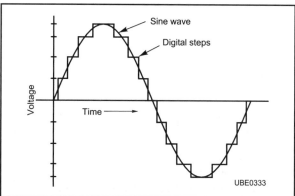

Figure 26-9 — This "stair-step" graph is a digital representation of a sine wave. Digital signals have values at specific, defined levels. If the analog signal value falls between two steps, the digital signal rounds up or down to the closest value.

There are many logic functions, and there is a digital IC for each function or possible combination. There are far too many ICs to discuss each one and its operation here. We will cover a few common circuits, to give you an idea of the possibilities.

One simple logic function is the *inverter*. An inverter takes a digital-signal input and creates the opposite signal output. **Figure 26-11** shows the schematic symbol that represents an inverter. We drew the input and output waveforms with the symbol. When the input signal is a 1, the output is a 0. When the input is a 0, the output is a 1. We sometimes call this the NOT function. The small circle on the output tells you the circuit performs the NOT function, or inversion.

Table 26-1 is an inverter *truth table*. A *truth table* lists all possible input-signal combinations, and the resulting output signals for each input-signal combination. A truth table is a valuable tool to help you understand a logic circuit's operation.

A logical AND circuit has two or more inputs. An output of 1 is possible only when all the inputs are 1s. If all inputs are 0s, or some inputs are 1s and others are 0s, the output is 0. **Table 26-2** is a truth table for the logical AND circuit. **Figure 26-12** shows the schematic-diagram symbol for a two-input AND *gate*. (*Gate* is the term used to describe digital-logic ICs.)

Another logic circuit is the OR gate. An OR circuit has two or more inputs and one output. If any input is a 1, the output will be 1. **Figure 26-13** is the schematic symbol for a two-input OR gate. **Table 26-3** is the truth table for this circuit.

You can use these digital

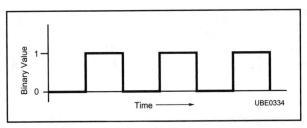

Figure 26-10 — These pulses represent the output from a binary digital circuit. The output circuit is either ON, representing a binary 1, or it is OFF, representing a binary 0.

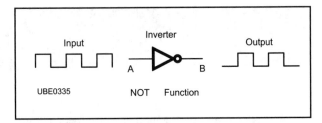

Figure 26-11 — This symbol represents an inverter circuit on schematic diagrams. The input and output signals illustrate inverter operation.

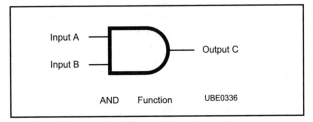

Figure 26-12 — This symbol represents a two-input AND gate. Both inputs must be 1s to produce a 1 output. If either or both inputs are 0s, the output is 0.

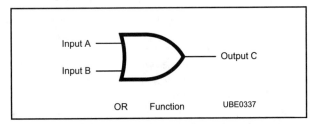

Figure 26-13 — We use this symbol to represent a two-input OR gate on schematic diagrams. If either input is 1 the output will be 1.

IC building blocks to form nearly any logic circuit imaginable. Manufacturers combine many of these building blocks into integrated circuits. A *latch* is a digital circuit that stores a single *binary digit*, or *bit* of information. When you press the CAPS LOCK key on your computer, a *latch* remembers that you pressed the key (that is, its output had been logic 0, and changes to logic 1). When you press the CAPS LOCK key again, the *latch* output returns to logic 0.

When you press a key on your keyboard for a single letter or digit, then eight *latches* will store the 8 *bits* representing that letter or digit. These 8 *bits* are one *byte* of information.

Figure 26-14A shows a latch made from OR gates and inverters. B shows the schematic symbol for this latch made as a single IC. Part C gives the truth table

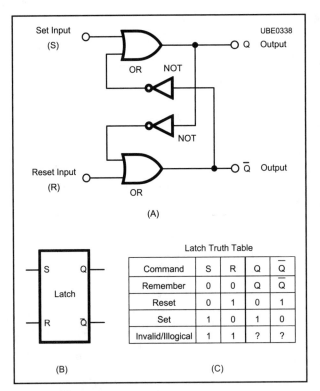

Figure 26-14 — You can make a latch with two OR gates and two inverters. Part B shows the schematic diagram symbol that represents an IC latch. Part C shows the truth table for this latch. The "Illogical" (Invalid) command should not be used. If both S and R change from logic 1 to logic 0 at the same time, nobody can predict what the two outputs will be.

Latch Truth Table

Command	S	R	Q	$\overline{Q}$
Remember	0	0	Q	$\overline{Q}$
Reset	0	1	0	1
Set	1	0	1	0
Invalid/Illogical	1	1	?	?

for the latch. The two inputs are SET (S) and RESET (R).

When S = 1 and R = 0, the Q output is 1. This is the SET command. When S = 0 and R =1, the Q output is 0. This is the RESET command. Notice there is a second output, labeled $\overline{Q}$. (Read this as Q NOT, which means an inverted Q, or the opposite of Q.) The Q NOT output is always the opposite of the Q output, with one exception: if you make S = 1 and R = 1, which is an *invalid* and *illogical* command.

When both the S and R inputs are 0, the outputs don't change. This is called the *Remember* command. The truth table also shows that if both inputs are logic 1, the outputs will both be "?". Actually, they will both be logic 1. Remember that if an OR gate has a logic 1 at one or both inputs, the output will be logic 1. The question mark indicates that if the *Invalid/Illogical* command is followed by the Remember command, it is not possible to predict what Q and Q NOT will be.

If S = 1 and R = 1, we are giving the latch an *invalid* and *illogical* command. We are telling the latch to both SET and RESET. It's like telling a car to go forward and reverse at the same time. You can do it (with a latch, but not with a car), but there's a big problem with the *invalid* command: there is no way to determine what the outputs will be *if both S and R change from logic 1 to logic 0 simultaneously*. Remember this when you work with latches.

A digital device which is very similar to a latch is a *flip-flop*. They both have Q and $\overline{Q}$ outputs, and both have two inputs for controlling the device. A *flip-flop* adds another input, called the *clock* input. While a latch responds immediately to its inputs, a flip-flop will respond only when the clock tells it to do so.

There are several construction techniques used to make these digital ICs. Generally, you should use devices that are all made with the same construction method. One digital IC *family* is called transistor-transistor logic, or TTL. This name comes from the bipolar transistors used to make the ICs. Part numbers in the 7400 series indicate TTL ICs. A 7404 IC has six inverters in a single package, and is often called a *hex inverter*. A 7432 has four OR gates.

Another family uses both P- and N-channel metal-oxide semiconductor field-effect transistors on the same substrate. We say the P- and N-channel MOSFETs are complementary. We call this construction *complementary metal-oxide semiconductor*, or *CMOS*. Part numbers in the 4000 series indicate CMOS ICs. A 4069 has six inverters, for example, and a 4081 has four AND *gates*. There are other logic families as well, including ECL, HCT and I2L (or I^2L). Each has certain advantages (for example speed and cost) and limitations (for example power consumption and noise immunity), and if you work with logic circuits you'll certainly learn about the different logic families.

Timers

There are many special-purpose digital integrated circuits. These are combinations of other digital devices built into a single IC. You can buy an IC to count signal pulses or to divide a series of pulses by some preset value. You can buy a chip that changes digital signals to analog signals or one to change analog signals to digital signals. There are many ICs designed for use with digital computers.

In this section we will study the timer IC. This useful building block has many applications. The most common timer IC is the 555. **Figure 26-15** shows the schematic-diagram symbol, with pin labels.

Let's study the Figure 26-15 circuit to learn about the timer IC. Normally pin 2, the trigger pin, is at +5 volts. We'll pull this pin to ground for an instant by applying a negative input pulse, or by touching a wire from pin 2 to ground (pin 1). This causes a positive output pulse to appear on pin 3, which we call the Q output. Current from the power supply flows through R1 to charge capacitor C1. When the capacitor voltage exceeds 2/3 the supply voltage (about 3.3 volts for this example) the discharge pin, pin 7, quickly discharges the capacitor to ground. Then the output at pin 3 returns to 0. The output remains at 0 until there is another negative trigger pulse.

It may help you to understand what this circuit, a *monostable multivibrator* or *one-shot*, is by thinking of a toilet. Toilets are hydraulic *monostable multivibrators*. A toilet sits there all day, in its *stable state* (not flushing, tank full of water), until you press the flush handle (you apply a *trigger signal* with your hand*). That trigger puts the toilet into its *unstable state* (tank emptying into the bowl, followed by the tank

Figure 26-15 — This 555 timer IC circuit is a monostable multivibrator, or one-shot. A negative pulse on the trigger pin produces a positive output pulse on the output, pin 3. Resistor R1 and capacitor C1 determine the output-pulse duration.

refilling). Once the tank is full, the toilet returns to its *stable state*, patiently awaiting the next flush. That may occur in a few seconds, or a few weeks. *Mono* means "one," so a *monostable multivibrator*, either a toilet or a 555 circuit, has one stable state. It is triggered into its unstable state, but always returns to the stable state. *Multivibrator* means the circuit jumps between two output conditions.

The output pulse length depends on the values used for R1 and C1. These two parts set the circuit *time constant*. When you studied capacitor circuits you learned how to calculate time constants. Multiply the resistor value, measured in ohms, times the capacitor value, measured in farads. Longer time constants produce longer output pulses.

Equation 26-1 shows you how to calculate the output pulse length.

$$T = 1.1 \times R1 \times C1 \quad \text{(Equation 26-1)}$$

where T is the output pulse length in seconds.

Suppose the Figure 26-15 circuit

has a 10-kilohm resistor for R1 and a 10-microfarad capacitor for C1. How long will the output pulse last?

First change the resistance measurement to ohms and the capacitance measurement to farads.

$$10 \text{ kilohms} = 10 \times 10^3 \text{ ohms}$$

$$10 \text{ microfarads} = 10 \times 10^{-6} \text{ farads}$$

Now substitute these values into Equation 26-1.

$$T = 1.1 \times 10 \times 10^3 \text{ ohms} \times 10 \times 10^{-6} \text{ farads}$$

$$T = 1.1 \times 100 \times 10^{-3} = 0.11 \text{ seconds} = 110 \text{ milliseconds}$$

Each output pulse lasts 0.11 seconds for this example.

There are two possible conditions for the Figure 26-15 circuit. As long as the voltage on pin 2 remains near 5 volts, the output voltage is 0. This is a *stable* circuit condition. When the voltage on pin 2 goes to 0 V (ground), the output voltage at pin 3 jumps to 5 volts. This condition only lasts a short time, however. This is an unstable condition.

There are many applications for this type of circuit. We call a circuit with one stable condition and one unstable condition a *one-shot* or a *monostable multivibrator*. You could build a one-shot with individual components, but the 555 timer, being an integrated circuit, makes a convenient package.

Figure 26-16 shows another multivibrator circuit that has many electronics applications. It is an *astable* or *free-running* multivibrator. An *astable multivibrator* has two *unstable* output conditions (high and low, or logical 1 and 0), and it alternates between those outputs. This circuit produces a never ending string of output pulses, and doesn't need an input signal to do so. We used a 555 timer IC for this circuit also. You can make an astable multivibrator with other components, but the 555 only needs a few additional resistors and capacitors.

Figure 26-16 — A 555 timer IC also can form an astable multivibrator, or free-running multivibrator. The circuit produces a string of output pulses with no input signal. Resistors R1 and R2, with capacitor C1, determine the output-pulse frequency.

This circuit operation is similar to Figure 26-15. The output (pin 3) is high while capacitor C1 charges through R1 and R2 until the voltage across C1 reaches about ⅔ the supply voltage. At that instant, the pin 3 output goes low and the capacitor

begins to discharge through R2 until it reaches about ⅓ the supply voltage. At that instant, C1 begins charging again, the output goes high, and the whole process begins again.

The values of R1, R2 and C1 determine the output pulse duration and the time between pulses. The output pulses shown in Figure 26-16 are on about half the time and off half the time. You can set nearly any pulse times by selecting the resistor and capacitor values.

Equation 26-2 gives the output pulse frequency. Resistance values must be in ohms and capacitor values must be in farads for this equation,

$$f = \frac{1.46}{[R1 + (2 \times R2)] \times C1}$$

(Equation 26-2)

where f is the frequency in hertz.

Let's choose a 10-kilohm resistor for R1 and a 100-kilohm resistor for R2. Pick a 0.01-microfarad capacitor for C2. What frequency will the

Figure 26-17 — You can build this astable multivibrator circuit on an experimenters' circuit board. Adjust R3 and R4 while you listen to the output signal. You also can try other values for the resistors and capacitor C1. Replace the switch with a Morse code key, and you will have a code-practice oscillator.

output signal have?

$$f = \frac{1.46}{[10 \times 10^3 + (2 \times 100 \times 10^3)] \times 0.01 \times 10^{-6}}$$

$$f = \frac{1.46}{[10 \times 10^3 + (200 \times 10^3)] \times 0.01 \times 10^{-6}}$$

$$= \frac{1.46}{[210 \times 10^3] \times 0.01 \times 10^{-6}}$$

$$f = \frac{1.46}{2.10 \times 10^{-3}} = 695 \text{ hertz}$$

The output signal from this circuit is in the range of signals you can hear. If you connect the output to a speaker, you will hear a tone.

Figure 26-17 shows another astable multivibrator. This is a good circuit with which to experiment. Resistors R2 and R3 replace R2 in the Figure 26-16 circuit. R4 serves as a volume control. C4 improves the sound by rounding the corners of the square-wave output pulses.

Try changing the values of R1, R2, R3 and C1. Listen to the effects of adjusting R3 and R4. Use Equation 26-2 to calculate the output frequency for this circuit. Calculate the frequency when you add the values of R2 and R3 to take the place of R2 in Equation 26-2. Also calculate the frequency without R3 (that is, variable R3 is set to 0 ohms). This gives the range of output tones you can expect from the circuit.

You can use this circuit as a code-practice oscillator to learn Morse code. Replace switch S1 with a code key. You can build the circuit on a small experimenters' circuit board.

Review Questions

26.1 Linear integrated circuits generally work with the following kinds of signals:

a) square waves

b) extraterrestrial

c) digital data streams

d) sine waves

26.2 Op amps are so named because they:

a) are used by surgeons when they perform medical operations

b) were used originally to perform mathematical operations, including calculus

c) are ideally suited to amplify ops

d) were invented by Sir Hiram Op

26.3 List as many characteristics of an *ideal* op amp as you can.

26.4 What is the meaning of the term *integrated* in an integrated circuit?

26.5 Negative feedback is used in an op amp circuit in order to:

a) stabilize the circuit and set the gain of an amplifier

b) make negative voltages become positive

c) reduce the power consumption of the op amp

d) change the back feed into useful feedback

26.6 The digital IC that has one input and one output is the:

a) AND gate

b) OR gate

c) inverter

d) NAND gate

26.7 A truth table for a digital logic gate:

a) is where everyone sits calmly and stops telling lies

b) lists all possible input combinations, and the output for each

c) is the first place you should look for digital IC specifications

d) truthfully, I really don't know what a truth table is

26.8 How is a digital *latch* different from a *flip-flop*?

26.9 A *one-shot* circuit is another name for a:

a) monostable multivibrator

b) astable multivibrator

c) flip-flop

d) latch

Answers

26.1 d

26.2 b

26.3 Infinite gain, infinite input impedance, zero output impedance, infinite bandwidth, zero noise, zero drift with time and temperature. If you got three or more from memory, pat yourself on the back.

26.4 A single *substrate* of semiconductor contains diodes, transistors, resistors and capacitors. This is done by adding N-type or P-type impurities to the semiconductor material, often silicon. In this way, many of the components needed to make an electronic circuit are integrated on one chip of semiconductor material.

26.5 a

26.6 c

26.7 b

26.8 Both a *latch* and a *flip-flop* have two outputs, and *remember* or store one bit of digital information. The *latch* responds immediately to its controlling inputs, while the *flip-flop* also has a clock input, so the *flip-flop* outputs change only when the clock input tells it to change.

26.9 a

Scientific and Engineering Notation

$$250{,}000 = 25 \times 10^{4}$$
$$5 \times 10^{5} = 500{,}000$$

Contents

Exponential and Scientific Notation

Modern electronics often uses numbers that are either quite large or very close to zero. At either extreme, it is difficult to write the numbers because of all the zeros. Even the most careful person will occasionally drop a zero, or add an extra one when calculating with such numbers. For most of us, calculations like these can be a real nightmare!

The lamp in a small flashlight may have an electrical current of 0.1 ampere flowing through it. The current flowing from the 9-volt battery in a smoke detector is close to 0.000010 ampere. This smoke detector battery current, expressed not in amperes but in electrons per second, is about 63,000,000,000,000 electrons per second.

A resistor in an electronic circuit may have a resistance of 910,000 ohms. The size of the microscopic conductors ("wires" that interconnect components) in an integrated circuit are on the order of 0.0000005 meters wide, or 0.0005 millimeters wide. By contrast, the graphite in a mechanical pencil is about 0.5 millimeters in diameter. Big numbers, and small numbers, can be difficult to deal with because of all the zeros.

Suppose you want to multiply 250,000 times 500,000. You can see how easily you could skip a zero, or get the numbers out of line when you are doing multiplication. See **Figure A-1**. With this many zeros in the answer, (125,000,000,000) it is just too easy to make a mistake — even with a few commas thrown in to help you count the zeros.

There's an easier way to keep track of all the zeros, though. Every time you multiply a number by 10, you just move the decimal point one place to the right and add another zero. So you can represent a number by writing its digits up to the last nonzero digit. Then multiply that part by 10 for every zero you omitted. In our example, 250,000 becomes $25 \times 10 \times 10 \times 10 \times 10$. (You may not think this is much better right now, but be patient for a minute.)

If we multiply a number by itself several times, we can say that the number is "raised to a power." If we raise 10 to the second power we say the number 10 is *squared*, or write it as 10^2. The 2 is an *exponent* or power of 10.

```
    250000
×   500000
  --------
    000000
    000000
    000000
    000000
    000000
   1250000
  -----------
  125000000000
```

Figure A-1 — This work may look extremely sloppy compared to the way you would do the problem. If you are just a little careless, though, you can become hopelessly lost.

Remember that 10^2 just means 10×10, or 100.

Going back to our example, we can write the first number in our multiplication problem (250,000) as $25 \times 10 \times 10 \times 10 \times 10$. Using the "power of 10" idea, you also can write this as 25×10^4 because we have 10 multiplied by itself four times (**Figure A-2**). Remember that you just move the decimal point one place to the right (add a zero) every time you multiply by 10. Then we can "expand" 25×10^4 back out to the normal form by writing 25 followed by four zeros (250000). This means that the exponent, or power of 10, always tells us how many places to move the decimal point. The second number in our example (500000) becomes 5×10^5. When we write a number with a power of 10, we express it in *exponential notation*. As another example, we could write 670,310,000 as 67031×10^4.

For numbers less than one, getting closer and closer to zero, we have a similar situation. In this case the number has many zeros right after the decimal point, such as 0.0000045. If it seems to you that dividing by 10 has the same effect as moving the decimal point to the left one place, you're right! And if you're also wondering, "Gee, does that mean I can write 0.0000045 as $0.45 \div 10 \div 10 \div 10 \div 10 \div 10$, or as $45 \div 10 \div 10 \div 10 \div 10 \div 10 \div 10 \div 10$?" the answer is Yes!. You can write this number either way.

If we write the nonzero part of the number as 45, then we must divide by 10 seven times to get the original number. So we can combine the divide-by-ten factors as a power of 10, or 10^7. Then we can write $45 \div 10^7$. (Notice that we could also write this as $0.45 \div 10^5$ or $4.5 \div 10^6$.) If you prefer, you can write the number as a fraction:

$$\frac{45}{10^7}$$

There is a nifty little trick that we often use when working with exponents. If the power of 10 is in the denominator (the bottom part) of a fraction, we can move it into the numerator (the top part) just by changing the sign of the exponent. So instead of writing $45 \div 10^7$ to show that we must divide by 10 seven times, we can write it as 45×10^{-7} (**Figure A-3**). Now the –7 tells us to move the decimal point 7 places to the left to write the number in its expanded form. If we move the decimal point two

$$250,000 = 25 \times 10^4$$
$$5 \times 10^5 = 500,000$$

Figure A-2 — We can easily write large numbers in exponential form or expand numbers written in exponential or scientific notation back to normal form.

$$0.0000045 = 4.5 \times 10^{-6} = 45 \times 10^{-7}$$

Figure A-3 — When we write small numbers (close to zero) in exponential or scientific notation, the power of 10 takes a negative value.

$\longleftarrow$ Negative Numbers $5.204 \times 10^{-5} = 0.00005204$	Positive Numbers $\longrightarrow$ $4.025 \times 10^{7} = 40,250,000$
Move the decimal point to the left when expanding negative powers of 10.	Move the decimal point to the right when expanding positive powers of 10.

Figure A-4 — Here is a simple key to remembering how to move the decimal point when expanding numbers out of exponential notation.

places to the left, so it is just before the 4, then it still has five places to go, and we have

0.45×10^{-5}.

Try to keep in mind that when you are working in exponential notation, if the power of 10 is a *positive* number, the decimal point moves to the *right*. If the power of 10 is a *negative* number, the decimal point moves to the *left*. See **Figure A-4**.

There is a special form of exponential notation, called *scientific notation*. Numbers expressed in scientific notation always have a single nonzero digit before the decimal point. The remaining nonzero digits come after the decimal point, followed by the power of 10.

Let's look at a few examples:

Number Notation	Number in Scientific
8.19	8.19×10^{0}
62.4	6.24×10^{1}
536.2	5.362×10^{2}
7209	7.209×10^{3}
0.819	8.19×10^{-1}
0.0624	6.24×10^{-2}
0.00536	5.36×10^{-3}

Some Rules for Working with Exponential Notation

Let's become familiar with a few rules about working with numbers in exponential notation. You will enter numbers into your scientific calculator using exponential notation (or scientific notation or engineering notation) to solve electronics problems. The calculator will keep track of the powers of 10 for you as it calculates the answer. Knowing the rules for powers of 10, however, will make it easier for you to understand the calculations (and to allow you to see if the answer seems reasonable — sometimes we make errors entering numbers into a calculator). Let's go over some of these basic rules before working a few problems with your calculator.

The first rule is about multiplication. To multiply numbers in exponential or scientific notation, first multiply the "plain number" parts of the numbers. Next, add the exponents of the powers of 10. Put these two parts together, and you have the answer!

Let's look at an example — we will multiply 250,000 times 500,000. First, write these numbers in exponential notation:

$250,000 = 25 \times 10^{4}$

$500,000 = 5 \times 10^{5}$

Next, set up the multiplication problem:

$$25 \times 10^{4}$$
$$\underline{\times 5 \times 10^{5}}$$

Multiply the "plain number" parts to get 125 (that is, $25 \times 5 = 125$). Then add the powers of 10 to get 10^{9} (that is, $4 + 5 = 9$). Combine these two parts to get the final answer:

$25 \times 10^{4} \times 5 \times 10^{5}$

$= 125 \times 10^{9}$

You can expand this answer by moving the decimal point 9 places to the right:

$125 \times 10^{9} = 125,000,000,000$

Or you could write

$125 \times 10^{9} = 1.25 \times 10^{11}$

Notice that we made 125 become 1.25 by dividing 125 by 10^{2}, so to keep the number the same we had to multiply 10^{9} by 10^{2}.

Figure A-5 shows this work. If you want to try multiplying these numbers without using exponential

$$250{,}000 = 25 \times 10^4$$
$$500{,}000 = 5 \times 10^5$$

(A)

$$\begin{array}{r} 25 \times 10^4 \\ \times\ 5 \times 10^5 \\ \hline 125 \times 10^{4+5} = 125 \times 10^9 \end{array}$$

(B)

$$125 \times 10^9 = 125{,}000{,}000{,}000$$

(C)

Figure A-5 — To multiply numbers written in exponential notation, first multiply the number parts, then add the exponents for the powers of 10.

numbers in exponential form and set up the problem. See Figure A-2.

$$5 \times 10^5$$
$$\underline{\times 45 \times 10^{-7}}$$

Multiply the numbers and add the exponents:

$5 \times 45 = 225$ and $10^{[5 + (-7)]} = 10^{-2}$

How did we get 10^{-2}? Don't forget that one of the exponents was –7, so when we add 5 and –7 we have:

$5 + (-7) = -2$

Figure A-6 reviews the steps.

Our second important rule has to do with division. To divide numbers written in exponential or scientific form, first divide the "plain number" parts. Then subtract the denominator power from the numerator power. (The denominator is the bottom part of a fraction and the numerator is the top part.) **Figure A-7A** shows a division problem, with the numbers converted to exponential and scientific notation. Part B shows how you can move the power of 10 from the denominator into the numerator. Then you can add the powers of 10. Part C shows the final answer.

You may have learned that you should "cancel" the same number of zeros from the numerator and denominator

$$500{,}000 = 5 \times 10^5$$
$$0.0000045 = 45 \times 10^{-7}$$

(A)

$$\begin{array}{r} 45 \times 10^{-7} \\ \times\ 5 \times 10^5 \\ \hline 225 \times 10^{-7+5} = 225 \times 10^{-2} \end{array}$$

(B)

$$225 \times 10^{-2} = 2.25$$

(C)

Figure A-6 — When you must multiply a number that has a negative exponent, be sure to add the exponent as a negative value.

notation, please go ahead. It's probably worthwhile for you to prove that the answer is the same whichever way you do it. Be extra careful, though. If the two answers do not agree, go back and check your work, because it's very likely you made a mistake somewhere!

What happens if we have to multiply 500,000 times 0.0000045? Well, let's write these

$$\frac{764{,}000{,}000}{382{,}000} = \frac{764 \times 10^6}{382 \times 10^3} = \frac{7.64 \times 10^8}{3.82 \times 10^5}$$

(A)

$$\frac{7.64 \times 10^8 \times 10^{-5}}{3.82} = 2 \times 10^{8 + (-5)}$$

(B)

$$2 \times 10^3 = 2000$$

(C)

Figure A-7 — To divide numbers written in exponential notation, first divide the number parts. Then move the exponent (power of 10) from the denominator of the fraction to the numerator by changing its sign (B). Finally, add the exponents in the numerator (C).

$$\frac{75{,}000{,}000}{50{,}000{,}000} = \frac{75}{50} = 1.5$$

(A)

$$\frac{75 \times 10^6}{5 \times 10^7} = \frac{75 \times 10^{6 + (-7)}}{5} = 15 \times 10^{-1}$$
$$= 1.5$$

(B)

Figure A-8 — You can divide numbers by canceling the same number of zeros in the numerator and denominator (A). You also can write the numbers in exponential form first (B).

before dividing. That's following the rule for division with powers of 10. Suppose there are six zeros in the numerator and seven in the denominator. You can get rid of six of them right away. See **Figure A-8A**. Part B shows how to solve this problem using exponential notation.

As another example, let's divide 250,000 by 500,000. We can write this as:

$$\frac{25 \times 10^4}{5 \times 10^5} = 5 \times 10^{-1} = 0.5$$

The 10^{-1} comes about because we have $(4 - 5 = -1)$ for the exponents. See **Figure A-9**.

It's very convenient to write numbers in exponential notation when we have to multiply or divide very large or very small numbers. However, when you must add or subtract numbers with a lot of zeros, you must remember a few different rules.

$$\frac{250,000}{500,000} = \frac{25 \times 10^4}{5 \times 10^5}$$

(A)

$$5 \times 10^{4 + (5)} = 5 \times 10^{-1} = 0.5$$

(B)

Figure A-9 — If the denominator power of 10 is larger than the numerator power, the answer will have a negative power of 10. (This means the answer will be less than 1.) This is reasonable, because you know that you always get a value less than 1 when you divide by a larger number. For example, ½, ¼ and ⅜ all give answers of 0.5, which is less than 1.

To add or subtract, be certain to express all the numbers with the *same power of 10*. Do the arithmetic with the "plain number" parts as you normally would. The power of 10 for your answer is the same power the numbers are expressed in. (When you add or subtract numbers, always be careful that the decimal point lines up in all the numbers. That is what you are doing by expressing all numbers in the same power of 10). For example, if you have to add 2,000 and 508,000, you might write the problem as:

$$2 \times 10^3$$
$$+\ 508 \times 10^3$$
$$\overline{\ 510 \times 10^3}$$

You can also write this answer as 51×10^4, 5.1×10^5 or even 510,000.

Figure A-10 shows several other examples of addition and subtraction problems with numbers written in exponential notation. Study those examples, and be sure you understand the work.

This discussion gives you a good background in working with exponential notation. You can understand calculations with very large and very small numbers.

$$12,300,000,000 + 45,000,000$$
$$12300 \times 10^6$$
$$+45 \times 10^6$$
$$\overline{12345 \times 10^6}$$
$$=12.345 \times 10^9$$

(A)

7.5×10^4	75×10^3
126×10^3	126×10^3
415×10^5	41500×10^3
$+\ 25 \times 10^2$	$+\ 2.5 \times 10^3$
	$\overline{41703.5 \times 10^3}$

(B)

$$7,930,000,000 - 7,137,000,000$$
$$7930 \times 10^6$$
$$-\ 7137 \times 10^6$$
$$\overline{\ 793 \times 10^6}$$

(C)

$$0.000000753 - 0.000000008$$
$$7.53 \times 10^{-7}$$
$$-\ 0.08 \times 10^{-7}$$
$$\overline{7.45 \times 10^{-7}}$$

(D)

Figure A-10 — Examples of addition and subtraction with numbers written in exponential notation. Notice that we must write all the numbers in a problem with the same power of 10, to align the decimal points.

Many quantities that we deal with every day in electronics involve numbers that we usually write in exponential form. It will be very helpful to work with numbers written in this way.

Using Exponential Notation on Your Calculator

Learning to express numbers in exponential notation on your scientific calculator will be rather easy. See **Appendix B** for specifics on your Texas Instruments calculator. This calculator has a **EE** key, used to Enter the *Exponent* of 10 when you are entering a number. After pressing the **EE** key, the next one (or two) digits are the power of 10.

Figure A-11 gives you some simple problems with numbers that you should write in scientific notation. There are also some problems with numbers written in exponential notation for you to expand into normal notation. Take the time to work through these problems, since doing so will make you more comfortable with exponential and scientific notation. The answers to these problems are in **Figure A-13**.

The problems in **Figure A-12** will give you some practice solving problems involving numbers expressed in exponential notation. These problems will help you become familiar with the basic operation of your calculator. After you solve the problems, you'll know how to enter numbers expressed in exponential notation almost without thinking about it. **Figure A-14** lists the answers to these problems.

There may be some variation in the answers your calculator gives. The number of digits displayed by your calculator, and the way the calculator rounds off numbers that are too large to fit in the display, will affect the result. So your answers may not agree exactly with the ones given in Figure A-14. Check your work if the last digit on your display differs by more than one or two from the

---

a) 9,460,000,000,000

b) 186,000

c) 0.00001578

d) 300,000,000

e) 0.000000000001113

Expand the following numbers to normal notation, without a power of 10.

f) 147.1×10^6

g) 83.14×10^2

h) 6.67×10^{-11}

i) 6.022×10^{23}

j) 1.3806×10^{-23}

Figure A-11 — Here are some numbers for you to practice converting between scientific or exponential and expanded notations. Check your answers with the ones given in Figure A-13.

---

a) $12.5 \times 10^{-3} \times 6.8 \times 10^3 =$

b) $625 \times 10^{-3} \times 5.6 \times 10^3 =$

c) $6.28 \times 3.75 \times 10^6 \times 2.48 \times 10^{-4} =$

d) $22.0 \times 10^6 \times 0.045 \times 10^{-6} =$

e) $1.38 \times 10^{-23} \times 290 \times 5 \times 10^2 =$

f) $\dfrac{1}{6.28 \times 21.15 \times 10^6 \times 5.96 \times 10^3} =$

g) $\dfrac{7.125 \times 10^6}{1.2 \times 10^2} =$

h) $\dfrac{10.0 \times 10^2 \times 2.00 \times 10^3}{50 + 2.00 \times 10^2} =$

i) $\dfrac{15 \times 10^2 + 3.4 \times 10^3}{7.0 \times 10^1} =$

j) $\dfrac{6.67 \times 10^{-11} \times 6.02 \times 10^{24} \times 7.34 \times 10^{22}}{(3.925 \times 10^8)^2}$

Figure A-12 — Work these practice problems with your scientific calculator or computer. Figure A-14 gives the answers for them.

a) 9.46×10^{12}

b) 1.86×10^{5}

c) 1.578×10^{-5}

d) 3×10^{8}

e) 1.113×10^{-12}

f) $147,100,000$

g) 8314

h) 0.0000000000667

i) $602,200,000,000,000,000,000,000$

j) $0.0000000000000000000000013806$

Figure A-13 — Compare your work on the exercises from Figure A-11 with the answers shown here.

a) 85

b) 35×10^{2}

c) 5.8404×10^{3}

d) 0.99

e) 2.001×10^{-18}

f) $\dfrac{1}{7.9161912 \times 10^{11}} = 1.263233763 \times 10^{-12}$

(The reciprocal, or $1/x$ key on your calculator is handy for problems like this.)

g) 5.9375×10^{4}

h) $\dfrac{2.00 \times 10^{6}}{2.50 \times 10^{2}} = 8000$

i) $\dfrac{4900}{7.0 \times 10^{1}} = 70$

j) $\dfrac{2.94725956 \times 10^{37}}{1.5405625 \times 10^{17}} = 1.913106128 \times 10^{20}$

(Notice that the denominator term is squared, or multiplied by itself.)

Figure A-14 — The answers you find to the problems in Figure A-12 may be slightly different from the ones given here. Your calculator may display a different number of digits than the calculator used to get these answers. That will cause it to round off the numbers differently, giving a different result.

same digit in the listed answer, however.

You should be aware of two important limitations to using a calculator. The first limitation is that most calculators can work only with exponent numbers between −99 and 99. This limitation applies to both numbers you enter, and the calculated results. In nearly every calculation you may run across in electronics, this won't be a problem, so let's not worry about this limitation.

What is Engineering Notation, and How is it Different from Scientific Notation?

Engineering notation is easy to understand and use if you are comfortable with *scientific* notation. In scientific notation, the exponent (power of 10) can be any integer (whole number), such as –4, –3, 2 or 5. Engineering notation is a form of scientific notation that requires that the exponent be a multiple of 3, such as –6, –3, 3, 6 or 9. For commonly used exponents that are multiples of 3 there are *metric prefix* names. Engineering notation and metric prefixes are used extensively in engineering and science. While they are something new to learn, becoming familiar with them will make your study of electronics much easier.

You're probably familiar with some of these metric prefixes: lengths measured in *milli*meters, distances measured in *kilo*meters, volumes of liquid expressed in *milli*liters, and town or city budgets expressed in *mega*dollars or *giga*dollars. The metric prefixes, and their values expressed as powers of 10, are given in the table below.

Prefix	Symbol	Value	Value
Giga	G	10^9	1,000,000,000
Mega	M	10^6	1,000,000
Kilo	k	10^3	1,000
milli	m	10^{-3}	1/1,000
micro	μ	10^{-6}	1/1,000,000
nano	n	10^{-9}	1/1,000,000,000
pico	p	10^{-12}	1/1,000,000,000,000

Let's get familiar with expressing some familiar quantities in scientific notation, and then we'll use the metric prefixes.

Sally is 1.8 meters tall. That's 1.8×10^0 meters. If we want to express Sally's height in millimeters, we know that a millimeter is 10^{-3} meters. So we make the number 1.8 bigger by 10^3, and the unit of meter smaller by 10^3. Recall that

$$10^3 \times 10^{-3} = 10^{[3 + (-3)]} = 10^0 = 1$$

so by making the number *bigger by 10^3*, and the unit

smaller by 10^3, we have expressed Sally's height in the new unit of millimeters. It may look different, but her height is the same.

Height = 1.8 meters = $1.8 \times (10^3 \times 10^{-3}$ meters)
= $(1.8 \times 10^3) \times (10^{-3}$ meters) = 1800 millimeters

Although it's rather silly and impractical, we could also express this height in kilometers, as follows:

Height = 1.8 meters = $1.8 \times (10^{-3} \times 10^3$ meters)
= $(1.8 \times 10^{-3}) \times (10^3$ meters) = 0.0018 kilometers

The power line voltage on some electric distribution lines is 23,000 volts. We can express this as 23 kilovolts, or 23 kV. What if we wanted to express this voltage using the unit of *megavolts*?

Well, mega is 10^6, and kilo is 10^3. So to make the unit of voltage be *bigger* by a factor of 1000 (10^6 is 10^3 times bigger than 10^3), we should make the voltage *smaller* by the same factor of 1000). Here's how to do it:

Voltage = 23 kV

= 23×10^3 volts

= $23 \times (10^{-3} \times 10^3) \times 10^3$ volts

= $(23 \times 10^{-3}) \times (10^3 \times 10^3)$ volts

= 0.023×10^6 volts

= 0.023 megavolts

You will soon become familiar with using engineering notation by doing problems, and learning to interpret what your calculator display is telling you. Your calculator has three modes for expressing numbers: floating, scientific notation and engineering notation.

Appendix B will explain how to tell your calculator which of these three modes to use, how to enter numbers in scientific notation and engineering notation, and how to interpret the display.

Understanding and Using Your TI-30X IIS Scientific Calculator

The examples of calculator use in this book are done with the Texas Instruments TI-30X IIS calculator. It is quite affordable, easy to learn, widely available and capable of doing all the calculations you will need to do. It also has many capabilities that are not needed for the purposes of this book (fractions, trigonometry, hyperbolics, rectangular and polar coordinates, statistics and probability). So don't become intimidated by all the keys; you will quickly master the few keys you need to use.

You may already have a calculator that will work very well. All you have to do is determine which keys to press on *your* calculator, based on the examples given in this book.

At the end of this Appendix is a list of where to find additional information about using your TI calculator.

Figure B-1 — The Texas Instruments TI-30X IIS calculator is recommended for performing the calculations used throughout this book.

Information About the Calculator

• If no key is pressed for about 5 minutes, the calculator will turn itself off. When you turn it back on, all the information in the 2-line display will be there.
• If it won't turn on, replace the battery.
• If the screen goes blank, replace the battery.
• If you get results you don't expect, replace the battery.
• The calculator has a two-line display. The upper line can hold up to 88 characters including digits and mathematical operators like × (the *multiply* symbol), but you can see only 11 at a time. The left and right arrow keys (← and →) allow you to "move" anywhere on the upper line display. In **Figure B-1**, you can see the equation 123 + 456 in the upper line, and 579 in the lower line.
• If you perform a calculation, the answer will appear in

the lower line of the display, and you can insert that answer into a new calculation by pressing the keys 2nd (–). There's no need to re-enter an answer if you use this handy feature.
• There are two other keys that can be real time savers. Once you enter an equation, and press the equals sign (=) to see the result of your calculation, the equation you entered is stored in a memory. To retrieve the equation, simply press the up arrow key (↑). There's no need to re-enter an equation if you use this handy feature, and then you can change a number in the equation to quickly see the effect. Using the up arrow key and the down arrow key (↓), you can scroll through many equations you've entered recently.
• There are two keys that at first look alike. The *subtract* key, which is dark blue and has a white minus sign on it, should be used when subtracting two numbers (for example, 7 – 4 = 3). The *negation* key is white and has a black minus sign enclosed in parentheses (–) on it. Use it when entering a negative number like an exponent: $10^{-2} = 1/10^2 = 1/100$.
• At the top left of the keypad is a light blue key labeled 2nd. Above many other keys is a light blue label, which is a second function for that key, *if* you first press the key labeled 2nd. For example, if you want to take the square root of 16, you would press

2nd X^2 1   6

since above the X^2 key is the square root symbol, in light blue.
• When in doubt, use parentheses to make it clear to the calculator what you're trying to do. For example, if you wanted to add 2 and 3, and then multiply the result by 4, pressing the following keys will *not* give the correct answer: 2 + 3 × 4. The calculator has a very particular order in which it performs calculations. To get the correct answer, enter (2 + 3) × 4, and the correct answer of 20 will appear. Remember, the upper display can hold 88 characters, so a few parentheses, even if not needed, don't cause any problems. They may just help you to get the right answer.
• As you use your calculator, you'll become very proficient at making it do what you want it to. For example, instead of keying in (2 + 3) × 4, you can leave out the × (meaning multiply) key, and simply key in (2 + 3) 4 and get the same result.
• The default mode for expressing angles is the *degree*. There are 360 degrees in a circle, and 90 degrees in a right angle. When you first turn on your calculator, or if you reset it, the mode for angles is the degree. You *could* change the angle mode to *radians* or *gradians*, if

Table B-1
Keystrokes Needed to Perform Basic Operations

Operation	Key(s) to Press
Turn the calculator on	ON
Turn the calculator off	2nd ON
Reset the calculator	ON CLEAR *(press both keys at the same time)*
Reset the calculator	2nd RESET
Fix the number of digits displayed	2nd FIX → → *(or more)* =
Delete the last character entered	DEL
Delete any character entered	DEL *(put cursor on the character you want to delete)*
Insert a character between 2 others	2nd INS *(put cursor on a character; the new character will be inserted to its left)*
Enter Scientific Notation mode	2nd SCI/ENG → =
Enter Engineering Notation mode	2nd SCI/ENG → → = *(Engineering Notation is the best mode to use for all calculations in this book)*

you wanted to, but for the purposes of this book, leaving degrees as the angle mode is best.

- In Figure B-1 you can see the ENG and DEG labels at the bottom of the display. These tell us that the calculator has been set to Scientific *Eng*ineering Mode, and that the Angle Mode is *deg*rees (not radians or gradians — these are not needed for anything in this book). Engineering Notation is the best mode to use for all calculations in this book.

Table B-1 summarizes the keystrokes needed for basic operations.

Examples

The following examples show how to use your TI-30X IIS calculator to solve equations.

From Unit 2, Chapter 11, on Ohm's Law:

Example 1

$E = I \times R$

$E = 5 \text{ mA} \times 2 \text{ k}\Omega$

$E = 5 \times 10^{-3} \text{ A} \times 2 \times 10^3 \text{ }\Omega = 10 \text{ V}$

Calculator keystrokes:

5 2nd EE – 3 × 2 2nd EE 3 =

[Note that the – (minus sign) key in the equation above is the *white key* under the 3 key. There is a – (subtract) key above the + (add) key. *Do NOT use the blue subtract key* when you mean to use the white minus sign key.]

The calculator's second display line shows: **10 × 10⁰⁰**

[Note that $10^{00} = 10^0 = 1$, so $10 \times 10^{00} = 10 \times 1 = 10$ (volts).]

Example 2

$R = E / I$

$R = 15 \text{ V} / 2 \text{ mA} = 15 \text{ V} / (2 \times 10^{-3} \text{ A})$

$R = 7.5 \times 10^3 = 7.5 \text{ k}\Omega$

Calculator keystrokes:

1 5 ÷ 2 2nd EE – 3 =

The calculator's second display line shows: **7.5 × 10⁰³**

From Unit 3, Chapter 15, on Frequency, Period and Examples of AC Voltages:

Example 3

$$f = \frac{c}{\lambda} \qquad \text{(Equation 15-3)}$$

$$f = \frac{c}{\lambda} = \frac{3.00 \times 10^8 \text{ m/s}}{80.5 \text{ meters}} = 3.727 \times 10^6 \text{ Hz} = 3.727 \text{ MHz}$$

Calculator keystrokes

3 2ⁿᵈ EE 8 ÷ 8 0 . 5 =

The calculator's second display line shows the result: **3.7267 × 10⁰⁶**

[Note that $10^{06} = 10^6 = 1,000,000$ so $3.7267 \times 10^{06} = 3.7267 \times 1,000,000 = 3.7267 \text{ MHz}$]

Additional Information for Your TI Calculator

The calculator comes with:
- A two-sided card in the cover of the calculator
- An information sheet explaining nearly everything about the calculator
- A sheet with examples of what each key does, and how to use it

A 5-page *Quick Reference Guide* on how to use all of the functions of the TI-30X IIS calculator may be found online:
education.ti.com/downloads/guidebooks/ scientific/30xii/30xiiqrg-eng.pdf

A comprehensive *Guidebook for Teachers*, with 118 pages, may be found online:
education.ti.com/downloads/guidebooks/ scientific/30xii/teacher_guide/30xiitg-eng.pdf

Vacuum Tubes

Most beginners in Amateur Radio and basic electronics will no longer encounter vacuum tubes, but they were the mainstay of all electronics for many decades, until solid-state devices, including diodes, transistors and integrated circuits, became the rule. For historic interest, and for practical information if you decide to work with older equipment, this Appendix gives an overview of Vacuum Tubes. Also, although transistors have replaced vacuum tubes for many applications, we still use tubes for some high power amplifiers and other applications.

Contents

Thermionic Emission

Electric current consists of a movement of electrons. Remember that electrons bump from atom to atom in their journey along a copper wire. Each electron must gain some energy to become free of an atom before it can move along the wire. Chemical energy in a battery supplies that energy for circuits like the one shown in **Figure C-1**.

You also can give the electrons additional energy by heating the material. When the temperature of a metal is high enough, electrons gain the energy they need to jump free. These *free electrons* can leave the solid and form a kind of cloud near the metal surface. We say the electrons *boil off* the metal. (See **Figure C-2**.)

These *negatively charged electrons* leave *positively charged ions* behind when they leave the metal. This process of heating the metal to remove electrons is *thermionic emission*. A thermal (temperature-related) process emits the ions.

Normally, we expect these electrons to lose some of this heat energy and return to the metal. The positive ions left in the metal attract the negative electrons, pulling them back onto the metal surface.

Suppose we place another piece of metal close to the first, as **Figure C-3** shows. We call these elements *electrodes*, because they connect to the voltage supply in an electric circuit. We connect the first electrode to the negative battery terminal and the second one to the positive terminal. We call the first electrode the *cathode* because it connects to the negative voltage supply. The second electrode is the *anode*, because it connects to the positive supply. Sometimes we also refer to the anode as the *plate*.

When we place the whole assembly inside a glass enclosure and remove the air inside, we have a *vacuum tube*. Removing the air ensures the free electrons can move from the cathode to the anode. Any gas molecules inside the tube would scatter the electrons and absorb energy from them. **Figure C-4** shows the construction of this basic vacuum tube. The cathode and anode leads go

Figure C-2 — Heating a metal gives some electrons the energy they need to break free from the material. These electrons move a short distance into the space surrounding the metal. When an electron leaves an atom of the metal, it leaves a positive ion behind. These positive ions attract the electrons, keeping them close to the surface. These positive ions attract some of the electrons back onto the metal.

Figure C-1 — The battery's chemical energy helps free electrons from copper atoms in the wire. This enables the electrons to move from atom to atom along the wire.

Electrons flow across space between metal plates.

Figure C-3 — A second metal piece placed close to the first attracts the free electrons if we apply a positive voltage to it.

Figure C-4 — This diagram illustrates the construction of a simple vacuum tube. Wire leads extend through the glass envelope so you can connect the tube to a circuit. One power supply feeds a current through the cathode to heat it. A second supply puts a positive voltage on the anode.

Figure C-5 — Some vacuum tubes use a separate filament to heat the cathode.

through the glass to provide connections to the external circuit.

You may be wondering how we heat the cathode inside this vacuum tube. There are two ways we can accomplish this. Both methods involve an electric current, since current produces heat when it flows through a metal.

Passing an electric current through the cathode will heat the cathode metal. One voltage supply feeds current through the cathode and a second supply connects between the cathode and anode. Tubes using this method have a *directly heated* cathode. The diode shown in Figure C-4 has a directly heated cathode.

Some vacuum tubes have a separate element to heat the cathode. A current through this *filament* heats the filament wire, which then *indirectly* heats the cathode. **Figure C-5** illustrates the construction of a tube with an *indirectly heated* cathode.

Diodes

A vacuum-tube diode contains two circuit elements. We sometimes call these circuit elements electrodes. You probably knew this tube has two electrodes because the prefix *di* means two.

The *cathode* gives up electrons to produce current through the tube. The cathode connects to the negative supply lead. Current through the cathode heats the wire to "boil off" electrons in a directly heated cathode. A *filament* close to an indirectly heated cathode produces the heat needed to free electrons.

The *plate*, or *anode*, collects the electrons that come off the cathode. The plate connects to the positive supply lead. This positive voltage attracts the electrons, pulling them across the space between the two electrodes.

Figure C-6 shows two symbols used to represent vacuum-tube diodes on schematic diagrams. You may wonder why we don't count three elements in the tube with an indirectly heated cathode. The filament is not part of the *circuit* in which we use the tube. The filament's only function is to heat the cathode to boil off electrons.

Figure C-6 — These symbols represent vacuum-tube diodes on schematic diagrams. The symbol at A represents a tube with a directly heated cathode. We use the symbol shown at B to represent a tube with an indirectly heated cathode.

Therefore, we don't count the filament as one of the active elements in the tube.

Figure C-7 shows a diode, with filament, connected to a battery. We included an ammeter to measure current through the tube. The positive plate voltage attracts the electrons given off by the cathode. The electrons move through the vacuum inside the tube, producing a current through the tube.

Figure C-8 is a cut-away view of the diode construction. The plate surrounds the cathode so electrons given off any side can travel directly to the plate. This ensures that the plate can collect all the electrons given off by the cathode.

How will the plate voltage affect the current through the tube? Let's conduct a simple experiment. Replace the battery in Figure C-7 with a variable-voltage power supply. With no voltage applied to the plate, there is no current through the tube. Now increase the plate voltage to 10 volts. The ammeter indicates 25 mA through the tube.

Continue to increase the plate voltage, 10 volts at a time, and read the plate current for each new voltage

Table C-1
Diode Plate Current and Voltage Characteristics

Plate Voltage (volts)	Plate Current (milliamperes)
0	0
10	25
20	70
30	130
40	200
50	275
60	360
70	450
80	560
90	660
100	775
110	890

Figure C-7 — The positive supply lead connects to the diode plate lead. This tube has a filament to heat the cathode. A separate supply powers the filament circuit. The ammeter measures current through the tube.

Figure C-8 — This cut-away view illustrates typical vacuum-tube diode construction.

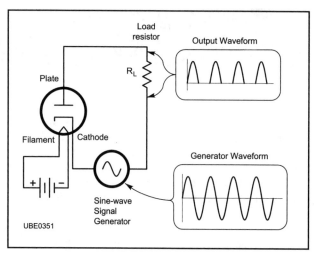

Figure C-10 — A vacuum-tube diode converts a sine-wave ac input to a series of dc pulses.

Figure C-9 — This characteristic curve graphs the data measured for Table C-1. It displays the changes in tube current as the plate voltage changes.

setting. **Table C-1** lists a set of measurements for one tube. **Figure C-9** is a *characteristic curve* plotted from this data.

Various vacuum-tube diode types have different characteristic curves. While the voltage and current numbers won't be the same, the general shape of the curve will be the same. Notice the current drops to zero when the plate voltage is zero.

What will happen if we connect the plate to the negative supply lead and the cathode to the positive lead? The plate will not attract electrons that come off the cathode. The negative plate will now *repel* those electrons, blocking any current through the tube. (The plate won't emit any electrons because it is not hot enough.) A diode tube with *reverse voltage* across its cathode and plate is *cut off*. That means there is no current through the tube.

A vacuum-tube diode works the same way a solid-state diode works. With an alternating voltage supply connected to the cathode and plate, the diode conducts during one-half cycle of the waveform. **Figure C-10** shows a diode connected to an alternating current supply. The tube output waveform is a series of pulses, which occur when the positive half-cycle connects to the plate.

The Triode — A Field-Effect Device

We seldom use vacuum-tube diodes to rectify ac signals in modern electronics. They produce a lot of heat and are less reliable than solid-state diodes. These tubes illustrate the basic operation of all vacuum tubes, however. Although transistors have replaced vacuum tubes for many applications, we still use tubes for high power amplifiers and other applications.

We must have some means to control the current through a tube so it can serve as an amplifier. The *triode* adds a third electrode to the cathode and anode in a diode. This third element is the *control grid*. **Figure C-11** shows the schematic-diagram symbols used to represent triode vacuum tubes.

The control grid is a metal screen placed between the cathode and anode, or plate. Electrons can easily pass through this screen.

We usually connect the *control grid*, or *grid*, to a negative voltage. The positive side of this supply connects to the cathode. Connected this way, the grid repels some of the electrons flowing from the cathode to the plate. **Figure C-12** is a circuit we might use to study the operation of a triode.

To begin our analysis of the triode, let's assume the control grid has no voltage. (Replace battery E_{GRID} in Figure C-12 with a piece of wire.) The cathode may be directly heated or indirectly heated. When it becomes hot, it emits electrons. Since the anode is positive when compared to the cathode, it attracts these electrons. Electrons move through the tube from cathode to plate. Does this sound identical to the vacuum-tube diode? For this experiment, we will assume the plate-current meter reads 4.5 mA.

Now let's put the grid battery back into the Figure C-12 circuit. We can adjust this voltage to any value we like for our experiment, so let's set it to 3 volts. Because the negative side of this supply connects to the control grid, the voltage tries to repel electrons emitted from the cathode. This time the plate-current meter only reads 0.15 mA. Making the control grid negative reduced the plate current.

Increase the grid voltage to 10 volts. This time the grid repels all the electrons coming from the cathode, so none get through to the plate. The plate-current meter reads zero now. We say the tube is *cutoff* when the control-grid voltage is high enough to block all plate current.

What do you think would happen if we made the grid positive with respect to the cathode? (In other words, what would happen if we turned battery E_{GRID} around in Figure C-12?) Like the plate, the grid would attract the electrons emitted from the cathode. The grid is just a wire screen, though, so most of the electrons would go right through it. Then the plate would continue to attract them, so the plate current would be even larger than when the grid voltage was zero. Some electrons would strike the grid, and this

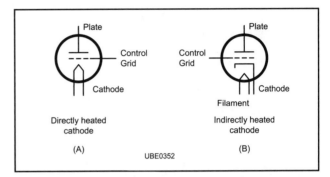

Figure C-11 — These symbols represent triode vacuum tubes on schematic diagrams. Some triodes have directly heated cathodes and some have indirectly heated cathodes. Notice we can draw the control-grid lead coming out of either side of the symbol.

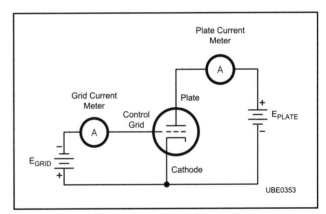

Figure C-12 — We can use this circuit to study the triode operation. One voltage supply connects between the cathode and plate, as it does with a diode. A second battery connects between the cathode and control grid, to make the grid negative compared to the cathode.

would increase the grid current also.

We call the voltages that set up the tube's operating conditions *bias voltages*. The plate gets a positive bias voltage compared to the cathode. The control grid has a negative bias voltage for normal operation.

There are two ways to change a triode's plate current. Increasing the plate voltage will increase the plate current, just as it does with a diode. (You should never apply a higher plate voltage than the tube manufacturer specifies. You also must use care not to allow the plate current to exceed the manufacturer's rating.) Changing the grid bias voltage also changes the plate current, as we learned in our earlier experiment.

Figure C-13 — This graph shows a typical set of characteristic curves for a triode vacuum tube. For each grid voltage shown, we increase the plate voltage from zero.

Figure C-14 — This simplified circuit illustrates how a triode vacuum tube amplifies the voltage of an input signal. Small variations in the input signal voltage add to and subtract from the grid bias battery, E$_{GRID}$. The changing grid voltage produces a changing plate current, which results in a large change of the output voltage.

Figure C-13 is a graph that plots a typical set of triode *characteristic curves*. We could measure these curves using a circuit like the one shown in Figure C-12. We would set a certain value of grid voltage, and then vary the plate voltage from zero to the maximum value. Then we would adjust the grid voltage to a new value and vary the plate voltage over the same range. After collecting the data for a range of grid voltages, we would plot the Figure C-13 graph.

Each triode tube type has a particular set of characteristic curves. Different tube types will have different values of plate voltage and current, and different values of grid voltage. Even the shape of the curves may vary somewhat. Figure C-13 is a representative

sample of a triode characteristic curve.

A complete description of how a triode tube amplifies a signal is beyond the scope of this book. We'll just give a brief, simplified description to help you understand why this tube is so important.

The circuit of **Figure C-14** illustrates how a triode amplifies a signal. A practical amplifier circuit requires many more parts. You wouldn't find two batteries supplying the plate and grid voltages. The grid bias battery and plate-voltage battery set the operating conditions for the tube in this example.

Figure C-15 is a copy of the Figure C-13 triode characteristics with the operating conditions added. The sinusoidal input signal voltage varies between plus 4 volts and minus 4 volts. This input signal adds to (and subtracts from) the grid battery voltage, E$_{GRID}$, which is –6 V. The grid bias voltage varies between –2 volts and –10 volts.

Variations in grid voltage cause changes in plate current, as Figure C-15 shows. In this example, the plate current varies between 17.5 mA and 8.7 mA.

Figure C-15 also shows how the

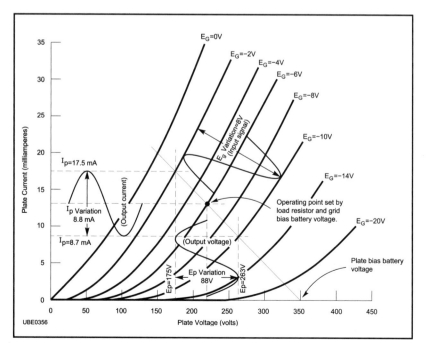

Figure C-15 — This graph shows the grid-voltage variations produced by the input signal. It also shows the resulting plate current variations and output-voltage variations. This illustrates how a triode vacuum tube amplifies a signal.

output voltage changes when the plate current varies. The plate current flows through the load resistor, creating a voltage drop that you can calculate using Ohm's Law. (If the plate current is 8.7 mA, there is an 87-volt drop across R_{LOAD}.)

$E = I\,R$

$E = 8.7 \times 10^{-3}\ A \times 10 \times 10^3\ \Omega = 87\ V$

This voltage drop subtracts from the battery voltage, to give the output-signal voltage. (In this case, 350 V – 87 V = 263 V.)

If the plate current increases to 17.5 mA, there is a larger voltage drop across the load resistor.

$E = 17.5 \times 10^{-3}\ A \times 10 \times 10^3\ \Omega = 175\ V$

Subtracting this value from the 350-V battery voltage, we have an output voltage of 175 volts. While the input voltage varies 8 volts between its positive and negative peaks, the output voltage varies 88 volts between peaks! The output voltage is an amplified version of the input voltage. The voltage gain is 88 volts peak-to-peak divided by 8 volts peak-to-peak, a gain of 11.

The Tetrode and Pentode Have Additional Control Elements

Triode vacuum tubes make good amplifiers. One triode characteristic can lead to problems, however. The plate current is very sensitive to changes in plate voltage. **Figure C-16** shows a set of triode characteristic curves.

Even small plate voltage variations can cause significant plate current changes. This means we must have a well-regulated plate-voltage supply to produce a stable amplifier.

Tube manufacturers added another grid to the triode to help solve this problem. They called the new grid a *screen grid*. This tube has four elements, not counting the filament, which heats the cathode. A four-element tube became known as a *tetrode*. (*Tetra* means four in Greek.)

A tetrode has a positive voltage applied to the screen grid, as **Figure C-17** shows. The screen grid helps attract the electrons emitted from the cathode. As its name implies, we make the screen grid from wire mesh or screen, so electrons easily pass through it. The positive voltage applied to the plate is higher than the screen voltage. The plate attracts the electrons through the screen grid and collects them. The screen collects some of the electrons as they move through the tube. The screen current is much smaller than the plate current, however.

The screen grid is physically much closer to the cathode than the plate. The positive screen voltage has a larger effect on the electrons as they leave the cathode than does the plate voltage. Small variations in plate voltage produce almost no change in plate current.

The tetrode solves the biggest problem with triode amplifiers. **Figure C-18** shows a set of theoretical tetrode characteristic curves. Notice the plate current is almost independent of plate voltage.

We don't use tetrodes in modern electronic circuits because they create another problem. Both the screen grid and the plate have positive voltages to attract the electrons from the cathode. This attraction force pulls the electrons across the vacuum inside the tube, so electrons that hit the plate are moving very fast.

When the electrons strike the plate they knock other electrons loose from the surface. We call this process of

Figure C-17 — A tetrode vacuum tube has all the elements of a triode tube, plus an additional grid, called the screen grid. The screen grid makes the plate current almost independent of variations in plate voltage.

Figure C-16 — This graph represents the plate current and voltage characteristics of a triode vacuum tube. Notice how the plate current changes as the plate voltage changes for each grid voltage setting.

Figure C-18 — We seldom use tetrode vacuum tubes in modern electronics. This graph represents a set of characteristic curves for an idealized tetrode. Notice the plate current is almost independent of the plate voltage for a given control-grid voltage.

Figure C-19 — This drawing shows the symbol used to represent a pentode vacuum tube on schematic diagrams. The battery connections illustrate the bias polarities used in a typical amplifier.

knocking other electrons free *secondary emission*. Many of the secondary electrons fly off the plate and the positive voltage on the screen grid attracts them. These electrons travel backward through the tube and increase the screen-grid current. Worse, they decrease the plate current, and

lower the gain of an amplifier made with a tetrode tube.

We add a fifth tube element to maintain the advantage of the tetrode, while eliminating its disadvantage. The new element fits between the screen grid and the plate. This tube is the *pentode*, because it has five electrodes. (*Penta* is Greek for five.)

This new element, called a *suppressor grid*, connects to the cathode. The connection may be inside or outside the tube. The cathode and suppressor grid have the same voltage. The suppressor grid repels secondary electrons as they travel toward the screen grid, pushing them back to the plate.

Figure C-19 shows the symbol used on schematic diagrams to represent a pentode vacuum tube. Separate batteries show the bias-voltage polarities applied to a pentode.

Figure C-20 shows a typical set of plate characteristics for a pentode vacuum tube. Like other tubes, each type of pentode has its own particular set of characteristic curves. The curves shown here are meant only to provide an example of the typical curve shapes.

Many high-power radio frequency amplifiers use triode or pentode tubes. The cathode, plate and control grid in a pentode operate the same way they do in a triode. A pentode amplifier works much the same as a triode amplifier.

Figure C-20 — This graph represents a typical set of characteristic curves for a pentode vacuum tube.

The Cathode-Ray Tube (CRT) Display

Historically, vacuum tubes have had many applications in electronic circuits. Solid-state devices such as bipolar and field-effect transistors have taken the place of vacuum tubes in most applications, however. When we think about vacuum tubes today, high-power radio-frequency amplifiers will likely come to mind.

Perhaps the most widely used vacuum tube of all, though, is the *cathode-ray tube*, or *CRT*. This vacuum tube is a display device, and until recently it was used in TVs, computer monitors and many other products.

Several very important pieces of electronics test equipment use CRT displays. An oscilloscope uses a CRT to draw a picture of the signal waveform in a circuit. **Figure C-21** is a schematic diagram of a simple full-wave rectifier circuit. We connected an oscilloscope to the circuit output, and the display shows a picture of the diode output pulses.

Spectrum analyzers use CRTs to display a bar graph of the sine-wave signal frequencies that make up a waveform. **Figure C-22** shows the spectrum-analyzer display resulting from a radio-frequency transmitter test. We feed two audio-frequency sine-wave signals into a radio transmitter microphone input. This display shows each output-signal frequency from the transmitter. The height of each line represents the strength of that signal.

Figure C-23 shows the construction of a basic cathode-ray tube. You should recognize the filament or heater, the cathode, the grid and the anode. These are the same basic parts used in the other vacuum tubes we studied.

The filament heats the cathode, causing it to give off electrons. The grid controls the flow of these electrons toward the anode. By increasing or decreasing the number of electrons in the beam, we can control the brightness of the display screen. The anode attracts the electrons, accelerating them so they move very fast as they approach the anode. The anode does not collect most of the electrons, however.

The anode has three sections that function as an *electron lens*. This lens focuses the electrons into a thin beam, which goes through a hole in the end of the anode. We call this assembly an *electron gun* because it shoots a thin electron beam toward the tube's front surface.

The front of the tube has a coating of a special material, called a *phosphor*. When electrons from the beam strike this phosphor, they give extra energy to electrons in the phosphor. Then these electrons radiate this energy to return to their normal position in the phosphor atoms. The energy they radiate appears as visible light, of a color specific to the phosphor used. Some phosphors give off a green glow. Others radiate white light. Still others produce the red, blue and green light needed for a color display.

After the electrons leave the electron-gun portion of the tube, they pass through two sets of *deflection plates*.

Figure C-21 — We can use an oscilloscope to draw a picture of signal waveforms. Here the scope display shows the output pulses from a full-wave rectifier circuit.

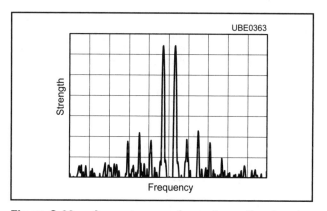

Figure C-22 — A spectrum analyzer shows the signal frequency and strength on a bar-graph display. This is especially useful for studying a waveform that includes several sine waves combined. Here we show the spectral display from a transmitter during a two-tone test. We feed two audio-frequency sine wave signals into the microphone input and measure the output signal frequencies and strengths.

One set of deflection plates moves the beam horizontally and the other set moves the beam vertically. **Figure C-24** shows the electron beam bent as it passes through the vertical deflection plates. Oscilloscopes and other pieces of test equipment normally use electrostatic deflection.

Most TV picture tubes use another method to deflect the electron beam: *magnetic deflection*. One advantage of magnetic deflection is that you can position the electromagnets around the outside of the tube neck. The magnetic field bends the electron beam, changing the position where it strikes the phosphor on the tube front. **Figure C-25** illustrates the electromagnetic deflection

Figure C-23 — This drawing shows the basic construction of a cathode-ray vacuum tube. Typical operating voltages are shown by each tube section. High voltages of several thousand volts are typical, and indicate the dangers involved with such tubes. The text explains how the various sections operate.

Figure C-24 — The electron beam bends as it passes between the deflection plates, when there is a voltage across plates. Higher voltages bend the beam farther.

Figure C-25 — A TV picture tube uses magnetic deflection to move the electron beam across the tube face. These coils produce a horizontal magnetic field and a vertical magnetic field. The magnetic fields deflect the beam left to right across the screen and move the beam from top to bottom. The beam scans the entire tube surface 30 times each second.

coils around the neck of a TV picture tube.

Electrostatic deflection provides better high-frequency operation, which is why oscilloscopes use this method. With no voltage applied to the deflection plates, the beam hits the center of the screen. A positive voltage on the right-hand plate and a negative voltage on the left deflects the beam to the right. The positive voltage attracts the electrons and the negative voltage repels them. The electrons pass right through and don't strike the deflection plates, however, because they are moving so fast.

Reversing the deflection-plate voltage polarity deflects the beam to the left. The vertical deflection plates operate the same way, moving the beam up and down from the center position.

The deflection amount depends on the applied voltage. A small voltage moves the beam a small amount and a

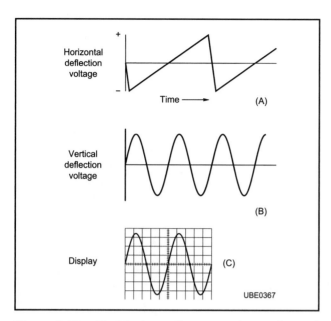

Horizontal
deflection
voltage

Time ———→   (A)

Vertical
deflection
voltage

                    (B)

Display   (C)

UBE0367

Figure C-26 — Part A shows the sawtooth waveform of the horizontal deflection voltage. Part B shows a sine-wave vertical input voltage. These deflection voltages combine to draw the waveform shown at C on the oscilloscope screen.

large voltage deflects it farther.

An oscilloscope usually operates with an internally generated voltage applied to the horizontal deflection plates. The vertical deflection plates get a signal voltage from the circuit under test.

The horizontal plates have a sawtooth-waveform voltage applied. This voltage starts the beam off at the screen's left edge, then sweeps it horizontally across the tube. During the short time the sawtooth waveform goes from its positive peak to its negative peak, the beam jumps back to the left screen edge.

Any voltage on the vertical deflection plates moves the electron beam up and down on the screen. The beam moves up and down while it sweeps from left to right. In this way, the oscilloscope draws a picture of the input waveform. You must adjust the horizontal sweep rate to match the waveform's frequency to get a useful picture. See **Figure C-26**.

Special circuits in a TV set move the electron beam horizontally and vertically, to scan the entire tube surface. One complete scan occurs 30 times each second. A control voltage from the received TV signal goes to the grid, changing the beam strength. This changes the brightness of the light given off from the screen phosphor, creating an image on the screen.

Common Schematic Symbols Used in Circuit Diagrams

Decibels

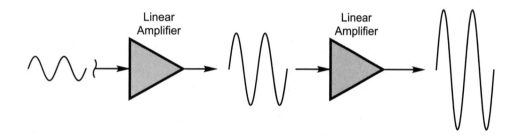

Each of these amplifiers has a gain of 3 decibels (3 dB). That means the output signal is twice as strong as the input signal.

Contents

Defining the Bel

The *decibel* is one unit that you will hear used (and sometimes misused) quite often in electronics. Just what does this term mean? First we'll define the term, and then we'll take a look at some of the ways we use decibels in electronics.

You have probably recognized *deci* as the metric prefix that means one-tenth. So the unit we are really talking about here is the *bel*, and a decibel is just $^1/_{10}$ of a bel. We often use a capital B to abbreviate *bel*. Since a lower case d is the abbreviation for deci, the proper abbreviation for a decibel is dB. The bel is named for Alexander Graham Bell. Most people remember Bell for his invention of the telephone. Bell was also very interested in working with deaf people and studying the way we hear sounds. Bell tried to invent a device that would amplify sounds, to help people with a partial hearing loss. The telephone is a result of this work.

We can hear very soft sounds, like a leaf rustling through the other leaves on a tree as it falls. We also can hear sounds that are extremely loud. A jackhammer pounding the pavement on a city street or the roar of a nearby jet engine are some examples. Some sounds can be so loud that they actually cause us pain. These painfully loud sounds can be nearly 1×10^{12} (yes, that's a million million) times louder than the soft rustling of the leaves or a

quiet whisper, yet we can hear sounds within this full range.

To make the numbers easier to work with, we often use logarithms to represent the numbers on such a wide scale. We could say that our ears have a logarithmic response to sound loudness or *intensity*. The *bel* compares the loudness of two sounds with each other. One of these sounds serves as a reference for the comparison. To calculate how many bels louder or softer the second sound is, simply divide the reference intensity into the other value. Then find the logarithm of that result.

$$bels = \log\left(\frac{I_1}{I_0}\right) \qquad \text{(Equation E-1)}$$

where:

I_0 is the intensity (or loudness) of the reference sound

I_1 is the intensity of the sound compared to the reference

Use the quieter sound intensity (a smaller number) as the reference sound to get a positive value of bels. If you use the louder sound intensity as the reference sound, however, you get the same value but with a negative sign. So a positive value of bels indicates a sound is louder than the reference sound. A negative value of bels indicates a sound is quieter than the reference.

Painfully loud sounds can be as much as 1×10^{12} times louder than the softest sounds we can hear.

Use that number as the ratio I_1/I_0 in Equation E-1, and calculate the range of our hearing, in bels.

$$bels = \log\left(\frac{I_1}{I_0}\right) \qquad \text{(Equation E-1)}$$

$$bels = \log (1 \times 10^{12}) = 12$$

We can hear sounds that differ in intensity by as much as 12 bels. Normal sounds in your home, like soft music, conversation or the TV are about 4 to 7 bels louder than the softest sounds you can hear.

Sound intensity is similar to sound power, so we can apply the bel to power levels in electronics. The bel is a rather large unit, even to compare sound intensity levels, so we normally use the decibel. It takes 10 decibels to make one bel. Therefore, the equation to compare two power levels in decibels is 10 times the equation to calculate bels.

$$dB = 10 \log\left(\frac{P_1}{P_0}\right) \qquad \text{(Equation E-2)}$$

where

P_0 is the reference power level

P_1 is the power level compared to the reference

Let's look at an example to help you understand bels and decibels. Remember that we use a ratio of two power levels, which means we divide one power by a reference,

Figure E-1 — This diagram shows a power level measured at the output of an Amateur Radio transmitter. The diagram also shows power levels after the signal goes through a power amplifier and a long length of coaxial cable.

or comparison, power.

Suppose we measure the output power from an Amateur Radio transmitter, and find that it is 15 watts. If we use a power amplifier after the transmitter, and measure the power again, we measure 1500 W, as shown in **Figure E-1**. What is the gain, or power increase, provided by this amplifier? To solve this problem, we will use the 15 W power as the reference. We want to compare the amplified power with this value. Equation E-2 will help us answer the question.

$$dB = 10 \log \left(\frac{P_1}{P_0} \right)$$

$$dB = 10 \log \left(\frac{1500 \text{ W}}{15 \text{ W}} \right)$$

$$dB = 10 \log (100) = 10 \log (10^2)$$

$$dB = 10 \times 2 = 20 \text{ decibels}$$

The amplifier provides a 20 dB increase in power. This example shows how to do the calculation. In a real Amateur Radio station, we would probably use one amplifier to go from 15 to 150 watts. Then another amplifier would increase the power from 150 to 1500 watts. Each amplifier would have a gain of 10 dB, which is a more realistic figure.

Did you notice in the equations above that the log of 100, which is the log of 10^2, is 2. Log is short for logarithm, and two words that mean the same as logarithm are *exponent* and *power*. So the log of 1000 equals the log of 10^3 equals 3. What's the log of one million?

If you thought that one million is 10^6, and the log of 10^6 is simply 6, you're right! When you need to find the log of a number that's not 10, or 100, or 1000 (etc.), that's when your calculator will come in handy. Find the log of 500 on your calculator by pressing the following calculator keys:

LOG 5 0 0 =

The answer is that the log of 500 = log (500) = 2.7.

What happens if the power decreases? Well, let's look at an example and find out. We can continue with the problem above, and measure the actual power arriving at the antenna. In this station, a long length of coaxial cable connects the transmitter to the antenna. Because some power is lost in this cable, we measure only 150 watts at the antenna. This time we'll use the 1500 W amplifier output as our reference. We want to compare the power at the antenna with the amplifier power. Again, Equation E-2 helps us answer our question.

$$dB = 10 \log \left(\frac{P_1}{P_0} \right)$$

$$dB = 10 \log \left(\frac{150 \text{ W}}{1500 \text{ W}} \right)$$

$$dB = 10 \log (0.10) = 10 \log (10^{-1})$$

$$dB = 10 \times (-1) = -10 \text{ decibels}$$

The negative sign tells us that we have less power than our reference. Of course, we knew that because there was less power at the antenna than the amplifier was producing. What happened to that power? Some of the energy going through the coaxial cable changed to heat, and there may be other losses in the cable. All coaxial cables would have some loss. If you have a cable with 10 dB of loss in any reasonable length, however, it's probably no good! 10 dB of cable loss means that 90% of the power entering it is lost to heat, and that leaves only 10% at the cable output. If the loss were 20 dB (a *really bad* situation), then 99% of the power entering it would be lost to heat, and that would leave only 1% at the cable output. It would be time to change something: either move the antenna and transmitter closer together (shorter cable means less loss), or get a much better cable.

Decibels and Power Ratios

We often use decibels to compare power levels in electronic circuits. How do you find the number of decibels? First select the power you want to use as the *reference power* to which other power levels will be compared. This reference power often is the beginning power. It may be the power before the signal goes through an amplifier or through a line to an antenna. Next, divide the new power (the amplifier output power, or the power that reaches the antenna) by your chosen reference power. Now find the logarithm of that power-level ratio. Finally, multiply the result by ten. A few examples will show you how easy it is to calculate decibels.

You won't even need a calculator to find the logarithm when the ratio is a number like 10, 100, 1000 and so on! Multiples of 10 less than 1, like 0.1, 0.01, 0.001 and so on are also easy. Use your calculator as we work through a few examples. You'll soon be doing logarithms like these without it, though. Here are some simple examples.

$$\log (1) = \log (10^0) = 0$$

$$\log (10) = \log (10^1) = 1$$

$$\log (100) = \log (10^2) = 2$$

$$\log (1000) = \log (10^3) = 3$$

$$\log (0.1) = \log (10^{-1}) = -1$$

$$\log (0.01) = \log (10^{-2}) = -2$$

$$\log (0.001) = \log (10^{-3}) = -3$$

Let's suppose you have an amateur transmitter that operates on the 2-meter band. Your transmitter has an output power of 10 watts, but you would like a little more power to use to make contact with a distant station. An amplifier is just what you need. After connecting your new amplifier, you measure the output power again, and find it is now 100 watts. How many dB increase is this? We'll use the 10-W signal as the reference in this case. Divide 100 W by 10 W to find the power ratio.

$$\text{Power Ratio} = \frac{P_1}{P_0} \quad \text{(Equation E-3)}$$

where
  P_0 is the reference power level
  P_1 is the power level compared to the reference power

$$\text{Power Ratio} = \frac{P_1}{P_0} = \frac{100 \text{ W}}{10 \text{ W}} = 10$$

Now find the logarithm of the power ratio.

$$\log (10) = \log (10^1) = 1$$

Finally, multiply this result by

$$10 \text{ decibels} = 10 \times 1 = 10$$

Your amplifier has increased the power of your 2-meter signal by 10 dB!

Now suppose the amplifier increased your signal to 1000 watts. Choose the reference power to be 10 W again, and divide the new power by the reference.

$$\text{Power Ratio} = \frac{P_1}{P_0}$$

$$\text{Power Ratio} = \frac{P_1}{P_0} = \frac{1000 \text{ W}}{10 \text{ W}} = 100$$

Find the logarithm of the power ratio.

$$\log (100) = \log (10^2) = 2$$

Multiply this result by 10 to find the number of decibels.

$$\text{decibels} = 10 \times 2 = 20$$

If we put all these steps together into a single equation, we have the definition of a decibel.

$$\text{decibels (dB)} = 10 \log \left(\frac{P_1}{P_0} \right)$$

$$\text{(Equation E-4)}$$

where
  P_0 is the reference power level
  P_1 is the power level compared to the reference power

Use this equation to calculate the number of decibels between power levels.

You should be aware of certain power ratios, because they occur so often. For example, let's see what happens if we double a given power. Suppose we start with a circuit that has a power of 2 mW. What dB increase occurs if we double the power to 4 mW? We'll start with the basic definition of a decibel.

$$\text{dB} = 10 \log \left(\frac{P_1}{P_0} \right)$$

$$\text{dB} = 10 \log \left(\frac{4 \text{ mW}}{2 \text{ mW}} \right)$$
$$= 10 \log (2) = 10 \times 0.3 = 3.0 \text{ dB}$$

When we double the power, there is a 3 dB increase. This is true no matter what the actual power levels are. Let's look at an example with higher power levels to show that the dB increase is the same.

We measure the transmitter output power at an Amateur Radio station like the one shown in **Figure E-2**, and find that it is 10 W. Use this power as a reference power for the station. After making some adjustments to the circuit, we measure the transmitter output power again. This time we find that the output power has increased to 20 W. What is the power increase, in dB? Equation E-4 will help us answer this question.

$$\text{dB} = 10 \log \left(\frac{P_1}{P_0} \right)$$

$$\text{dB} = 10 \log \left(\frac{20 \text{ W}}{10 \text{ W}} \right)$$
$$= 10 \log (2) = 10 \times 0.3 = 3.0 \text{ dB}$$

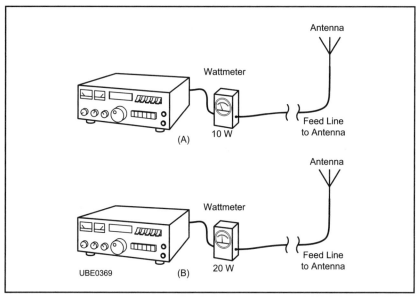

Figure E-2 — The output power from an Amateur Radio transmitter is 10 watts. After making some adjustments to the transmitter tuning, you measure the power again. Now you find the power has increased to 20 watts. The text describes how to calculate the decibel increase that occurred.

we still had a 3 dB change. This is an important point about the decibel. It compares two power levels. The number of decibels depends on the ratio of those levels, not on the actual power. The 3 dB value is also important, because it shows that one power level was twice the other one. Increasing a power by two gives a 3 dB increase and cutting a power in half gives a 3 dB decrease.

Whenever you multiply or divide the reference power by a factor of 2, you will have a 3 dB change in power. You might guess, then, that if you multiplied the power by 4 it would be a 6 dB increase. If you multiplied the power by 8 it would be a 9 dB increase. You would be right in both cases!

Suppose the power in part of a circuit such as the one shown in **Figure E-3** measures 5 milliwatts and in another part of the circuit it measures 40 mW. Using the 5-mW value as the reference power, how many decibels greater is the 40-mW power?

So our transmitter adjustments gave us a 3 dB increase in transmitter power.

Suppose you measured the power output from another transmitter, and found it to be 100 W. Later, after experimenting with a new circuit in the transmitter, you measure the output power as 50 W. What effect did your experiment have on the output power? What is the power change in decibels? Again, Equation E-4 will help answer this question.

$$dB = 10 \log \left(\frac{P_1}{P_0} \right)$$

$$dB = 10 \log \left(\frac{50 \text{ W}}{100 \text{ W}} \right)$$
$$= 10 \log (0.50)$$
$$= 10 \times (-0.30) = -3.0 \text{ dB}$$

Although the power levels in our two examples were much different,

$$dB = 10 \log \left(\frac{P_1}{P_0} \right)$$

$$dB = 10 \log \left(\frac{40 \text{ mW}}{5 \text{ mW}} \right)$$
$$= 10 \log (8.0) = 10 \times 0.9 = 9.0 \text{ dB}$$

Figure E-3 — A simple amateur transmitter amplifies the signal from an oscillator and then feeds that signal to an antenna. It uses several amplifier stages. The input power to one of those stages is 5 milliwatts and the output from that stage is 40 milliwatts. The text describes how to calculate the gain of that amplifier stage.

A Glossary of Electronics and Amateur Radio Terms

In addition to terms used in *Understanding Basic Electronics*, this Glossary includes many topics encountered in discussion of Amateur Radio, communications and more advanced areas of electronics.

Absorption — The loss of energy from an electromagnetic wave as it travels through any material. The energy may be converted to heat or other forms. Absorption usually refers to energy lost as the wave travels through the ionosphere.

Absorption wavemeter — A device for measuring frequency or wavelength. It takes some power from the circuit under test when the meter is tuned to the same resonant frequency.

Adcock array — A radio direction finding antenna array consisting of two vertical elements fed 180° apart and capable of being rotated.

Admittance — The reciprocal of impedance, often used to aid the solution of a parallel-circuit impedance calculation.

Alpha (α) — The ratio of transistor collector current to emitter current. Alpha is between 0.92 and 0.98 for a junction transistor.

Alpha cutoff frequency — A term used to express the useful upper frequency limit of a transistor. The point at which the gain of a common-base amplifier is 0.707 times the gain at 1 kHz.

Alternating current (ac) — Electrical current that flows first in one direction in a wire and then in the other direction. The applied voltage changes polarity and causes the current to change direction. This direction reversal continues at a rate that depends on the frequency of the ac.

Alternator — A machine used to generate alternating-current electricity.

Alternator whine — A common form of conducted interference typified by an audio tone being induced onto the received or transmitted signal. The pitch of the noise varies with alternator speed.

Amateur Auxiliary — A voluntary organization, administered by ARRL Section Managers. The primary objectives are to foster amateur self-regulation and compliance with the rules.

Amateur Radio communication — Noncommercial radio communication by or among Amateur Radio stations solely with a personal aim and without pecuniary or business interest. (Pecuniary means payment of any type, whether money or other goods.)

Amateur Radio operator — A person holding a valid license to operate an Amateur Radio station. In the US this license is issued by the Federal Communications Commission.

Amateur Radio station — A station licensed in the Amateur Radio Service, including necessary equipment at a particular location, used for Amateur Radio communication.

Amateur Service — A radio communication service of self-training, intercommunication, and technical investigation carried on by radio amateurs.

Ampere (A) — The basic unit of electrical current, equal to 6.24×10^{18} electrons moving past a point in one second. We abbreviate amperes as amps.

Amplifier — A device usually employing electron tubes or transistors to increase the voltage, current, or power of a signal. The amplifying device may use a small signal to control voltage and/or current from an external supply. A larger replica of the small input signal appears at the device output.

Amplitude modulation (AM) — A method of combining an information signal and an RF carrier. In double-sideband voice AM transmission, we use the voice information to vary (modulate) the amplitude of a radio-frequency signal. Shortwave broadcast stations use this type of AM, as do stations in the Standard Broadcast Band (510-1600 kHz). Amateurs seldom use double-sideband voice AM, but a variation, known as single sideband (SSB), is very popular.

AMTOR — Amateur Teleprinting Over Radio. AMTOR provides error-correcting capabilities. See Automatic Repeat Request (ARQ) and Forward Error Correction (FEC).

Analog-to-digital converter (ADC) — A device that samples an analog signal and outputs a digital number representing the amplitude of the signal.

AND gate — A logic circuit whose output is 1 only when all of its inputs are 1.

Anode — The terminal that connects to the positive supply lead for current to flow through a device.

Antenna — An electric circuit designed specifically to radiate the energy applied to it in the form of electromagnetic waves. An antenna is reciprocal; a wave moving past it will induce a current in the circuit also. Antennas are used to transmit and receive radio waves.

Antenna bandwidth — A range of frequencies over which an antenna will perform well. Antenna bandwidth is usually specified as a range of frequencies where the antenna SWR will be below some given value.

Antenna effect — One of two operational modes of a simple loop antenna wherein the antenna exhibits the characteristics of a small, nondirectional vertical antenna.

Antenna efficiency — The ratio of the radiation resistance to the total resistance of an antenna system.

Antenna switch — A switch used to connect one transmitter, receiver or transceiver to several different antennas.

Apogee — That point in a satellite's orbit (such as the moon) when it is farthest from the earth.

Apparent power — The product of the RMS current and voltage values in a circuit without consideration of the phase angle between them.

Ascending Pass — With respect to a particular ground station, a satellite pass during which the spacecraft is headed in a northerly direction while it is in range.

ASCII — American National Standard Code for Information Interchange. This is a seven-bit digital code used in computer and radioteleprinter applications.

Astable (free-running) multivibrator — A circuit that alternates between two unstable states. This circuit could be considered as an oscillator that produces square waves.

Asynchronous flip-flop — A circuit, also called a *latch*, that changes output state depending on the data inputs, without requiring a clock signal.

Atom — A basic building block of all matter. Inside an atom, there is a positively charged, dense central core, surrounded by a "cloud" of negatively charged electrons. There are the same number of negative charges as there are positive charges, so the atom is electrically neutral.

Attenuate — To reduce in amplitude.

ATV (amateur television) — A wideband TV system that can use commercial transmission standards. ATV is only permitted on the 70-cm band and higher frequencies.

Audio frequency (AF) — The range of frequencies that the human ear can detect. Audio frequencies are usually listed as 20 Hz to 20,000 Hz.

Audio rectification — Interference to electronic devices caused by a strong RF field that is rectified and amplified in the device.

Audio-frequency shift keying (AFSK) — A method of transmitting radioteletype information by switching between two audio tones fed into an FM transmitter microphone input. This is the RTTY mode most often used on VHF and UHF.

Aurora — A disturbance of the atmosphere around the earth's poles, caused by an interaction between electrically charged particles from the sun and the earth's magnetic field. Often a display of colored lights is produced, which is visible to those who are close enough to the magnetic-polar regions. Auroras can disrupt HF radio communication and enhance VHF communication. They are classified as visible auroras and radio auroras.

Automatic gain control — An amplifier circuit designed to provide a relatively constant output amplitude over a wide range of input values. Its abbreviation is AGC.

Automatic Repeat Request (ARQ) — An AMTOR communication mode. In ARQ, also called Mode A, the two stations constantly confirm each other's transmissions. If information is lost, it is repeated until the receiving station confirms correct reception.

Autopatch — A device that allows repeater users to make telephone calls through a repeater.

Avalanche point — That point on a diode characteristic curve where the amount of reverse current increases greatly for small increases in reverse bias voltage.

Average power — The product of the RMS current and voltage values associated with a purely resistive circuit, equal to one half the peak power when the applied voltage is a sine wave.

Azimuth-equidistant projection map — A map made with its center at one geographic location and the rest of the continents projected from that point. Also called a great-circle map, this map is the most useful type for determining where to point a directional antenna to communicate with a specific location.

Back EMF — An opposing electromotive force (voltage) produced by a changing current in a coil. It can be equal to the applied EMF under some conditions.

Backscatter — A small amount of signal that is reflected from the earth's surface after traveling through the ionosphere. The reflected signals may go back into the ionosphere along several paths and be refracted to earth again. Backscatter can help provide communications into a station's skip zone.

Balanced line — A symmetrical feed line with two conductors having equal but opposite voltages. Neither conductor is at ground potential.

Balanced modulator — A circuit used in a single-sideband suppressed-carrier transmitter to combine a voice signal and the RF signal. The balanced modulator isolates the input signals from each other and the output, so that only the difference of the two input signals reaches the output.

Balun — Contraction for balanced to unbalanced. A device to couple a balanced load to an unbalanced source, or vice versa. A balun is often used to feed a balanced antenna with an unbalanced feed line.

Band-pass filter — A circuit that allows signals to go through it only if they are within a certain range of frequencies. It attenuates signals above and below this range.

Band plan — An agreement for operating within a certain portion of the radio spectrum. Band plans set aside certain frequencies for each different mode of amateur operation, such as CW, SSB, FM, repeaters and simplex.

Band spread — A receiver quality used to describe how far apart stations on different nearby frequencies will seem to be. We usually express band spread as the number of kilohertz that the frequency changes per tuning-knob rotation. Note that band spread affects frequency resolution.

Bandwidth — The frequency range (measured in hertz) over which a signal is stronger than some specified amount below the peak signal level. For example, if a certain signal is at least half as strong as the peak power level over a range of ± 3 kHz, the signal has a 3-dB bandwidth of 6 kHz.

Base loading — The technique of inserting a coil with specific reactance at the bottom of a vertical antenna in order to cancel the capacitive reactance of the antenna, producing a resonant antenna system.

Battery — A device that converts chemical energy into electrical energy. It provides excess electrons to produce a current and the voltage or EMF to push those electrons through a circuit.

Baud — The unit used to describe the transmission speed of a digital signal. For a single-channel signal, one baud is equal to one digital bit per second.

Baudot — A five-bit digital code used in teleprinter applications.

Beam antenna — A directional antenna. A beam antenna must be rotated to provide coverage in different directions.

Beamwidth — As related to directive antennas, the width (measured in degrees) of the major lobe between the two directions at which the relative power is one half (-3 dB) of the value at the peak of the lobe.

Beat-frequency oscillator (BFO) — An oscillator that provides a signal to a receiver's product detector. In the product detector, the BFO signal mixes with the incoming signal to produce an audio signal.

Beta (β) — The ratio of transistor collector current to base current. Betas show wide variations, even between individual devices of the same type.

Beta cutoff frequency — The point at which the gain of a common-emitter amplifier is 0.707 times the gain at 1 kHz.

Bipolar junction transistor (BJT) — A transistor made of two PN semiconductor junctions using two layers of similar-type material (N or P) with a third layer of the opposite type between them.

Bistable multivibrator — Another name for a flip-flop circuit that has two stable output states.

Blanking — Portion of a video signal that is "blacker than black," used to be certain that the return trace is invisible.

Bleeder resistor — A large-value resistor added across the filter capacitor in a power supply. The bleeder resistor dissipates any charge left on the filter capacitor when the supply is switched off.

Block diagram — A picture using boxes to represent sections of a complicated device or process. The block diagram shows the connections between sections.

Blocking — A receiver condition in which reception of a desired weak signal is prevented because of a nearby, unwanted strong signal.

Breakdown voltage — The voltage that will cause a current in an insulator. Different insulating materials have different breakdown voltages. Breakdown voltage is also related to the thickness of the insulating material.

Butterworth filter — A filter whose passband frequency response is as flat as possible. The design is based on a Butterworth polynomial to calculate the input/output characteristics.

Bypass capacitor — A capacitor that provides an alternating-current path of comparatively low impedance around some circuit element.

Calling frequencies — Frequencies set aside for establishing contact. Once two stations are in contact, they should move their QSO to an unoccupied frequency.

Capacitive coupling (of a dip meter) — A method of transferring energy from a dip-meter oscillator to a tuned circuit by means of an electric field.

Capacitor — An electrical component composed of two or more conductive plates separated by an insulating material. A capacitor stores energy in an electrostatic field.

Capacitor-input filter — A power-supply filter having a capacitor connected directly to the rectifier output.

Capture effect — An effect especially noticed with FM and PM systems whereby the strongest signal to reach the demodulator is the one to be received. You cannot tell whether weaker signals are present.

Carbon-composition resistor — An electronic component designed to limit current in a circuit; made from ground carbon mixed with clay.

Carbon-film resistor — A resistor made by depositing a gaseous carbon deposit on a round ceramic form.

Cardioid radiation pattern — A heart-shaped antenna pattern characterized by a single, large lobe in one direction, and a deep, narrow null in the opposite direction.

Cathode — The terminal that connects to the negative supply lead for current to flow through the device.

Cathode-ray tube (CRT) — An electron-beam tube in which the beam can be focused on a luminescent screen. The spot position can be varied to produce a pattern on the screen. CRTs were used in oscilloscopes and as the "picture tube" in television receivers.

Cavity — A high-Q tuned circuit that passes energy at one frequency with little or no attenuation but presents a high impedance to another nearby frequency.

Center loading — A technique for adding a series inductor at or near the center of an antenna element in order to cancel the capacitive reactance of the antenna. This technique is usually used with elements that are less than $1/4$ wavelength.

Centi — The metric prefix for 10^{-2}, or divide by 100.

Ceramic capacitor — An electronic component composed of two or more conductive plates separated by a ceramic insulating material.

Characteristic impedance — The opposition to electric current that a circuit presents. Impedance includes factors other than resistance, and applies to alternating currents. Ideally, the characteristic impedance of an antenna feed line will be the same as the transmitter output impedance and the antenna input impedance.

Chassis ground — A common connection for all parts of a circuit that connect to the power supply.

Chebyshev filter — A filter whose passband and stopband frequency response has an equal-amplitude ripple, and a sharper transition to the stop band than does a Butterworth filter. The design is based on a Chebyshev polynomial to calculate the input/output characteristics.

Choke-input filter — A power-supply filter having an inductor (choke) connected directly to the rectifier output.

Circular polarization — Describes an electromagnetic wave in which the electric and magnetic fields are rotating. If the electric field vector is rotating in a clockwise sense, then it is called right-hand circular polarization. If the electric field is rotating in a counterclockwise sense, it is called left-hand circular polarization. Note that the polarization sense is determined by standing behind the antenna for a signal being transmitted, or in front of it for a signal being received.

Clipping — Occurs when the peaks of a voice waveform are cut off in a transmitter, usually because of overmodulation. Also called flattopping.

Coaxial cable — coax (pronounced ko'-aks). This is a type of feed line with one conductor inside the other. Plastic, foam or gaseous insulation surrounds the center conductor. The insulation is covered by a shielding conductor. The entire cable is usually covered with vinyl insulation.

Coaxial capacitor — A cylindrical capacitor used for noise-suppression purposes. The line to be filtered connects to the two ends of the capacitor, and a third connection is made to electrical ground. One side of the capacitor provides a dc path between the ends, while the other side of the capacitor connects to ground.

Code key — A device used as a switch to generate Morse code.

Code-practice oscillator — A device that produces an audio tone, used for learning the code.

Coefficient of coupling — A measure of the mutual inductance between two coils. The greater the coefficient of coupling, the more mutual inductance between the coils. It is a measure of the amount of energy that will be transferred from one coil to another.

Coil — A conductor wound into a series of loops. Also known as *inductor*.

Color code — A system where numerical values are assigned to various colors. Colored stripes are painted on the body of resistors and sometimes other components to show their value.

Communications terminal — A computer-controlled device that demodulates RTTY and CW for display by a computer or ASCII terminal. The communications terminal also accepts information from a computer or terminal and modulates a transmitted signal.

Complementary metal-oxide semiconductor (CMOS) — A type of construction used to make digital integrated circuits. CMOS is composed of both N-channel and P-channel MOS devices on the same chip.

Complex number — A number that includes both a real and an imaginary part. Complex numbers provide a convenient way to represent a quantity (like impedance) that is made up of two different quantities (like resistance and reactance).

Composite video signal — A complete video signal, consisting of the actual picture information, blanking pulses and sync pulses.

Conductance — The reciprocal of resistance. This is the real part of a complex admittance.

Conducted noise — Electrical noise that is imparted to a radio receiver or transmitter through the power connections to the radio.

Conductor — A material that has a loose grip on its electrons, so that an electrical current can pass through it.

Connected — The condition in which two packet-radio stations are sending information to each other. Each is acknowledging when the data has been received correctly.

Constant-k filter — A filter design based on the image-parameter technique. The product of the series and shunt impedances is independent of frequency within the filter passband.

Contests — On-the-air operating events. Different contests have different objectives: contacting as many other amateurs as possible in a given amount of time, contacting amateurs in as many different countries as possible or contacting an amateur in each county in one particular state, to name only a few.

Continuous wave (CW) — A term used by amateurs as a synonym for Morse code communication. Hams usually produce Morse code signals by interrupting the continuous-wave signal from a transmitter to form the dots and dashes.

Control operator — A licensed amateur designated to be responsible for the transmissions of an Amateur Radio station.

Coordinated Universal Time (UTC) — A system of time referenced to time at the prime meridian, which passes through Greenwich, England.

Core — The material in the center of a coil. The material used for the core affects the inductance value of the coil.

Corona discharge — A condition when a static-electricity charge builds up on an antenna, usually a mobile antenna, and then discharges as the air insulation around the antenna becomes ionized and glows light blue.

Counter (divider, divide-by-n counter) — A circuit that is able to change from one state to the next each time it receives an input signal. A counter produces an output signal every time a predetermined number of input signals have been received.

Coupling capacitor — A capacitor that provides a relatively low-impedance path from one stage to the next for ac signals above some frequency, while providing a high impedance to lower-frequency ac and dc signals. Also called a blocking capacitor because it blocks dc and low-frequency ac signals.

CQ — The general call when requesting a conversation with anyone.

Critical angle — If radio waves leave an antenna at an angle greater than the critical angle for that frequency, they will pass through the ionosphere instead of returning to earth.

Critical frequency — The highest frequency at which a vertically incident radio wave will return from the ionosphere. Above the critical frequency, radio signals pass through the ionosphere instead of returning to the earth.

Cross modulation — A type of intermodulation caused by the carrier of a desired signal being modulated by an unwanted signal.

Crystal oscillator — An oscillator in which the main frequency-determining element is the mechanical resonance of a piezoelectric crystal (usually quartz).

Crystal-lattice filter — A filter that employs piezoelectric crystals (usually quartz) as the reactive elements. They are most often used in the IF stages of a receiver or transmitter.

Crystal-controlled marker generator — An oscillator circuit that uses a quartz crystal to set the frequency, and which has an output rich in harmonics that can be used to determine band edges on a receiver. An output every 100 kHz or less is normally produced.

Cubical quad antenna — An antenna built with its elements in the shape of four-sided loops.

Current — A flow of electrons in an electrical circuit.

Cutoff frequency — In a high-pass, low-pass, or band pass filter, the cutoff frequency is the frequency at which the filter output is reduced to ½ of the power (–3 dB) available at the filter input.

D layer — The lowest layer of the ionosphere. The D layer contributes very little to short-wave radio propagation. It acts mainly to absorb energy from radio waves as they pass through it. This absorption has a significant effect on signals below about 7.5 MHz during daylight.

D'Arsonval meter movement — A type of meter movement in which a coil is suspended between the poles of a permanent magnet. DC flowing through the coil causes it to rotate an amount proportional to the current. A pointer attached to the coil indicates the amount of deflection on a scale.

Dash — The long sound used in Morse code. Pronounce this as "dah" when verbally sounding Morse code characters.

Decibel (dB) — The smallest change in sound level that can be detected by the human ear. Power gains and losses are also expressed in decibels. One tenth of a bel, denoting a logarithm of the ratio of two power levels. $dB = 10 \log (P2/P1)$

Declination angle — The angle measured north or south from the celestial equator to an object in the sky.

Delta loop antenna — A variation of the cubical quad antenna with triangular elements.

Delta match — A method for impedance matching between an open-wire transmission line and a half-wave radiator that is not split at the center. The feed-line wires are fanned out to attach to the antenna wire symmetrically around the center point. The resulting connection looks somewhat like a capital Greek delta.

Depletion mode — Type of operation in a JFET or MOSFET where current is reduced by reverse bias on the gate.

Depletion region — An area around the semiconductor junction where the charge density is very small. This creates a potential barrier for current flow across the junction. In general, the region is thin when the junction is forward biased, and becomes thicker under reverse-bias conditions.

Descending pass — With respect to a particular ground station, a satellite pass during which the spacecraft is headed in a southerly direction while it is in range.

Desensitization — A reduction in receiver sensitivity caused by the receiver front end being overloaded by noise or RF from a local transmitter.

Detector — The stage in a receiver in which the modulation (voice or other information) is recovered from the RF signal.

Deviation — The peak difference between an instantaneous frequency of the modulated wave and the unmodulated-carrier frequency in an FM system.

Deviation ratio — The ratio of the maximum frequency deviation to the maximum modulating frequency in an FM system.

Dielectric — An insulating material. A dielectric is a medium in which it is possible to maintain an electric field with little or no additional energy supplied after the field has been established.

Dielectric constant — A property of insulating materials that serves as a measure of how much electric charge can be stored in the material with a given voltage.

Dielectric materials — Materials in which it is possible to maintain an electric field with little or no additional energy being supplied. Insulating materials or nonconductors.

Digipeater — A packet-radio station used to retransmit signals that are specifically addressed to be retransmitted by that station.

Digital communications — The term used to describe Amateur Radio transmissions that are designed to be received and printed automatically. The term also describes transmissions used for the direct transfer of information from one computer to another.

Digital IC — An integrated circuit whose output is either on (1) or off (0).

Digital signal processing — The processing of sequences of digital numbers that represent signals.

Digital signal processor (DSP) — A device to do digital signal processing. The term normally is understood to refer to a microprocessor-type device with special capabilities for signal processing.

Digital-to-analog converter (DAC) — A device that converts digital numbers to an analog signal with an amplitude proportional to the digital numbers.

Dip meter — A tunable RF oscillator that supplies energy to another circuit resonant at the frequency that the oscillator is tuned to. A meter indicates when the most energy is being coupled out of the circuit by showing a dip in indicated current.

Dipole antenna — An antenna with two elements in a straight line that are fed in the center; literally, two poles. For amateur work, dipoles are usually operated at half-wave resonance.

Direct-conversion receiver — A receiver that converts an RF signal directly to an audio signal with one mixing stage.

Direct current (dc) — Electrical current that flows in one direction only.

Direct digital synthesis (DDS) — The generation of a periodic waveform by directly calculating the values of the waveform samples.

Directive antenna — An antenna that concentrates the radiated energy to form one or more major lobes in specific directions. The receiving pattern is the same as the transmitting pattern.

Directivity — The ability of an antenna to focus transmitter power into a beam. Also its ability to enhance received signals from specific directions.

Director — A parasitic element located in front of the driven element of a beam antenna. It is intended to increase the strength of the signals radiated from the front of the antenna. Typically about 5% shorter than the driven element.

Direct sequence — A spread-spectrum communications system where a very fast binary bit stream is used to shift the phase of an RF carrier.

Direct waves — Radio waves that travel directly from a transmitting antenna to a receiving antenna. Also called "line-of-sight" communications.

Distributed capacitance — The capacitance that exists between turns of a coil.

Doping — The addition of impurities to a semiconductor material, with the intent to provide either excess electrons or positive charge carriers (holes) in the material.

Doppler shift — A change in the observed frequency of a signal, as compared with the transmitted frequency, caused by satellite movement toward or away from you.

Dot — The short sound used in Morse code. Pronounce this as "dit" when verbally sounding Morse code characters if the dot comes at the end of the character. If the dot comes at the beginning or in the middle of the character, pronounce it as "dih."

Double-pole, double throw (DPDT) switch — A switch that has six contacts. The DPDT switch has two center contacts. The two center contacts can each be connected to one of two other contacts.

Doubly balanced mixer (DBM) — A mixer circuit that is balanced for both inputs, so that only the sum and the difference frequencies, but neither of the input frequencies, appear at the output. There will be no output unless both input signals are present.

Drain — The point at which the charge carriers exit an FET. Corresponds to the plate of a vacuum tube.

Drift — As related to op amps, the change of offset voltage with temperature changes, typically a few microvolts per degree Celsius.

Driven element — Any antenna element connected directly to the feed line.

Dual-trace oscilloscope — An oscilloscope with two separate vertical input circuits. This type of oscilloscope can be used to observe two waveforms at the same time.

Duct — A radio waveguide formed when a temperature inversion traps radio waves within a restricted layer of the atmosphere.

Dummy load (dummy antenna) — A resistor that provides a transmitter with a proper load. The resistor gets rid of the transmitter output power without radiating a signal. A dummy load is used when testing transmitters.

Duplexer — A device, usually employing cavities, to allow a transmitter and receiver to be connected simultaneously to one antenna. Most often, as in the case of a repeater, the transmitter and receiver operate at the same time on different frequencies.

DX — Distance, foreign countries.

DX Century Club (DXCC) — A prestigious award given to amateurs who can prove contact with amateurs in at least 100 DXCC countries.

Dynamic (edge-triggered) input — An input, such as for a flip-flop, that is sampled only when the rising (or falling) edge of a clock pulse is detected.

Dynamic range — A measure of receiver performance. The difference, in decibels, between the minimum usable signal level and the maximum signal that does not produce distortion in the audio output.

E layer — The second lowest ionospheric layer, the E layer exists only during the day, and under certain conditions may refract radio waves enough to return them to earth.

Earth ground — A circuit connection to a cold-water pipe or to a ground rod driven into the earth.

Earth-moon-earth (EME) — A method of communicating with other stations by reflecting radio signals off the moon's surface.

Earth operation — Earth-to-space-to-earth Amateur Radio communication by means of radio signals automatically retransmitted by stations in space operation.

Effective isotropic radiated power (EIRP) — A measure of the power radiated from an antenna system. EIRP takes into account transmitter output power, feed-line losses and other system losses, and antenna gain as compared to an isotropic radiator.

Effective radiated power (ERP) — The relative amount of power radiated in a specific direction from an antenna, taking system gains and losses into account.

Effective voltage — The value of a dc voltage that will heat a resistive component to the same temperature as the ac voltage that is being measured.

Electric field — An invisible force of nature. An electric field exists in a region of space if an electrically charged object placed in the region is subjected to an electrical force.

Electric force — A push or pull exerted through space by one electrically charged object on another.

Electrolytic capacitor — A polarized capacitor formed by using thin foil electrodes and chemical-soaked paper.

Electromagnetic radiation — Another term for electromagnetic waves, consisting of an electric field and a magnetic field that are at right angles to each other.

Electromagnetic waves — A disturbance moving through space or materials in the form of changing electric and magnetic fields.

Electromotive force (EMF) — The force or pressure that pushes a current through a circuit. A synonym is *voltage*.

Electron — A tiny, negatively charged particle, normally found in an area surrounding the nucleus of an atom. Moving electrons make up an electrical current.

Electronic keyer — A device used to generate Morse code dots and dashes electronically. One input generates dots, the other, dashes. Character speed is usually adjusted by turning a control knob. Speeds range from 5 or 10 words per minute up to 60 or more.

ELI the ICE man — A mnemonic to remember the phase relationships between current and voltage for inductors and capacitors. ELI tells us voltage (E) leads current (I) for an inductor (L), and ICE tells us current (I) leads voltage (E) for a capacitor (C).

Elliptical filter — A filter with equal-amplitude passband ripple and points of infinite attenuation in the stop band. The design is based on an elliptical function to calculate the input/output characteristics.

Emission — The transmitted signal from an Amateur Radio station.

Emission privilege — Permission to use a particular emission type (such as Morse code or voice).

Energy — The ability to do work; the ability to exert a force to move some object.

Engineering notation — A form of scientific notation that requires that the exponent be a multiple of 3, such as –6, –3, 3, 6 or 9. For commonly used exponents that are multiples of 3 there are *metric prefix* names. See Appendix A.

Enhancement mode — Type of operation in a MOSFET where current is increased by forward bias on the gate.

Equinoxes — One of two spots on the earth's orbital path around the sun at which it crosses a horizontal plane extending through the center of the sun. The vernal equinox marks the beginning of spring and the autumnal equinox marks the beginning of autumn.

Exclusive OR gate — A logic circuit whose output is 1 when either of two inputs is 1 and whose output is 0 when neither input is 1 or when both inputs are 1.

F layer — A combination of the two highest ionospheric layers, the Fl and F2 layers. The F layer refracts radio waves and returns them to earth. The height of the F layer varies greatly depending on the time of day, season of the year and amount of sunspot activity.

Facsimile (fax) — The process of scanning pictures or images and converting the information into signals that can be used to form a likeness of the copy in another location.

False or deceptive signals — Transmissions that are intended to mislead or confuse those who may receive the transmissions. For example, distress calls transmitted when there is no actual emergency are false or deceptive signals.

Farad — The basic unit of capacitance.

Faraday rotation — A rotation of the polarization plane of radio waves when the waves travel through the ionized magnetic field of the ionosphere.

Fast-scan TV (ATV) — A television system used by Amateurs that employs the same video-signal standards as commercial TV.

Feed line (feeder) — The wires or cable used to connect your transmitter and receiver to an antenna. Also see Transmission line.

Ferrite loop (loopstick) — A loop antenna wound on a ferrite rod to increase the magnetic flux. Also called a loopstick antenna.

Field — Any of the invisible forces in nature, such as gravity, electric force or magnetic force. This term also refers to the region of space through which these forces act.

Field Day — An annual event in which amateurs set up stations in outdoor locations. Emergency power is also encouraged.

Field-effect transistor (FET) — A voltage-controlled semiconductor device. Output current can be varied by varying the input voltage. The input impedance of an FET is very high.

Field-effect transistor volt-ohm-milliammeter (FET VOM) — A multiple-range meter used to measure voltage, current and resistance. The meter circuit uses an FET amplifier to provide a high input impedance. This leads to more accurate readings than can be obtained with a VOM.

Field-strength meter — A simple test instrument used to show the presence of RF energy and the relative strength of the RF field.

Fills — Repeats of parts of a previous transmission — usually requested because of interference.

Filter — A circuit that will allow some signals to pass through it but will greatly reduce the strength of others. In a power supply circuit, a filter smooths the ac ripple.

Filter choke — A large-value inductor used in a power-supply filter to smooth out the ripple in the pulsating dc output from the rectifier.

Fist — The unique rhythm of an individual amateur's Morse code sending.

Fixed resistor — A resistor with a nonadjustable value of resistance.

Flip-flop (bistable multivibrator) — A circuit that has two stable output states, and which can change from one state to the other when the proper input signals are detected.

Folded dipole — An antenna consisting of two (or more) parallel, closely spaced half-wave wires connected at their ends. One of the wires is fed at its center.

Forward bias — A voltage applied across a semiconductor junction so that it will tend to produce current.

Forward biased — A condition in which the anode of a diode is positive with respect to the cathode, so it will conduct.

Forward Error Correction (FEC) — A mode of AMTOR communication. In FEC mode, also called Mode B, each character is sent twice. The receiving station checks the mark/space ratio of the received characters. If an error is detected, the receiving station prints a space to show that an incorrect character was received.

Frequency — The number of cycles of an alternating current that occur per second.

Frequency bands — A group of frequencies where amateur communications are authorized.

Frequency coordinator — A volunteer who keeps records of repeater input and output frequencies and recommends frequencies to amateurs who wish to put new repeaters on the air.

Frequency counter — A digital-electronic device that counts the cycles of an electromagnetic wave for a certain amount of time and gives a digital readout of the frequency.

Frequency deviation — The amount the carrier frequency in an FM transmitter changes as it is modulated.

Frequency discriminator — A circuit used to recover the audio from an FM signal. The output amplitude depends on the deviation of the received signal from a center (carrier) frequency.

Frequency domain — A time-independent way to view a complex signal. The various component sine waves that make up a complex waveform are shown by frequency and amplitude on a graph or the CRT display of a spectrum analyzer.

Frequency hopping — A spread-spectrum communications system where the center frequency of a conventional carrier is altered many times a second in accordance with a pseudo-random list of channels.

Frequency modulation (FM) — The process of varying the frequency of an RF carrier in response to the instantaneous changes in a modulating signal. The signal that modulates the carrier frequency may be audio, video, digital data or some other kind of information.

Frequency privilege — Permission to use a particular group of frequencies.

Frequency resolution — The space between markings on a receiver dial. The greater the frequency resolution, the easier it is to separate signals that are close together. Note that frequency resolution affects band spread.

Frequency-shift keying (FSK) — A method of transmitting radioteletype information by switching an RF carrier between two separate frequencies. This is the RTTY mode most often used on the HF amateur bands.

Front-to-back ratio — The energy radiated from the front of a directional antenna divided by the energy radiated from the back of the antenna.

Full-break-in (QSK) — With QSK, an amateur can hear signals between code characters. This allows another amateur to break into the communication without waiting for the transmitting station to finish.

Full-wave bridge rectifier — A full-wave rectifier circuit that uses four diodes and does not require a center-tapped transformer.

Full-wave rectifier — A circuit composed of two half-wave rectifiers. The full-wave rectifier allows the full ac waveform to pass through; one half of the cycle is reversed in polarity. This circuit requires a center-tapped transformer.

Fuse — A thin strip of metal mounted in a holder. When too much current passes through the fuse, the metal strip melts and opens the circuit.

GaAsFET — Gallium-arsenide field-effect transistor. A low-noise device used in UHF and higher frequency amplifiers.

Gain (antenna) — An increase in the effective power radiated by an antenna in a certain desired direction, or an increase in received signal strength from a certain direction. This is at the expense of power radiated in, or signal strength received from, other directions.

Galactic plane — An imaginary plane surface extending through the center of the Milky Way galaxy. This plane is used as a reference for some astronomical observations.

Gamma match — A method for matching the impedance of a feed line to a half-wave radiator that is split in the center (such as a dipole). It consists of an adjustable arm that is mounted close to the driven element and in parallel with it near the feed point. The connection looks somewhat like a capital Greek gamma.

Gate — Control terminal of an FET. Corresponds to the grid of a vacuum tube. Gate also refers to a combinational logic element with two or more inputs and one output. The output state depends upon the state of the inputs.

General-coverage receiver — A receiver used to listen to both the shortwave-broadcast frequencies and the amateur bands.

Geomagnetic disturbance — A dramatic change in the earth's magnetic field that occurs over a short period of time.

Giga — The metric prefix for 10^9, or times 1,000,000,000.

Gray line — A band around the earth that is the transition region between daylight and darkness.

Gray-line propagation — A generally north-south enhancement of propagation that occurs along the gray line, when D layer absorption is rapidly decreasing at sunset, or has not yet built up around sunrise.

Gray scale — A photographic term that defines a series of neutral densities (based on the percentage of incident light that is reflected from a surface), ranging from white to black.

Great circle — An imaginary circle around the surface of the earth formed by the intersection of the surface with a plane passing through the center of the earth.

Great-circle path — Either one of two direct paths between two points on the surface of the earth. One of the great-circle paths is the shortest distance between those two points. Great-circle paths can be visualized if you think of a globe with a rubber band stretched around it connecting the two points.

Greenwich Hour Angle (GHA) — The angle measured east or west from the prime meridian to an object in the sky.

Grid — The control element (or elements) in a vacuum tube.

Ground connection — A connection made to the earth for electrical safety.

Ground-plane antenna — A vertical antenna built with a central radiating element one-quarter-wavelength long and several radials extending horizontally from the base. The radials are slightly longer than one-quarter wave, and may droop toward the ground.

Ground waves — Radio waves that travel along the surface of the earth.

Ground-wave signals — Radio signals that are propagated along the ground rather than through the ionosphere or by some other means.

Half-power points — Those points on the response curve of a resonant circuit where the power is one half its value at resonance.

Half section — A basic L-section building block of image-parameter filters.

Half-wavelength dipole antenna — A fundamental antenna one-half wavelength long at the desired operating frequency, and connected to the feed line at the center. This is a popular amateur antenna.

Half-wave rectifier — A circuit that allows only half of the applied ac waveform to pass through it.

Ham-bands-only receiver — A receiver designed to cover only the bands used by amateurs.

Hand key — A simple switch used to send Morse code.

Heat sink — A piece of metal used to absorb excess heat generated by a component, and dissipate the heat into the air.

Henry — The basic unit of inductance.

Hertz (Hz) — An alternating-current frequency of one cycle per second. The basic unit of frequency.

High-pass filter — A filter that allows signals above the cutoff frequency to pass through. It attenuates signals below the cutoff frequency.

Horizontally polarized wave — An electromagnetic wave with its electric lines of force parallel to the ground.

Horizontal polarization — Describes an electromagnetic wave in which the electric field is horizontal, or parallel to the earth's surface.

Horizontal synchronization pulse — Part of a TV signal used by the receiver to keep the CRT electron-beam scan in step with the camera scanning beam. This pulse is transmitted at the beginning of each horizontal scan line.

Hot-carrier diode — A type of diode in which a small metal dot is placed on a single semiconductor layer. It is superior to a point-contact diode in most respects.

Imaginary number — A value that sometimes comes up in solving a mathematical problem, equal to the square root of a negative number. Since there is no real number that can be multiplied by itself to give a negative result, this quantity is imaginary. In electronics work, the symbol j is used to represent $\sqrt{-1}$ since i, used in mathematics, is already used for current in electronics. The reactance and susceptance of complex impedances and admittances are normally given in terms of j.

Impedance — A term used to describe a combination of reactance and resistance in a circuit.

Impedance-matching network — A device that matches the impedance of an antenna system to the impedance of a transmitter or receiver. Also called an antenna-matching network or Transmatch.

Inclination — The angle at which a satellite crosses the equator at an ascending node. Inclination is also equal to the highest latitude reached in an orbit.

Induced EMF — A voltage produced by a change in magnetic lines of force around a conductor. When a magnetic field is formed by current in the conductor, the induced voltage always opposes changes in that current.

Inductive coupling (of a dip meter) — A method of transferring energy from a dip-meter oscillator to a tuned circuit by means of a magnetic field between two coils.

Inductor — An electrical component usually composed of a coil of wire wound on a central core. An inductor stores energy in a magnetic field.

Input frequency — A repeater's receiving frequency.

Insulator — A material that maintains a tight grip on its electrons, so that an electrical current cannot pass through it.

Integrated circuit — A device composed of many bipolar or field-effect transistors manufactured on the same chip, or wafer, of silicon.

Intercept point — As related to receiver performance, it is the input (or output) signal level at which the desired output power and the distortion product power have the same value.

Intermediate frequency (IF) — The output frequency of a mixing stage in a superheterodyne receiver. The subsequent stages in the receiver are tuned for maximum efficiency at the IF.

Intermodulation distortion (IMD) — A type of interference that results from the mixing of integer multiples of signal frequencies in a nonlinear stage or device. The resulting mixing products can interfere with desired signals on the mixed frequencies.

International Telecommunication Union (ITU) — The international body that regulates the use of the radio spectrum.

Inverted-V dipole — A half-wave dipole antenna with its center elevated and the ends drooping toward the ground. Amateurs sometimes call this antenna an "inverted V."

Inverter — A logic circuit with one input and one output. The output is 1 when the input is 0, and the output is 0 when the input is 1.

Ion — An electrically charged atom or molecule. An ion is an atom that is surrounded by too few or too many valence electrons, and thereby has a net positive or negative charge.

Ionosphere — A region in the atmosphere about 30 to 260 miles above the earth. The ionosphere is made up of charged particles, or ions. The ionosphere bends radio waves as they travel through it, returning them to earth.

Ion trap — A magnet installed in a cathode-ray tube to prevent negative ions from burning a brown spot on the center of the CRT.

Isolator — A passive attenuator in which the loss in one direction is much greater than the loss in the other.

Isotropic radiator — An imaginary antenna in free space that radiates equally in all directions (a spherical radiation pattern). It is used as a reference to compare the gain of various real antennas.

Joule — The unit of energy in the metric system of measure.

Junction diode — An electronic component formed by placing a layer of N-type semiconductor material next to a layer of P-type material. Diodes allow current to flow in one direction only.

Junction field-effect transistor (JFET) — A field-effect transistor created by diffusing a gate of one type of semiconductor material into a channel of the opposite type of semiconductor material.

K index — A geomagnetic-field measurement that is updated every few hours. The K index can be used to indicate HF propagation conditions.

Kepler's Laws — Three laws of planetary motion, used to mathematically describe satellite-orbit parameters.

Kilo — The metric prefix for 10^3, or times 1000.

L network — A combination of a capacitor and an inductor, one of which is connected in series with the signal lead while the other is shunted to ground.

Ladder line — Parallel-conductor feeder with insulating spacer rods every few inches.

Lambda (λ) — the symbol for wavelength of an electromagnetic wave. Wavelength = velocity/frequency, $\lambda = v/f$.

Latch — Another name for a bistable multivibrator flip-flop circuit. The term latch reminds us that this circuit serves as a memory unit, storing a bit of information.

Libration fading — A fluttery, rapid fading of EME signals, caused by short-term motion of the moon's surface relative to an observer on earth.

Light-emitting diode (LED) — A device that uses a semiconductor junction to produce light when current flows through it.

Line of sight — The term used to describe VHF and UHF propagation in a straight line directly from one station to another.

Linear electronic voltage regulator — A type of voltage-regulator circuit that varies either the current through a fixed dropping resistor or the resistance of the dropping element itself.

Linear IC — An integrated circuit whose output voltage is a linear (straight line) representation of its input voltage.

Linear or plane polarization — Describes the orientation of the electric-field component of an electromagnetic wave. The electric field can be vertical or horizontal with respect to the earth's surface, resulting in either a vertically or a horizontally polarized wave.

Lissajous figure — An oscilloscope pattern obtained by connecting one sine wave to the vertical amplifier and another sine wave to the horizontal amplifier. The two signals must be harmonically related to produce a stable pattern.

Loading coil — An inductor that is inserted in an antenna element or transmission line for the purpose of producing a resonant system at a specific frequency.

Logic probe — A simple piece of test equipment used to indicate high or low logic states (voltage levels) in digital-electronic circuits.

Long-path communication — Communication made by pointing beam antennas in the directions indicated by the longer great-circle path between the stations. To work each other by long-path, an amateur in Hawaii would point his antenna west and an amateur in Florida would aim east.

Long-path propagation — Propagation between two points on the earth's surface that follows a path along the great circle between them, but is in a direction opposite from the shortest distance between them.

Loop antenna — An antenna configured in the shape of a loop. If the current in the loop, or in multiple parallel turns, is essentially uniform, and if the loop circumference is small compared with a wavelength, the radiation pattern is symmetrical, with maximum response in either direction of the loop plane.

Lower sideband (LSB) — The common mode of single sideband transmission used on the 40, 80 and 160-meter amateur bands.

Low-pass filter — A filter that allows signals below the cutoff frequency to pass through and attenuates signals above the cutoff frequency.

M-derived filter — A filter, designed using image-parameter techniques, that has a sharper transition from pass band to stop band than a constant-k type. This filter has one infinite attenuation frequency, which can be placed at a desired frequency by proper design.

Magnetic field — A region through which a magnetic force will act on a magnetic object.

Magnetic force — A push or pull exerted through space by one magnetically charged object on another.

Major lobe — The shape or pattern of field strength that points in the direction of maximum radiated power from an antenna.

Major lobe of radiation — A three-dimensional area in the space around an antenna that contains the maximum radiation peak. The field strength decreases from the peak level, until a point is reached where it starts to increase again. This area is known as the major lobe.

Malicious interference — Intentional, deliberate obstruction of radio transmissions.

Marker generator — An RF signal generator that produces signals at known frequency intervals. The marker generator can be used to calibrate receiver and transmitter frequency readouts.

Matching network — A device that matches one impedance level to another. For example, it may match the impedance of an antenna system to the impedance of a transmitter or receiver. Amateurs also call such devices a Transmatch, impedance-matching network, or match box.

Matching stub — A section of transmission line used to tune an antenna element to resonance or to aid in obtaining an impedance match between the feed point and the feed line.

Maximum average forward current — the highest average forward current that can flow through a diode for a given junction temperature.

Maximum usable frequency (MUF) — The greatest frequency at which radio signals will return to a particular location from the ionosphere. The MUF may vary for radio signals sent to different destinations.

MAYDAY — From the French "m'aider" (help me), MAYDAY is used when calling for emergency assistance in voice modes.

Mechanical filter — A nonelectrical filter that uses mechanically resonant disks at the design frequency, and a pair of electromechanical transducers to change the electrical signal into a mechanical wave and back again.

Mega — The metric prefix for 10^6, or times 1,000,000.

Metal-film resistor — A resistor formed by depositing a thin layer of resistive-metal alloy on a cylindrical ceramic form.

Metal-oxide semiconductor FET (MOSFET) — A field-effect transistor that has its gate insulated from the channel material. Also called an IGFET, or insulated gate FET.

Meteor — A particle of mineral or metallic material that is in a highly elliptical orbit around the sun. As the earth's orbit crosses the orbital path of a meteor, it is attracted by the earth's gravitational field, and enters the atmosphere. A typical meteor is about the size of a grain of sand.

Meteor-scatter communication — A method of radio communication that uses the ionized trail of a meteor, which has burned up in the earth's atmosphere, to reflect radio signals back to earth.

Metric prefixes — A series of terms used in the metric system of measurement. We use metric prefixes to describe a quantity compared to a basic unit. The metric prefixes indicate multiples of 10.

Metric system — A system of measurement developed by scientists and used in most countries of the world. This system uses a set of prefixes that are multiples of 10 to indicate quantities larger or smaller than the basic unit.

Mica capacitor — A capacitor formed by alternating layers of metal foil with thin sheets of insulating mica.

Micro — The metric prefix for 10^{-6}, or divide by 1,000,000.

Microphone — A device that converts sound waves into electrical energy.

Milli — The metric prefix for 10^{-3}, or divide by 1000.

Minimum discernible signal (MDS) — The smallest input-signal level that can just be detected by a receiver.

Minor lobe of radiation — Those areas of an antenna pattern where there is some increase in radiation, but not as much as in the major lobe. Minor lobes normally appear at the back and sides of the antenna.

Mixer — A circuit that takes two or more input signals, and produces an output that includes the sum and difference of those signal frequencies.

Mobile operation — Amateur Radio operation conducted while in motion or at temporary stops at different locations.

Modem — Short for modulator/demodulator. A modem modulates a radio signal to transmit data and demodulates a received signal to recover transmitted data.

Modulate — To vary the amplitude, frequency, or phase of a radio-frequency signal.

Modulation — The process of varying some characteristic (amplitude, frequency or phase) of an RF carrier for the purpose of conveying information such as voice or video.

Modulation index — The ratio of the maximum carrier frequency deviation to the frequency of the modulating signal at a given instant in an FM transmitter.

Modulator — A circuit designed to superimpose an information signal on an RF carrier wave.

Monitor mode — One type of packet-radio receiving mode. In monitor mode, everything transmitted on a packet frequency is displayed by the monitoring TNC. This occurs whether the transmissions are addressed to the monitoring station or not.

Monitor oscilloscope — A test instrument connected to an amateur transmitter and used to observe the shape of the transmitted-signal waveform.

Monostable multivibrator (one shot) — A circuit that has one stable state. It can be forced into an unstable state for a time determined by external components, but it will revert to the stable state after that time.

Moonbounce — A common name for EME (earth-moon-earth) communication.

Multiband antenna — An antenna that will operate well on more than one frequency band.

Multimeter — An electronic test instrument used to make basic measurements of current and voltage in a circuit. This term is used to describe all meters capable of making different types of measurements, such as the VOM, VTVM and FET VOM.

Multimode transceiver — A VHF or UHF transceiver capable of SSB, CW and FM operation.

Multipath — A fading effect caused by the transmitted signal traveling to the receiving station over more than one path.

Mutual coupling — When coils display mutual coupling, a current flowing in one coil will induce a voltage in the other. The magnetic flux of one coil passes through the windings of the other.

Mutual inductance — The ability of one coil to induce a voltage in another coil. Any two coils positioned so that the magnetic flux from one coil cuts through the turns of wire in the other are said to have mutual inductance.

N-type material — Semiconductor material that has been treated with impurities to give it an excess of electrons. We call this a "donor material."

NAND (NOT AND) gate — A logic circuit whose output is 0 only when both inputs are 1.

Negative charge — One of two types of electrical charge. The electrical charge of a single electron.

Negative-format modulation — A fax system that uses a minimum modulation level to produce white and a maximum modulation level to produce black.

Neon lamp — A cold-cathode (no heater or filament), gas-filled tube used to give a visual indication of voltage in a circuit, or of an RF field.

Nets — Groups of amateurs who meet on the air to pass traffic or communicate about a specific subject. One station (called the net control station) usually directs the net.

Network — A term used to describe several packet stations linked together to transmit data over long distances.

Neutral — Having no electrical charge, or having an equal number of positive and negative charges.

Neutralization — Feeding part of the output signal from an amplifier back to the input so it arrives out of phase with the input. This negative feedback neutralizes the effect of positive feedback caused by coupling between the input and output circuits in the amplifier.

Night effect — A special type of error in a radio direction-finding system, occurring mainly at night, when sky-wave propagation is most likely.

Node — A point where a satellite crosses the plane passing through the earth's equator. It is an ascending node if the satellite is moving from south to north, and a descending node if the satellite is moving from north to south.

Noise figure — A measurement used to characterize receiver sensitivity.

Noninverting buffer — A logic circuit with one input and one output, and whose output state is the same as the input state (0 or 1).

Nonresonant rhombic antenna — A diamond-shaped antenna consisting of sides that are each at least one wavelength long. The feed line is connected to one end of the diamond, and there is a terminating resistance of approximately 800 ohms at the opposite end. The antenna has a unidirectional radiation pattern.

NOR (NOT OR) gate — A logic circuit whose output is 0 if either input is 1.

Nucleus — The dense central portion of an atom. The nucleus contains positively charged particles.

Offset — The difference between a repeater's input and output frequencies. On 2 meters, for example, the offset is either plus 600 kilohertz (kHz) or minus 600 kHz from the receive frequency. Also the slight difference in transmitting and receiving frequencies in a transceiver.

Offset voltage — As related to op amps, the voltage needed between the input terminals to produce 0-V output. Ideally this is 0 volts.

Ohm — The basic unit of electrical resistance, used to describe the amount of opposition to current.

Ohm's Law — A basic law of electronics. Ohm's Law gives a relationship between voltage, resistance and current (E = IR).

Omnidirectional — Antenna characteristic meaning it radiates equal power in all compass directions.

Open circuit — An electrical circuit that does not have a complete path, so current can't flow through the circuit.

Open-wire feed line — Parallel-conductor feeder with air as its primary insulation material.

Operational amplifier (op amp) — A linear IC that can amplify dc as well as ac. Op amps have very high input impedance, very low output impedance and very high gain.

Operator license — The portion of an Amateur Radio license that gives permission to operate an Amateur Radio station.

Optical shaft encoder — A device consisting of two pairs of photoemitters and photodetectors, used to sense the rotation speed and direction of a knob or dial. Optical shaft encoders are often used with the tuning knob on a modern radio to provide a tuning signal for the microprocessor controlling the frequency synthesizer.

Optocoupler (optoisolator) — A device consisting of a photoemitter and a photodetector used to transfer a signal between circuits using widely varying operating voltages.

Orbital period — The time it takes for a complete orbit, usually measured from one equator crossing to the next. The higher the altitude, the longer the period.

OR gate — A logic circuit whose output is 1 when either input is 1.

Oscillator — A circuit built by adding positive feedback to an amplifier. It produces an alternating current signal with no input except the dc operating voltages.

Oscilloscope — A device using a cathode-ray tube to display the waveform of an electric signal with respect to time or as compared with another signal.

Output frequency — A repeater's transmitting frequency.

P-type material — Semiconductor material that has been treated with impurities to give it an electron shortage. This creates excess positive charge carriers, or "holes," so it becomes an "acceptor material."

Packet Bulletin-Board System (PBBS) — A computer system used to store packet-radio messages for later retrieval by other amateurs.

Packet radio — A system of digital communication whereby information is broken into short bursts. The bursts ("packets") also contain addressing and error-detection information.

Paper capacitor — A capacitor formed by sandwiching paper between thin foil plates, and rolling the entire unit into a cylinder.

Parabolic (dish) antenna — An antenna reflector that is a portion of a parabolic curve. Used mainly at UHF and higher frequencies to obtain high gain and narrow beamwidth when excited by one of a variety of low-gain antennas placed at the dish focus to illuminate the reflector.

Parallel circuit — An electrical circuit in which the electrons follow more than one path in going from the negative supply terminal to the positive terminal.

Parallel-conductor feed line — Feed line constructed of two wires held a constant distance apart. They may be encased in plastic or constructed with insulating spacers placed at intervals along the line.

Parallel-resonant circuit — A circuit including a capacitor, an inductor and sometimes a resistor, connected in parallel, and in which the inductive and capacitive reactances are equal at the applied-signal frequency. The circuit impedance is a maximum, and the current is a minimum at the resonant frequency.

Parasitic element — Part of a directive antenna that derives energy from mutual coupling with the driven element. Parasitic elements are not connected directly to the feed line.

Parasitics — Undesired oscillations or other responses in an amplifier.

Path loss — The total signal loss between transmitting and receiving stations relative to the total radiated signal energy.

Peak envelope power (PEP) — The average power of the RF cycle having the greatest amplitude. (This occurs during a modulation peak.)

Peak envelope voltage (PEV) — The maximum peak voltage occurring in a complex waveform.

Peak inverse voltage (PIV) — The maximum instantaneous anode-to-cathode reverse voltage that is to be applied to a diode.

Peak negative value — On a signal waveform, the maximum displacement from the zero line in the negative direction.

Peak positive value — On a signal waveform, the maximum displacement from the zero line in the positive direction.

Peak power — The product of peak voltage and peak current in a resistive circuit. (Used with sine-wave signals.)

Peak-to-peak (P-P) voltage — A measure of the voltage taken between the negative and positive peaks on a cycle.

Peak voltage — A measure of voltage on an ac waveform taken from the centerline (0 V) and the maximum positive or negative level.

Perigee — That point in the orbit of a satellite (such as the moon) when it is closest to the earth.

Period, T — The time it takes to complete one cycle of an ac waveform.

Phase — A representation of the relative time or space between two points on a waveform, or between related points on different waveforms. The time interval between one event and another in a regularly recurring cycle.

Phase angle — If one complete cycle of a waveform is divided into 360 equal parts, then the phase relationship between two points or two waves can be expressed as an angle.

Phase-locked loop (PLL) — A servo loop consisting of a phase detector, low-pass filter, dc amplifier and voltage-controlled oscillator.

Phase modulation — A method of superimposing an information signal on an RF carrier wave in which the phase of an RF carrier wave is varied in relation to the information signal strength.

Phone — Voice communications.

Photocell — A solid-state device in which the voltage and current-conducting characteristics change as the amount of light striking the cell changes.

Photoconductive effect — A result of the photoelectric effect that shows up as an increase in the electric conductivity of a material. Many semiconductor materials exhibit a significant increase in conductance when electromagnetic radiation strikes them.

Photodetector — A device that produces an amplified signal that changes with the amount of light-sensitive surface.

Photoelectric effect — An interaction between electromagnetic radiation and matter resulting in photons of radiation being absorbed and electrons being knocked loose from the atom by this energy.

Phototransistor — A bipolar transistor constructed so the base-emitter junction is exposed to incident light. When light strikes this surface, current is generated at the junction, and this current is then amplified by transistor action.

Pico — The metric prefix for 10^{-12}, or divide by 1,000,000,000,000.

PIN diode — A diode consisting of a relatively thick layer of nearly pure semiconductor material with a layer of P-type material on one side and a layer of N-type material on the other.

Pi network output-coupling circuits — A combination of two like reactances (coil or capacitor) and one of the opposite type. The single component is connected in series with the signal lead and the two others are shunted to ground, one on either side of the series element.

Plastic-film capacitor — A capacitor formed by sandwiching thin sheets of mylar or polystyrene between thin foil plates, and rolling the entire unit into a cylinder.

PN-junction — The contact area between two layers of opposite-type semiconductor material.

Point-contact diode — A diode that is made by a pressure contact between a semiconductor material and a metal point.

Polarization — A property of an electromagnetic wave that tells whether the electric field of the wave is oriented vertically or horizontally. The polarization sense can change from vertical to horizontal under some conditions, and even can be gradually rotating either in a clockwise (right-hand-circular polarization) or a counterclockwise (left-hand-circular polarization) direction.

Polar-coordinate system — A method of representing the position of a point on a plane by specifying the radial distance from an origin, and an angle measured counterclockwise from the 0° line.

Portable operation — Amateur Radio operation conducted away from the location shown on the station license.

Positive charge — One of two types of electrical charge. A positive charge is the opposite of a negative charge. Electrons have a negative charge. The nucleus of an atom has a positive charge.

Positive-format modulation — A FAX system that uses a maximum modulation level to produce black.

Potentiometer — Another name for a variable resistor. The value of a potentiometer can be varied over a range of values without removing it from a circuit.

Power — The rate at which energy is consumed. In an electric circuit, power is found by multiplying the voltage applied to the circuit by the current through the circuit.

Power factor — The ratio of real power to apparent power in a circuit. Also calculated as the cosine of the phase angle between current and voltage in a circuit.

Power supply — That part of an electrical circuit that provides excess electrons to flow into a circuit. The power supply also supplies the voltage or EMF to push the electrons along. Power supplies convert a power source (such as the ac mains) to a useful form. (A circuit that provides a direct-current output at some desired voltage from an ac input voltage.)

Prescaler — A divider circuit used to increase the useful range of a frequency counter.

Primary winding — The coil in a transformer that is connected to the energy source.

Procedural signal (prosign) — One or two letters sent as a single character. Amateurs use prosigns in CW (Morse Code) QSOs (contacts) as a short way to indicate the operator's intention. Some examples are "K" for "Go Ahead," or "AR" for "End of Message." We send the prosign as one character.

Product detector — A detector circuit whose output is equal to the product of a beat-frequency oscillator (BFO) and the modulated RF signal applied to it. A product detector can be used to demodulate an RF signal.

Propagation — The means by which radio waves travel from one place to another.

PSK31 — A narrowband digital communications system.

Pseudonoise (PN) — A binary sequence designed to appear to be random (contain an approximately equal number of ones and zeros). Pseudonoise is generated by a digital circuit and mixed with digital information to produce a direct-sequence spread-spectrum signal.

Pulsating dc — The output from a rectifier before it is filtered. The polarity of a pulsating dc source does not change, but the amplitude of the voltage changes with time.

Pulse modulation — Modulation of an RF carrier by a series of pulses. These pulses convey the information that has been sampled from an analog signal.

Pulse-amplitude modulation (PAM) — A pulse-modulation system where the amplitude of a standard pulse is varied in relation to the information-signal amplitude at any instant.

Pulse-code modulation (PCM) — A modulation process where an information waveform is converted from analog to digital form by sampling the information signal and then encoding the sample value in some digital form (such as binary-coded decimal).

Pulse-position modulation (PPM) — A pulse-modulation system where the position (timing) of the pulses is varied from a standard value in relation to the information-signal amplitude at any instant.

Pulse-width modulation (PWM) — A pulse-modulation system where the width of a pulse is varied from a standard value in relation to the information-signal amplitude at any instant.

Q — A quality factor describing how closely a practical coil or capacitor approaches the characteristics of an ideal component.

Q signals — Three-letter symbols beginning with "Q." 0 signals are used in amateur CW work to save time and for better communication.

QSL card — A postcard sent to another radio amateur to confirm a contact.

QSO — A conversation, or contact, between two radio amateurs.

Quarter-wavelength vertical antenna — An antenna constructed of a quarter-wavelength-long radiating element placed perpendicular to the earth. (See Ground-plane antenna.)

Radiate — To convert electric energy into electromagnetic (radio) waves. Radio waves radiate from an antenna.

Radiated noise — Usually referring to a mobile installation, noise that is being radiated from the ignition system or electrical system of a vehicle and causing interference to the reception of radio signals.

Radiation resistance — The equivalent resistance that would dissipate the same amount of power as is radiated from an antenna. It is calculated by dividing the radiated power by the square of the RMS antenna current.

Radio frequency (RF) — The range of frequencies that can be radiated through space in the form of electromagnetic radiation. We usually consider RF to be those frequencies higher than the audio frequencies, or above 20 kilohertz.

Radio-frequency interference (RFI) — Interference to an electronic device (radio, TV, stereo) caused by RF energy from an amateur transmitter or other source.

Radio horizon — The position at which a direct wave radiated from an antenna becomes tangent to the earth's surface. Note that as the wave continues past the horizon, the wave gets higher and higher above the surface.

Radio-path horizon — The point where radio waves are returned by tropospheric bending. The radio-path horizon is 15 percent farther away than the geometric horizon.

Radioteletype (RTTY) — Radio signals sent from one teleprinter machine to another machine. Anything that one operator types on his teleprinter will be printed on the other machine. (A type of digital communications.)

Ragchew — A lengthy conversation (or QSO) between two radio amateurs.

Random-length wire antenna — An antenna having a length that is not necessarily related to the wavelength of a desired signal.

Ratio detector — A circuit used to demodulate FM signals. The output is the ratio of voltages from either side of a discriminator-transformer secondary.

Reactance — The property of an inductor or capacitor (measured in ohms) that opposes current in an ac circuit without converting power to heat.

Reactance modulator — A device capable of modulating an ac signal by varying the reactance of a circuit in response to the modulating signal. (The modulating signal may be voice, data, video or some other kind, depending on what type of information is being transmitted.) The circuit capacitance or inductance changes in response to an audio input signal.

Reactive power — The apparent power in an inductor or capacitor. The product of RMS current through a reactive component and the RMS voltage across it. Also called wattless power.

Real power — The actual power dissipated in a circuit, calculated to be the product of the apparent power times the phase angle between the voltage and current.

Receiver — A device that converts modulated radio signals into audio signals.

Receiver incremental tuning (RIT) — A transceiver control that allows for a slight change in the receiver frequency without changing the transmitter frequency. Some manufacturers call this a Clarifier (CLAR) control.

Rectangular coordinates — A graphical system used to represent length and direction of physical quantities for the purpose of finding other unknown quantities.

Rectangular-coordinate system — A method of representing the position of a point on a plane by specifying the distance from an origin in two perpendicular directions.

Rectifier — An electronic component that allows current to pass through it in only one direction.

Reflected wave — A radio wave whose direction is changed when it bounces off some object in its path.

Reflectometer — A test instrument used to indicate standing wave ratio (SWR) by measuring the forward power (power from the transmitter) and reflected power (power returned from the antenna system).

Reflector — A parasitic antenna element that is located behind the driven element to enhance forward directivity. The reflector is usually about 5% longer than the driven element.

Refract — To bend. Electromagnetic energy is refracted when it passes through a boundary between different types of material. Light is refracted as it travels from air into water or from water into air.

Repeater — An amateur station that receives a signal and retransmits it for greater range.

Resistance — The ability to oppose an electric current.

Resistor — Any material that opposes a current in an electrical circuit. An electronic component specifically designed to oppose current.

Resonant frequency — That frequency at which a circuit including capacitors and inductors presents a purely resistive impedance. The inductive reactance in the circuit is equal to the capacitive reactance. Also the desired operating frequency of a tuned circuit. In an antenna, the resonant frequency is one where the feed-point impedance contains only resistance.

Resonant rhombic antenna — A diamond-shaped antenna consisting of sides that are each at least one wavelength long. The feed line is connected to one end of the diamond, and the opposite end is left open. The antenna has a bidirectional radiation pattern.

Reverse bias — A voltage applied across a semiconductor junction so that it will tend to prevent current flow.

Reverse biased — A condition in which the cathode of a diode is positive with respect to the anode, so it will not conduct.

RF burn — A flesh burn caused by exposure to a strong field of RF energy.

Rig — The radio amateur's term for a transmitter, receiver or transceiver.

Ripple — The amount of change between the maximum voltage and the minimum voltage in a pulsating dc waveform.

Root-mean square (RMS) voltage — Another name for effective voltage. The term refers to the method of calculating the value.

Rotary switch — A switch that connects one center contact to several individual contacts. An antenna switch is one common use for a rotary switch.

Rotor — The movable plates in a variable capacitor.

RST System — The system used by amateurs for giving signal reports. "R" stands for readability, "S" for strength and "T" for tone.

RF envelope — The shape of an RF signal as viewed on an oscilloscope.

S meter — A meter in a receiver that shows the relative strength of a received signal.

Sawtooth wave — A waveform consisting of a linear ramp and then a return to the original value. It is made up of sine waves at a fundamental frequency and all harmonics.

Scanning — The process of analyzing or synthesizing, in a predetermined manner, the light values or equivalent characteristics of elements constituting a picture area. Also the process of recreating those values to produce a picture on a CRT screen.

Schematic symbol — A drawing used to represent a circuit component on a wiring diagram.

Scientific notation — A special form of exponential notation in which numbers always have a single nonzero digit before the decimal point. The remaining nonzero digits come after the decimal point, followed by the power of 10. For example, 274 is 2.74×10^2 in scientific notation. See Appendix A.

Secondary station identifier (SSID) — A number added to a packet-radio station's call sign so that one amateur call sign can be used for several packet stations.

Secondary winding — The coil in a transformer that connects to the load.

Selective-call identifier — A four-character AMTOR station identifier.

Selective fading — A variation of radio-wave field intensity that is different over small frequency changes. It may be caused by changes in the material that the wave is traveling through or changes in transmission path, among other things.

Selectivity — A measure of the ability of a receiver to distinguish between a desired signal and an undesired one at some different frequency. Selectivity can be applied to the RF, IF and AF stages.

Self-resonant antenna — An antenna that is to be used on the frequency at which it is resonant, without the use of any added inductive or capacitive loading elements.

Semiconductor material — A material with resistivity between that of metals and insulators. Pure semiconductor materials are usually doped with impurities to control the electrical properties.

Semidiameter — The apparent radius of a generally spherical object (such as the moon) in the sky. Semidiameter is usually expressed in degrees of arc as measured between imaginary lines drawn from the observer to the center of the object and from the observer to one edge.

Sensing antenna — An omnidirectional antenna used in conjunction with an antenna that exhibits a bidirectional pattern to produce a radio direction-finding system with a cardioid pattern.

Sensitivity — A measure of the minimum input-signal level that will produce a certain audio output from a receiver.

Sequential logic — A type of circuit element that has at least one output and one or more input channels, and in which the output state depends on the previous input states. A flip-flop is one sequential-logic element.

Series circuit — An electrical circuit in which all the electrons must flow through every part of the circuit. There is only one path for the electrons to follow.

Series-resonant circuit — A circuit including a capacitor, an inductor and sometimes a resistor, connected in series, and in which the inductive and capacitive reactances are equal at the applied-signal frequency. The circuit impedance is at a minimum, and the current is a maximum at the resonant frequency.

Shack — The room where an Amateur Radio operator keeps his or her station equipment.

Short circuit — An electrical circuit where the current does not take the desired path, but finds a shortcut instead. Often the current goes directly from the negative power-supply terminal to the positive one, bypassing the rest of the circuit.

Short-path communication — Communication made by pointing beam antennas in the direction indicated by the shorter great-circle path.

Sidebands — The sum or difference frequencies generated when an RF carrier is mixed with an audio signal.

Signal generator — A test instrument that produces a stable low-level radio-frequency signal. The signal can be set to a specific frequency and used to troubleshoot RF equipment.

Signal tracer — A test instrument that shows the presence of RF or AF energy in a circuit. The signal tracer is used to trace the flow of a signal through a multistage circuit.

Silicon-controlled rectifier — A bistable semiconductor device that can be switched between the off and on states by a control voltage.

Simplex operation — A term normally used in relation to VHF and UHF operation. Simplex means you are receiving and transmitting on the same frequency.

Sine wave — A single-frequency waveform that can be expressed in terms of the mathematical sine function. A smooth curve, usually drawn to represent the variation in voltage or current over time for an ac signal.

Single sideband (SSB) — A common mode for voice operation on the amateur high-frequency bands. This is a variation of amplitude modulation.

Single-pole, double-throw (SPDT) switch — A switch that connects one center contact to either of two other contacts.

Single-pole, single-throw (SPST) switch — A switch that only connects one center contact to another contact.

Single-sideband, suppressed-carrier signal — A radio signal in which only one of the two sidebands generated by amplitude modulation is transmitted. The other sideband and the RF carrier wave are removed before the signal is transmitted.

Single-sideband, suppressed-carrier, amplitude modulation (SSB) — A technique used to transmit voice information in which the amplitude of the RF carrier is modulated by the audio input, and the carrier and one sideband are suppressed.

Skin effect — A condition in which ac flows in the outer portions of a conductor. The higher the signal frequency, the less the electric and magnetic fields penetrate the conductor, and the smaller the effective area of a given wire for carrying the electrons.

Skip — Radio waves that are bent back to earth by the ionosphere. Skip is also called sky-wave propagation.

Skip zone — A region between the farthest reach of ground-wave communications and the closest range of skip propagation.

Sky temperature — A measure of relative background noise coming from space, often expressed in kelvins. The sun is a source of much background noise, and so has a high noise temperature.

Sky waves — Radio waves that travel from an antenna upward to the ionosphere, where they either pass through the ionosphere into space or are refracted back to earth.

Sky-wave signals — Radio signals that travel through the ionosphere to reach the receiving station. Sky-wave signals will cause a variation in the measured received-signal direction, resulting in an error with a radio direction-finding system.

Slew rate — As related to op amps, a measure of how fast the output voltage can change with changing input signals.

Slope detection — A method for using an AM receiver to demodulate an FM signal. The signal is tuned to be part way down the slope of the receiver IF filter curve.

Sloper — A ½-wave dipole antenna that has one end elevated and one end nearer the ground.

Slow-scan television (SSTV) — A television system used by Amateurs to transmit pictures within a signal bandwidth allowed on the HF bands by the FCC. It takes approximately 8 seconds to send a single frame with SSTV.

Smith Chart — A coordinate system developed by Phillip Smith to represent complex impedances on a graph. This chart makes it easy to perform calculations involving antenna and transmission-line impedances and SWR.

Software-defined radio (SDR) — A transmitter and/or receiver whose principal signal processing functions are defined by software.

Solar flux index — A measure of solar activity. The solar flux index is a measure of the radio noise on 2800 MHz.

Solar wind — Electrically charged particles emitted by the sun, and traveling through space. The wind strength depends on how severe the disturbance on the sun was. These charged particles may have a sudden impact on radio communications.

Solid-state devices — Circuit components that use semiconductor materials. Semiconductor diodes, transistors and integrated circuits are all solid-state devices.

SOS — A Morse code call for emergency assistance.

Source — The point at which the charge carriers enter an FET. Corresponds to the cathode of a vacuum tube.

Space operation — Space-to-earth and space-to-space Amateur Radio communication from a station that is beyond the major portion of the earth's atmosphere.

Space wave — A radio wave arriving at the receiving antenna made up of a direct wave and one or more reflected waves.

Spectrum analyzer — A test instrument generally used to display the power (or amplitude) distribution of a signal with respect to frequency.

Speech processor — A device used to increase the average power contained in a speech waveform. Proper use of a speech processor can greatly improve the readability of a voice signal.

Spin modulation — Periodic amplitude fade-and-peak variations resulting from the Phase III satellite's 60 r/min spin.

Splatter — The term used to describe a very wide bandwidth signal, usually caused by overmodulation of a sideband transmitter. Splatter causes interference to adjacent signals.

Sporadic-E propagation — A type of radio-wave propagation that occurs when dense patches of ionization form in the E layer of the ionosphere. These "clouds" reflect radio waves, extending the possible VHF communications range.

Spread-spectrum modulation — A signal-transmission technique where the transmitted carrier is spread out over a wide bandwidth.

Square wave — A periodic waveform that alternates between two values, and spends an equal time at each level. It is made up of sine waves at a fundamental frequency and all odd harmonics.

SSTV scan converter — A device that uses digital signal-processing techniques to change the output from a normal TV camera into an SSTV signal or to change a received SSTV signal to one that can be displayed on a normal TV.

Stability — A measure of how well a receiver or transmitter will remain on frequency without drifting.

Standing-wave ratio (SWR) — Sometimes denoted as VSWR. A measure of the impedance match between the feed line and the antenna. Also, with a Transmatch in use, a measure of the match between the feeder from the transmitter and the antenna system. The system includes the Transmatch and the line to the antenna. The ratio of maximum voltage to minimum voltage along a feed line. Also the ratio of antenna impedance to feed line impedance when the antenna is a purely resistive load.

Standing-wave-ratio (SWR) meter — A device used for measuring SWR. SWR is a relative measure of the impedance match between an antenna, feed line and transmitter.

Static (level-triggered) input — An input, such as for a flip-flop, which causes the output to change when it changes state.

Station license — The portion of an Amateur Radio license that authorizes an amateur station at a specific location. The station license also lists the call sign of that station.

Stator — The stationary plates in a variable capacitor.

Subatomic particles — The building blocks of atoms. Electrons, protons and neutrons are the most common subatomic particles.

Sudden Ionospheric Disturbance — A blackout of HF sky-wave communications that occurs after a solar flare.

Summer solstice — One of two spots on the earth's orbital path around the sun at which it reaches a point farthest from a horizontal plane extending through the center of the sun. With the north pole inclined toward the sun, it marks the beginning of summer in the northern hemisphere.

Sunspots — Dark spots on the surface of the sun. When there are few sunspots, long-distance radio propagation is poor on the higher-frequency bands.

Superheterodyne receiver — A receiver that converts RF signals to an intermediate frequency before detection.

Susceptance — The reciprocal of reactance. This is the imaginary part of a complex admittance.

Sweep circuits — The circuits in an oscilloscope that set the time base for observing waveforms on the scope.

Switch — A device used to connect or disconnect electrical contacts.

Switching regulator — A voltage-regulator circuit in which the output voltage is controlled by turning the pass element on and off at a rate of several kilohertz.

SWR meter — A device used to measure SWR. A measuring instrument that can indicate when an antenna system is working well.

Sync — Having two or more signals in step with each other, or occurring at the same time. A pulse on a TV or FAX signal that ensures the transmitted and received images start at the same point.

Synchronous flip-flop — A circuit whose output state depends on the data inputs, but that will change output state only when it detects the proper clock signal.

Synchronous motor — An ac electric motor whose rotation speed is controlled by the frequency of the electric energy used to power it.

Telecommand operation — Earth-to-space Amateur Radio communication to initiate, modify or terminate functions of a station in space operation (an Amateur Radio satellite).

Teleprinter — A machine that can convert keystrokes (typing) into electrical impulses. The teleprinter can also convert the proper electrical impulses back into text. Hams use teleprinters for radioteletype work.

Television raster — A predetermined pattern of scanning lines that provide substantially uniform coverage of an area.

Temperature coefficient — A number used to show whether a component will increase or decrease in value as it gets warm.

Temperature inversion — A condition in the atmosphere in which a region of cool air is trapped beneath warmer air.

Terminal node controller (TNC) — A TNC accepts information from a computer or terminal and converts the information into packets by including address and error-checking information. The TNC also receives packet signals and extracts transmitted information for display by a computer.

Terminator — A band around the earth that separates night from day.

Thermal noise — A random noise generated by the interchange of energy within a circuit and surroundings to maintain thermal equilibrium.

Thevenin's Theorem — Any combination of voltage sources and impedances, no matter how complex, can be replaced by a single voltage source and a single impedance that will present the same voltage and current to a load circuit.

Third-party participation (or communication) — The way an unlicensed person can participate in Amateur Radio communications. A control operator must ensure compliance with FCC rules.

Third-party traffic — Messages passed from one amateur to another on behalf of a third person.

Thyristor — Another name for a silicon-controlled rectifier.

Ticket — The radio amateur's term for an Amateur Radio license.

Time constant — The product of resistance and capacitance in a simple series or parallel RC circuit, or the inductance divided by the resistance in a simple series or parallel RL circuit. One time constant is the time required for a voltage across a capacitor or a current through an inductor to build up to 63.2% of its steady-state value, or to decay to 36.8% of the initial value. After a total of 5 time constants have elapsed, the voltage or current is considered to have reached its final value.

Time domain — A method of viewing a complex signal. The amplitude of the complex wave is displayed over changing time. The display shows only the complex waveform, and does not necessarily indicate the sine-wave signals that make up the wave.

Top loading — The addition of inductive reactance (a coil) or capacitive reactance (a capacitance hat) at the end of a driven element opposite the feed point. It is intended to increase the electrical length of the radiator.

Toroidal inductor or toroid — A coil wound on a donut-shaped ferrite or powdered-iron form.

Traffic — Messages passed from one amateur to another in a relay system; the amateur version of a telegram.

Traffic net — An on-the-air meeting of amateurs, for the purpose of relaying messages.

Transceiver — A radio transmitter and receiver combined in one unit.

Transequatorial propagation — A form of F-layer ionospheric propagation, in which signals of higher frequency than the expected MUF are propagated across the earth's magnetic equator.

Transformer — Two coils with mutual inductance used to step up or step down the voltage level of an ac power source to one more suited for a particular circuit.

Transistor-transistor logic (TTL) — Digital integrated circuits composed of bipolar transistors, possibly as discrete components, but usually part of a single IC. The power supply voltage should be 5 V.

Transmatch — See Matching network.

Transmission line — The wires or cable used to connect a transmitter or receiver to an antenna. See Feed line.

Transmit-receive (TR) switch — A device used for switching an antenna between transmit and receive operation.

Transmitter — A device that produces radio-frequency signals.

Transponder — A repeater aboard a satellite that retransmits, on another frequency band, any type of signals it receives. Signals within a certain receiver bandwidth are translated to a new frequency band, so many signals can share a transponder simultaneously.

Traps — Parallel LC networks inserted in an antenna element to provide multiband operation.

Triac — A bidirectional SCR, primarily used to control ac voltages.

Triangulation — A radio direction-finding technique in which compass bearings from two or more locations are taken, and lines are drawn on a map to predict the location of a radio signal source.

Triode — A vacuum tube with three active elements: cathode, plate and control grid.

Troposphere — The region in the earth's atmosphere just above the surface of the earth and below the ionosphere.

Tropospheric bending — When radio waves are bent in the troposphere, they return to earth approximately 15 percent farther away than the geometric horizon.

Tropospheric ducting — A type of radio-wave propagation whereby the VHF communications range is greatly extended. Certain weather conditions cause portions of the troposphere to act like a duct or waveguide for the radio signals.

Tropospheric enhancement — A weather-related phenomenon. Tropo can produce unusually long propagation on the VHF and UHF bands.

True or Geometric horizon — The most distant point one can see by line of sight.

Truth table — A chart showing the outputs for all possible input combinations to a digital circuit.

Tuning-fork oscillator — An oscillator in which the main frequency-determining element is the mechanical resonance of a tuning fork.

Tunnel diode — A diode with an especially thin depletion region, so that it exhibits a negative resistance characteristic.

Twin lead — Parallel-conductor feeder with wires encased in insulation. See Parallel-conductor feed line.

Two-tone test — Problems in a sideband transmitter can be detected by feeding two audio tones into the microphone input of the transmitter and observing the output on an oscilloscope.

Unbalanced line — Feed line with one conductor at ground potential, such as coaxial cable.

Unidentified communications or signals — Signals or radio communications in which the transmitting station's call sign is not transmitted.

Unijunction transistor (UJT) — A three-terminal, signal-junction device that exhibits negative resistance and switching characteristics unlike bipolar transistors.

Upper sideband (USB) — The common single-sideband operating mode on the 20, 17, 15, 12 and 10-meter HF amateur bands. Hams also use upper sideband on all the VHF and UHF bands.

Varactor diode — A component whose capacitance varies as the reverse-bias voltage is changed.

Variable capacitor — A capacitor that can have its value changed within a certain range.

Variable resistor — A resistor whose value can be adjusted over a certain range.

Variable-frequency oscillator (VFO) — An oscillator used in receivers and transmitters. The frequency is set by a tuned circuit using capacitors and inductors. The frequency can be changed by adjusting the components in the tuned circuit.

Velocity factor — An expression of how fast a radio wave will travel through a material or transmission line. It is usually stated as a fraction of the speed the wave would have in free space (where the wave would have its maximum velocity). Velocity factor is also sometimes specified as a percentage of the speed of the radio wave in free space.

Vertical antenna — A common amateur antenna, usually made of metal tubing. The radiating element is vertical. There are usually four or more radial conductors parallel to or on the ground.

Vertically polarized wave — A radio wave that has its electric lines of force perpendicular to the surface of the earth.

Vertical sync pulse — Part of a TV signal used by the receiver to keep the CRT electron-beam scan in step with the camera scanning beam. This pulse returns the beam to the top edge of the screen at the proper time.

Vestigial sideband (VSB) — A signal-transmission method in which one sideband, the carrier and part of the second sideband are transmitted. Most commonly used for amateur television (ATV) transmissions.

Vidicon tube — A type of photo-sensitive vacuum tube used in older TV cameras.

Virtual height — The height that radio waves appear to be reflected from when they are returned to earth by refraction in the ionosphere.

Voice-operated relay (VOX) — Circuitry that activates the transmitter when the operator speaks into the microphone.

Volt (V) — The basic unit of electrical pressure or EMF.

Voltage — The EMF or pressure that causes electrons to move through an electrical circuit.

Voltage source — Any source of excess electrons. A voltage source produces a current and the force to push the electrons through an electrical circuit.

Volt-ohm-milliammeter (VOM) — A multiple-range meter used to measure voltage, current and resistance.

W1AW — The headquarters station of the American Radio Relay League. This station is a memorial to the League's cofounder, Hiram Percy Maxim. The station provides daily on-the-air code practice and bulletins of interest to hams.

Watt (W) — The unit of power in the metric system. The watt describes how fast a circuit uses electrical energy.

Wattmeter — A test instrument used to measure the power output (in watts) of a transmitter.

Wavelength — Often abbreviated λ (Greek letter lambda). The distance a radio wave travels in one RF cycle. The wavelength relates to frequency. Higher frequencies have shorter wavelengths.

White noise — A random noise that covers a wide frequency range across the RF spectrum. It is characterized by a hissing sound in your receiver speaker.

Winter solstice — One of two spots on the earth's orbital path around the sun at which it reaches a point farthest from a horizontal plane extending through the center of the sun. With the north pole inclined away from the sun, it marks the beginning of winter in the northern hemisphere.

Wire-wound resistor — A resistor made by winding a length of wire on an insulating form.

Yagi antenna — The most popular type of amateur directional (beam) antenna. It has one driven element and one or more additional elements.

Zener diode — A diode that is designed to be operated in the reverse-breakdown region of its characteristic curve. Zener diodes are used to keep power supply voltages constant.

Zener voltage — A reverse-bias voltage that produces a sudden change in apparent resistance across the diode junction, from a large value to a small value.

Zero beat — The condition that occurs when two signals are at exactly the same frequency. The beat frequency between the two signals is zero. When two operators in a QSO are transmitting on the same frequency the stations are zero beat.

INDEX

FEEDBACK

Please use this form to give us your comments on this book and what you'd like to see in future editions, or e-mail us at **pubsfdbk@arrl.org** (publications feedback). If you use e-mail, please include your name, call sign, e-mail address and the book title, edition and printing in the body of your message. Also indicate whether or not you are an ARRL member.

Where did you purchase this book? ☐ From ARRL directly   ☐ From an ARRL dealer

Is there a dealer who carries ARRL publications within:

☐ 5 miles   ☐ 15 miles   ☐ 30 miles   of your location?   ☐ Not sure.

License class:

☐ Novice   ☐ Technician   ☐ Technician with code   ☐ General   ☐ Advanced   ☐ Amateur Extra

Name _____   ARRL member? ☐ Yes ☐ No

_____   Call Sign _____

Address _____

City, State/Province, ZIP/Postal Code _____

Daytime Phone (   ) _____   Age _____

If licensed, how long? _____

Other hobbies _____   E-mail _____

_____

Occupation _____

For ARRL use only	UBE
Edition	2 3 4 5 6 7 8 9 10 11 12
Printing	2 3 4 5 6 7 8 9 10 11 12

From _____

_____

_____

EDITOR, UNDERSTANDING BASIC ELECTRONICS
ARRL—THE NATIONAL ASSOCIATION FOR AMATEUR RADIO
225 MAIN STREET
NEWINGTON CT 06111-1494

please fold and tape